The Nassi-Levy

Finn

Spanish

TWO

YEARS

WORKBOOK EDITION

AB Verbs

No radical
change

3 ortográfico
change

Lanzar
Lancé

Stephen L. Levy
Former Head, Foreign Language Department
Roslyn (New York) Public Schools

Robert J. Nassi
Former Teacher of Spanish
Los Angeles Valley Junior College
Los Angeles, California

AMSCO SCHOOL PUBLICATIONS, INC.,
a division of Perfection Learning®

With grateful acknowledgement to coauthor,
Bernard Bernstein

To Sergio,
El alma no tendría un arcoiris si los ojos no tuvieran lágrimas.
Q.E.P.D.

And to Jorge,
Con gratitud especial y sincero aprecio y cariño por tu amistad.

S.L.L.

Text design by A Good Thing
Cover photograph by Thinkstock
Illustrations by Felipe Galindo

Copyright © 2015 by Amsco School Publications, Inc., a division of Perfection Learning®

Please visit our Web sites at:
www.amscopub.com and *www.perfectionlearning.com*

When ordering this book, please specify:
Softcover: ISBN 978-1-62974-672-2 or **1486801**

5 6 7 8   EBM   20 19 18 17

Printed in the United States of America

Preface

THE NASSI / LEVY SPANISH TWO YEARS, THIRD EDITION is designed to give students a comprehensive review and thorough understanding of the elements of the Spanish language and the highlights of Hispanic culture. Abundant and varied exercises help students master each phase of the work.

This THIRD EDITION, contains the following features:

1. A proficiency-oriented communicative approach.

2. Grammatical topics are presented in smaller increments and exercises devoted to practice, drill, and mastery of these topics immediately follow the grammatical explanation.

3. The exercises are set in contexts that are both functional and realistic. Many of them are personalized to stimulate student response and internalization of the concepts under study.

4. The exercises are graded from easy to more challenging and provide opportunities for personalized self-expression by the learner.

5. There is an abundance of artwork used to elicit specific grammar topics and vocabulary.

6. Alternative-assessment activities, called **Actividades**, are introduced to enable students to show both their proficiency and creativity, while performing contextually organized tasks in the target language.

7. Rubrics for evaluating oral and written language are also included.

(ORGANIZATION)

For ease of study and reference, the book is divided into six parts. In Parts One through Three, the chapters are organized around related grammatical topics. The three chapters in Part Four are devoted to word building, synonyms and antonyms, and thematic vocabulary. Part Five covers geography, history, literature, art, music, architecture, science, and life-style. Part Six provides material for comprehensive practice and testing of the speaking, listening, reading, and writing skills.

(GRAMMAR)

Each grammar chapter deals fully with one major topic or several closely related ones. Explanations of structures are brief and clear. All points of grammar are illustrated by many examples, in which the key elements are typographically highlighted.

This second year review of Spanish covers a basic grammar sequence. Care has been taken to avoid the use of overly complex, structural elements. To enable students to concentrate on the structural practice, the vocabulary has been carefully controlled and systematically "recycled" throughout the chapters.

EXERCISES

For maximum efficiency in learning, the exercises directly follow the points of grammar to which they apply. Carefully graded, the exercises proceed from simple assimilation to more challenging manipulation of elements and communication. To provide students with meaningful practice of a grammar topic, the exercises are set in contexts that are functional, realistic, and communicative. Many are also personalized to stimulate student response and internalization of the concepts under study.

While the contents of the exercises afford extensive oral practice, the book's format also encourages reinforcement through written student responses, including English-to-Spanish exercises intended to sharpen composition skills. The grammatical chapters conclude with Mastery Exercises, in which all grammatical aspects in the chapter are again practiced in recombinations of previously covered elements. The communicative situations for each exercise and the directions are given in English.

FLEXIBILITY

The topical organization and the integrated completeness of each chapter permit the teacher to follow any sequence suitable to the objectives of the course and the needs of the students. This flexibility is facilitated by the detailed table of contents at the front of the book and the comprehensive grammatical index at the back. Teachers and students will also find the book useful as a reference source.

CULTURE

The cultural chapters in Part Five are presented in Spanish. Every effort has been made to keep the narratives clear and readable and to provide a wealth of cultural information. Each cultural chapter includes exercises designed to facilitate and check learning.

OTHER FEATURES

In order to help students demonstrate their performance in Spanish, almost all chapters in Parts One to Three contain alternative-assessment activities. Although these activities are grammatically organized, they are open-ended and enable students to demonstrate their proficiency in using the grammatical elements in personalized, contextually organized tasks.

The Appendix features complete model verb tables and the principal parts of common irregular verbs, as well as basic rules of Spanish punctuation, syllabication, and pronunciation. Spanish-English and English-Spanish vocabularies and a comprehensive Index complete the book.

The NASSI / LEVY SPANISH TWO YEARS, THIRD EDITION presents a comprehensive coverage of the elements of Spanish, clear and concise explanations, extensive contextualized practice materials, functional vocabulary, interesting cultural narratives in Spanish, and performance-oriented assessment activities, will help students strengthen their skills in the Spanish language. As students pursue proficiency, they will also gain valuable insights into the cultures of the Spanish-speaking world.

Contents

Part One
Verbal Structures

Part Two
Nouns, Pronouns, and Prepositions

Part Three
Adjective / Adverb and Related Structures

Part Four
Word Study

Part Five
Spanish and Spanish-American Civilizations

Part Six
Comprehensive Testing
Speaking, Listening, Reading, Writing *419*

PART

1

Verbal Structures

CHAPTER 1

Present Tense of Regular Verbs

◆ 1 ◆ REGULAR VERBS

a. The present tense of regular verbs is formed by dropping the infinitive ending (-*ar*, -*er*, -*ir*) and adding the following personal endings:

-o, –as, –a, –amos, –áis, –an for -ar verbs

-o, –es, –e, –emos, –éis, –en for -er verbs

-o, –es, –e, –imos, –ís, –en for -ir verbs

	bailar *to dance*	**comer** *to eat*	**vivir** *to live*
yo	bail*o*	com*o*	viv*o*
tú	bail*as*	com*es*	viv*es*
Ud., él, ella	bail*a*	com*e*	viv*e*
nosotros, -as	bail*amos*	com*emos*	viv*imos*
vosotros, -as	bail*áis*	com*éis*	viv*ís*
Uds., ellos, ellas	bail*an*	com*en*	viv*en*

b. The present tense has the following meanings in English.

yo como	*I eat, I'm eating, I do eat*
usted baila	*you dance, you're dancing, you do dance*
ellos viven	*they live, they're living, they do live*

NOTES:

1. In a negative statement, **no** follows the subject and goes immediately before the verb.

   Ellos *no* comen a las doce.   *They don't eat at twelve o'clock.*

2. In a question, the subject usually follows the verb.

   ¿Comen *ellos* a las doce?   *Do they eat at twelve o'clock?*

   ¿No comen *ellos* a las doce?   *Don't they eat at twelve o'clock?*

3. Unless required for clarity or for emphasis, subject pronouns are usually omitted.

   Colecciono MP3.   *I collect MP3s.*

   ¿Colecciona *Ud.* MP3 también?   *Do you collect MP3s too?*

◆ 2 ◆ FREQUENTLY USED -AR VERBS

ayudar *to help*	coleccionar *to collect*	desear *to want, wish*
bajar *to go down, descend*	comprar *to buy*	enseñar *to teach, show*
borrar *to erase*	contestar *to answer*	entrar *to enter*
buscar *to look for, seek*	cultivar *to cultivate*	escuchar *to listen (to)*
caminar *to walk*	dejar *to let, allow, leave*	esperar *to wait for, await, hope, expect*
cantar *to sing*	descansar *to rest*	estudiar *to study*

explicar	*to explain*	necesitar	*to need*	regresar	*to return*
gritar	*to shout*	pagar	*to pay (for)*	sacar	*to take out; to take (photo)*
hablar	*to speak, talk*	pasar	*to pass, spend (time)*	tomar	*to take, eat, drink*
hallar	*to find*	patinar	*to skate*	trabajar	*to work*
invitar	*to invite*	practicar	*to practice*	usar	*to use*
llenar	*to fill*	preguntar	*to ask*	viajar	*to travel*
llevar	*to carry, wear*	preparar	*to prepare*	visitar	*to visit*
mirar	*to look (at)*	quitar	*to take away*		

EXERCISE A. Alfredo is describing what happens in his classes at school. Express in complete sentences what he says.

EXAMPLE: yo / prestar atención   Yo **presto** atención.

1. la maestra / enseñar la lección

   La maestra enseña la lección

2. los alumnos / escuchar a la maestra

   Los alumnos escuchan [a] la maestra

3. Javier / contestar las preguntas

   Javier contesta las preguntas

4. yo / buscar las palabras en el diccionario

   yo busco las palabras

5. tú / preguntar muchas cosas

   tú preguntas muchas cosas

6. Gloria / entrar en la clase tarde

   Gloria entra la clase tarde

7. la clase / preparar la tarea

   La clase prepara la t

8. nosotros / estudiar mucho

   nosotros estudiamos

EXERCISE B. While talking to your grandmother on the telephone, she asks you what everyone in the family is doing at this moment. Tell her.

EXAMPLE: Felipe / mirar la televisión   Felipe **mira** la televisión.

1. mi hermana / pasar la aspiradora

   mi hermana pasa la aspiradora

2. Mamá / preparar la comida

   Mamá prepara la comida

3. Luis / trabajar en el jardín

   Luis trabaja en el jardín

4. Papá / lavar el carro

   Papá lava el carro

5. Rosita y yo / escuchar MP3

   Rosita y yo escuchamos

6. Adela / tocar el piano

   Adela toca el piano

EXERCISE C. Use the cues provided to write negative sentences.

EXAMPLE: los niños / coleccionar insectos   Los niños **no coleccionan** insectos.

1. las niñas / montar en bicicleta

   no montan la bicicleta

2. los amigos / caminar en el parque

3. Pierre y yo / nadar en la piscina

yo nadamos en la piscina

4. Kyoko / comprar un suéter

yo compra un suéter

5. yo / viajar en autobús

yo viaja en autobus

EXERCISE D. Write a list of **seven** things you and your classmates do **not** do in school. Use the following suggestions or create your own.

escuchar MP3	preparar la tarea	arreglar el monopatín
visitar otras clases	gritar en la clase	mirar por la ventana
hablar en voz alta	descansar en la clase	

EXAMPLE: Yo **no miro** por la ventana.

1. _____
2. _____
3. _____
4. _____
5. _____
6. _____
7. _____

EXERCISE E. Your father is watching his favorite program and isn't paying close attention to what you are telling him. After each statement, he asks a question. Tell what he asks in response to the statements below.

EXAMPLES: Rogelio gana muchos trofeos.   Yo colecciono insectos.
   ¿Gana Rogelio muchos trofeos?   **¿Coleccionas tú** insectos?

1. Guy y Lázaro toman muchos refrescos.   *¿Toman ellos muchos refrescos?*
2. Evelyn practica un deporte.   *¿Practica Evyle Evelyn una deporte?*
3. Gustavo escucha música clásica.   *¿Escucha Gustavo música clásica?*
4. Yo patino en un monopatín.   *¿Patinas tu en un monopatín?*
5. Lucy y Sean cantan en el coro.   *¿Cantan Lucy y Sean el coro?*
6. Marco descansa en una hamaca.   *¿Descansa en una hamaca Marco?*
7. Beto y yo sacamos muchas fotos.   *¿Sacan fotos ustedes?*

◆3◆ FREQUENTLY USED -ER VERBS

aprender *to learn*	**correr** *to run*	**leer** *to read*
beber *to drink*	**creer** *to believe*	**prometer** *to promise*
comer *to eat*	**deber** *to have to (should, ought); to owe*	**responder** *to answer*
comprender *to understand*	**esconder** *to hide (something)*	**vender** *to sell*

EXERCISE F.   Gladys and a friend describe what different people are doing at the beach. Express what they say.

EXAMPLE: un hombre / vender refrescos   Un hombre **vende** refrescos.

1. los niños / correr en la playa _los niños corren e la playa_

2. tú / aprender a nadar _tú aprendes_

3. Sofía / beber mucho jugo _Sofía bebe_

4. Rafael y yo / leer una revista _Rafael y yo luemos_

5. yo / esconder la pelota _yo escondo_

6. nosotros / comer en un café _nosotros comemos_

7. el salvavidas / responder a muchas preguntas _el salvavidas responden_

8. Cristina / prometer jugar al voleibol _Cristina promete_

EXERCISE G.   After Anabel's friends leave, her younger sister asks her a lot of questions. Answer the sister's questions according to the cues provided.

EXAMPLE: ¿Quién aprende a hablar español? (Robert)   **Robert aprende** a hablar español.

1. ¿Quién corre en el parque todos los días? (Diego)
Diego corre

2. ¿Quiénes comen muchos dulces? (Pedro y yo)
Pedro y yo commemos

3. ¿Quién lee las tiras cómicas? (nosotros)
nosotros leemos

4. ¿Quiénes beben muchos refrescos? (Gabriela y Carlos)
Gabriela y Carlos beben

5. ¿Quién debe estudiar más? (yo)
yo debo estudiar mas

6. ¿Quién promete estudiar mucho? (Donald)
Donald promete

7. ¿Quiénes deben aprender a patinar en monopatín? (Ramona e Isabel)
Ramona e Isabel deben

EXERCISE H. Luis and his friend Víctor always disagree with each other. Tell what Luis says and what Víctor responds.

EXAMPLE: deber comprar una bicicleta nueva / Samuel

LUIS: Samuel **debe** comprar una bicicleta nueva.
VÍCTOR: Samuel **no debe** comprar una bicicleta nueva.

1. esconder el dinero / Anita
LUIS: Anita escode
VÍCTOR: Anita no escode

2. aprender a hablar japonés / Oscar
LUIS: Oscar aprende
VÍCTOR: Oscar No aprende

3. prometer visitar la biblioteca / Esteban y Pablo
LUIS: Esteban y pablo prometen visitar
VÍCTOR: Esteban y pablo no prometen visitar

4. comer mucha fruta / Adriana
LUIS: Adriana come mucha fruta
VÍCTOR: Adriana no come mucha fruta

5. leer el periódico todos los días / nosotros
LUIS: nosotros leemos
VÍCTOR: nosotros no leemos

6. correr en un maratón / Silvia y Luz
LUIS: Silvia y luiz corren
VÍCTOR: Silvia y luiz no corren

EXERCISE I. A new exchange student asks you questions about the school and the students. Answer her questions using the cues provided in parentheses.

EXAMPLES: ¿Dónde comen los estudiantes? (*en la cafetería*)   ¿Lees muchas revistas? (*no*)
Los estudiantes **comen en** la cafetería.   **No, no leo** muchas revistas.

1. ¿Deben Uds. participar en la clase? (*sí*)
Debemos participar

2. ¿Aprenden muchos estudiantes a hablar español? (*sí*)
Sí Aprenden mucho

3. ¿Dónde corres? (*en el gimnasio*)
Corro en el gimnasio

4. ¿Qué lee el profesor en la clase de inglés? (*los exámenes*)
El profesor lee los exámenes

5. ¿Quién esconde su (*his*) teléfono celular? (*Felipe*)

Felipe esconde su teléfono

6. ¿Quiénes responden a las preguntas del profesor? (*los alumnos*)

Los alumnos responden a las preguntas

7. ¿Crees que esta escuela es buena? (*sí*)

Sí, creo que esta escuela es buena

◆4◆ FREQUENTLY USED -IR VERBS

abrir *to open*	**dividir** *to divide*	**recibir** *to receive*
asistir a *to attend*	**escribir** *to write*	**subir** *to go up, climb; to raise*
cubrir *to cover*	**insistir (en)** *to insist on*	**sufrir** *to suffer*
decidir *to decide*	**partir** *to leave, depart*	**vivir** *to live*
describir *to describe*	**permitir** *to permit, allow*	

EXERCISE J. To celebrate "El cinco de mayo," Tamara decides to have a party at her home. Express what she tells a friend about the party.

EXAMPLE: yo / abrir los refrescos   Yo **abro** los refrescos.

1. yo / decidir dar una fiesta

Yo decido dar un Fiesta

2. mis padres / permitir la fiesta

Mis padres permiten

3. tú y yo / escribir las invitaciones

Nosotros escribimos las...

4. tú / cubrir la mesa con un mantel mexicano

tu cubres la mesa

5. mi mamá / insistir en preparar tacos y enchiladas

Mi mamá insiste en...

6. mis hermanos / decidir no ayudarme

mis hermanos deciden no ayudarm

7. todos los amigos / asistir a la fiesta

a Todos... Asistan a la Fiesta

EXERCISE K. Gregory could not attend the team's first game today. His teammates, Ramón and Peter, tell him about it. Express what they say.

1. el equipo / asistir a un partido importante

el equipo asiste a un part

2. tú / decidir descansar

tú decides descansar

3. el entrenador / dividir el equipo en dos grupos

el entrenador divide el eq

4. nosotros / recibir los uniformes temprano

Nosotros Recibimos uniformes tempran

5. Gonzalo / insistir en ser el capitán

Gonzalo insiste ser el capitán

6. Juan y Enrique / decidir ser antipáticos

Juan y Enrique deciden ser antipáticos

7. yo / subir al autobús tarde

Yo subi al autobús tarde

8. el autobús / partir tarde

el Autobus parte tarde

EXERCISE L.   **Imagine you are an exchange student and it's your first day of class. Your classmate David asks you several questions. Answer negatively.**

EXAMPLE: ¿Vives con una familia que habla español?   **No, no vivo** con una familia que habla español.

1. ¿Viven Uds. cerca de la escuela?

No, no vivo cerca de la escuela.

2. ¿Escriben tus padres correos electrónicos todos los días?

No, no escriben correos electrónicos

3. ¿Insiste la familia en muchas reglas?

No, no la familia no insisten reglas. reglas

4. ¿Permiten ellos muchas fiestas en la casa?

No, no permiten ellos no permiten muchas fiestas

5. ¿Asistes a muchos conciertos?

No, no Asiste a muchos conciertos

6. ¿Descubres tú muchas cosas nuevas en tu tiempo libre?

No, no descubre muchas
descubre muchas cosas en mi tiempo libre

EXERCISE M.   **Lee is an avid joker and always responds to what you say with a question. Write the questions she asks for each statement you make.**

EXAMPLE: Los hermanos Silva viven en Costa Rica.   ¿**Viven los hermanos Silva** en Costa Rica?

1. Ellos asisten a un campamento de tenis.

¿Asisten ellos a un campamento?

2. Yo decido practicar con ellos.

¿decides tu a practicar con ellos?

3. Ángel escribe muchas tarjetas a sus amigos en Costa Rica.

¿Escribe muchas turgetas Ángel?

4. Luisa cubre los regalos con un mantel.

¿cubre los regalos con un mantel Luisa?

5. Nosotros siempre dividimos la cuenta.

¿Dividimos la cuenta? siempre

6. El tren para la ciudad parte a las tres y quince.

¿El tren para la ciudad parte a 3:15 el tren para el ciudad?

7. Tú insistes en contestar con preguntas.

¿Insistes tú en contestar con preguntas?

MASTERY EXERCISES

EXERCISE N. Gabriel is a fast talker and, when he speaks, one statement or question always follows another, even if they are not related. Complete his statements / questions with the appropriate form of the verbs given.

1. (*practicar*) Yo _____ el piano cada tarde. ¿Qué _____ tú? Elias _____ el fútbol americano.

2. (*vender*) Este señor _____ globos. Esos niños _____ limonada. Nosotros no _____ nada.

3. (*sufrir*) El equipo _____ cuando no gana. Mi perro _____ cuando hace calor. ¿_____ los gatos también?

4. (*prometer*) Yo _____ llegar a tiempo. Andrés _____ trabajar mucho. ¿Qué _____ tú?

5. (*viajar*) Tú siempre _____ en autobús. María _____ en taxi. ¿En qué _____ nosotros?

6. (*dividir*) Nosotros _____ los gastos. Tú _____ el trabajo. El señor Ramos no _____ la cuenta.

EXERCISE O. A young cousin asks you many questions about school. Answer his questions as indicated.

1. ¿Entras a la escuela a tiempo? *(sí)*

_____

2. ¿Quiénes saludan a la profesora? *(los alumnos)*

_____

3. ¿Quién explica la lección? *(la profesora)*

_____

4. ¿Pasa la clase mucho tiempo en la biblioteca? *(no)*

_____

5. ¿Responden los estudiantes en inglés o en español? *(español)*

_____

6. ¿Dónde comes? *(en la cafetería)*

_____

7. ¿Deben Uds. trabajar mucho? *(sí)*

_____

8. ¿Asisten tú y tus amigos a las mismas clases? *(no)*

_____

9. ¿Lees el periódico en la escuela? *(a veces)*

_____

10. ¿Reciben Uds. buenas notas en los exámenes? *(sí)*

_____

EXERCISE P. **Match the left and right columns and tell who does the following activities.**

yo	correr tres millas cada día
tú	practicar un deporte
mi amigo	leer muchas novelas
mis padres	asistir a una clase de baile
mi hermana y yo	escribir poemas

EXAMPLE: **Pedro ayuda** en casa.

1. _____

2. _____

3. _____

4. _____

5. _____

EXERCISE Q. **You are describing a new student in your school and classes in an electronic message to a friend in Mexico. Include the following information in your message:**

• where she lives

• the languages she speaks (Spanish and French)

• she is now learning English

• the sports she practices

• the classes you and she attend together

• the distance she runs every day

• how well her parents understand English

• how they practice English (newspapers, radio, television)

• the amount of time you spend together

• how she promises to help you in school

EXERCISE R.   **While reading a newspaper from Argentina, you read the following article. Answer the question based on it.**

Un estudio mostró que la gente considera más a la familia, a los hijos, la salud y el trabajo como los principales factores que afectan la felicidad. Por el contrario, las cuestiones relacionadas con el dinero son las que causan mayor infelicidad... la gente no menciona el dinero cuando piensa en felicidad. El dinero apareció como una de las razones de la infelicidad más mencionadas.

Según este artículo, ¿qué afecta poco la infelicidad de las personas?

1. la familia

2. los amigos

3. el dinero

4. las vacaciones

ACTIVIDADES

1. How many things do you do on a given day? In your Spanish journal, write a paragraph in which you describe eight different activities you do on a specific day. Include the people with whom you do some of them and try to use a different verb for each activity.

2. Write a list in Spanish of the chores you need to do around the house during the week and on the weekend. List eight chores using a different verb for each one.

3. Summer vacation has just begun and you would like to share some information about your summer activities with a new friend in Spain. Write a message in Spanish of at least ten sentences in which you describe some of the activities you usually do in the summer, the places you visit and the people with whom you do these things. Use as many different verbs as you can.

2

Present Tense of Stem-Changing Verbs

◆1◆ STEM-CHANGING -*AR* AND -*ER* VERBS

a. Many verbs that contain *e* in the stem change the *e* to *ie* in all present tense forms except those for *nosotros* and *vosotros*.

b. Many verbs that contain *o* in the stem change the *o* to *ue* in all present tense forms except those for *nosotros* and *vosotros*.

c. This change occurs in the syllable directly before the verb ending.

d. The verbs *cerrar, defender, contar,* and *volver* have regular endings in the present tense.

	cerrar *to close*	**defender** *to defend*	**contar** *to count*	**volver** *to return*
yo	c*ie*rro	def*ie*ndo	c*ue*nto	v*ue*lvo
tú	c*ie*rras	def*ie*ndes	c*ue*ntas	v*ue*lves
Ud., él, ella	c*ie*rra	def*ie*nde	c*ue*nta	v*ue*lve
nosotros, -as	cerramos	defendemos	contamos	volvemos
vosotros, -as	cerráis	defendéis	contáis	volvéis
Uds., ellos, ellas	c*ie*rran	def*ie*nden	c*ue*ntan	v*ue*lven

NOTE: All stem–changing verbs that change *e* to *ie* or *o* to *ue* are identified in the glossary by (*ie*) or (*ue*) after the verb.

Frequently Used Stem–Changing Verbs

E to IE

atravesar *to cross*	despertarse *to wake up*	pensar *to think; to intend*
calentar *to heat*	empezar *to begin*	perder *to lose*
cerrar *to close*	encender *to light*	quebrar *to break*
comenzar *to begin*	entender *to understand*	querer *to want; to wish; to love*
confesar *to confess*	gobernar *to govern*	sentarse *to sit down*
defender *to defend*	nevar *to snow*	temblar *to tremble*

O to UE

acordarse (de) *to remember*	envolver *to wrap up*	poder *to be able, can*
acostarse *to go to bed*	jugar (ue) *to play*	probar *to prove, to try, to test*
almorzar *to (eat) lunch*	llover *to rain*	recordar *to remember*
contar *to count*	morder *to bite*	sonar *to sound*
costar *to cost*	mostrar *to show*	soñar (con) *to dream*
devolver *to return, to give back*	mover *to move*	volar *to fly*
encontrar *to find, to meet*	oler (hue) *to smell*	volver *to return*

EXERCISE A. Thomas and his friends are talking about the future. Tell what each one intends to do.

EXAMPLE: Thomas / visitar a España   Thomas **piensa** visitar a España.

1. Elena / estudiar enfermería   _____

2. Ellos / ser jugadores de béisbol   _____

3. yo / escribir una novela   _____

4. Kyoto / volver al Japón   _____

5. Gabriel y yo / visitar un parque
    de atracciones   _____

6. tú / ganar un campeonato   _____

7. los hermanos Silva / trabajar
    con su padre   _____

8. Ignacio / ser abogado   _____

EXERCISE B. Tell what language each of these people understands.

EXAMPLE: Vicenzo / italiano   Vicenzo **entiende** italiano.

1. Marcel / francés   _____

2. Natasha / ruso   _____

3. Sofía y Josefina / rumano   _____

4. Hans y yo / alemán   _____

5. Tú / portugués   _____

6. Uds. / chino   _____

7. Ahmed / árabe   _____

8. el señor Kim / coreano   _____

EXERCISE C. Tell where each of these people eats lunch.

EXAMPLE: Carmen / cafetería de la escuela   Carmen **almuerza en** la cafetería de la escuela.

1. los primos / parque   _____

2. Papá / oficina   _____

3. yo / comedor   _____

4. Sasha y Felipe / restaurante   _____

5. tú / café de la plaza   _____

6. mis abuelos y yo /al aire libre _____

7. el médico / hospital _____

8. el salvavidas / la playa _____

EXERCISE D. **Tell at what time each person returns home.**

EXAMPLE: Florence / a las ocho   Florence **vuelve** a casa a las ocho.

1. yo / a las cuatro _____

2. mis padres / a las siete _____

3. mi hermano / a la una _____

4. tú / a la medianoche _____

5. Richard y Charles / a las once _____

6. Romi y yo / a las nueve _____

EXERCISE E. **Tell who does or doesn't do each of the following things.**

EXAMPLE: los soldados / defender la patria   Los soldados **defienden** la patria.

1. los niños / no atravesar la calle solos _____

2. el portero / cerrar las puertas _____

3. yo / soñar con unas vacaciones

en la playa _____

4. el perro / no morder al niño _____

5. tú / encender la luz del patio _____

6. Roberto y yo / no pensar jugar
al tenis esta tarde

_____

7. yo / calentar la sopa _____

8. tú / devolver el regalo a la tienda _____

9. Uds. / empezar a ahorrar dinero _____

10. nosotros / no probar la comida
japonesa

_____

EXERCISE F. **Answer the questions a Spanish–speaking pen pal asks you about you and your friends. Use the cues provided.**

1. ¿Piensan Uds. asistir a la universidad? *(sí)*

_____

2. ¿Te acuestas tarde todos los días? *(no)*

_____

3. ¿Juegan Uds. al fútbol cuando llueve? *(no)*

_____

4. ¿Piensas tú que el presidente gobierna bien? *(sí)*

_____

5. ¿Pierde frecuentemente el equipo de béisbol de tu escuela? *(no)*

_____

6. ¿Quieren tú y tus amigos visitar mi país? *(sí)*

_____

7. ¿Puedes recordar los cumpleaños de todos tus amigos? *(no)*

_____

8. ¿Cuentan contigo tus amigos? *(sí)*

_____

◆2◆ STEM-CHANGING *-IR* VERBS

a. Some *-ir* verbs that contain an *e* in the stem change the *e* to *ie* or to *i* in all present-tense forms, except those for *nosotros* and *vosotros*.

b. Some *-ir* verbs that contain an *o* in the stem change the *o* to *ue* in all present-tense forms, except those for *nosotros* and *vosotros*.

c. The change occurs in the syllable directly before the verb ending.

d. The verbs *sentir*, *dormir*, and *pedir* have regular endings in the present tense.

	sentir *to regret*	**dormir** *to sleep*	**pedir** *to ask for*
yo	siento	duermo	pido
tú	sientes	duermes	pides
Ud., él, ella	siente	duerme	pide
nosotros, -as	sentimos	dormimos	pedimos
vosotros, -as	sentís	dormís	pedís
Uds., ellos, ellas	sienten	duermen	piden

NOTE: All stem-changing verbs that change *e* to *ie*, *e* to *i*, or *o* to *ue* are identified in the end vocabulary by *(ie)*, *(i)*, or *(ue)* after the verb.

Frequently Used Stem-Changing Verbs

E to IE

preferir   *to prefer*   **referir**   *to tell; to narrate*   **sentir**   *to regret, be sorry; to feel*

O to UE

dormir   *to sleep*   **morir(se)**   *to die*

E to I

despedirse (de)   *to take leave (of),*
   to say goodbye (to)

impedir   *to prevent*

medir   *to measure*

pedir   *to ask for, request; to order (food)*

reír(se)   *to laugh*

reñir   *to quarrel; to scold*

repetir   *to repeat*

servir   *to serve*

sonreír(se)   *to smile*

vestirse   *to get dressed,*
   to dress (oneself)

NOTE: The verbs *reír* and *sonreír* have an accent mark over the *i* in all the present tense forms: *río, ríes, ríe, reímos, reís, ríen.*

EXERCISE G.   **You and your friends are planning a day's outing but can't decide where to go. Tell what each person prefers.**

EXAMPLE: Carina / ir a la piscina   Carina prefiere ir a la piscina.

1. Esther / sentarse en un café. _____

2. Berta y Homero / mirar la televisión _____

3. yo / visitar un museo _____

4. Uds. / caminar en el parque _____

5. Tú / ir al estadio _____

6. Roberto y yo / ver una película _____

EXERCISE H.   **Teddy is describing how the members of his family sleep. Tell what he says.**

EXAMPLE: mi padre / con la boca abierta   Mi padre **duerme** con la boca abierta.

1. yo / con los ojos cerrados _____

2. mi hermano / con un ojo abierto _____

3. mis abuelos / en la silla _____

4. tú / boca abajo _____

5. mi tía Aurora / tranquilamente _____

6. mis hermanos y yo / profundamente _____

EXERCISE I.   **You and several friends are in a Spanish restaurant. Tell what each person orders.**

EXAMPLE: Alex / arroz con pollo   Alex **pide** arroz con pollo.

1. Marisa / paella _____

2. Eddie y Verónica / mariscos _____

3. yo / una chuleta de cerdo _____

4. Larry / cocido _____

5. tú / caldo gallego   _____

6. nosotros / flan de postre   _____

EXERCISE J.   **Tell when each of these people laughs.**

EXAMPLE: Marina / lee las tiras cómicas   Marina **ríe cuando** lee las tiras cómicas.

1. tú / escuchas un chiste   _____

2. Amelia / tiene miedo   _____

3. Arthur y Freda / cometen un error   _____

4. mis amigos y yo / vemos algo cómico   _____

5. yo / mi hermana canta   _____

6. muchas personas / están nerviosas   _____

EXERCISE K.   **Sondra is writing a story about her grandmother. Help her complete it by writing the appropriate form of the verbs indicated in the spaces provided.**

Mi abuela siempre _____ muchos cuentos de su infancia y de su adolescencia. A veces
                           1. (referir)

ella _____ el mismo cuento cinco veces. Ella no nos _____ cuando nosotros se
        2. (repetir)   *3.* (reñir)

lo _____. Muchas veces ella _____ en ropa antigua mientras _____
      4. (recordar)   *5.* (vestirse)   *6.* (referir)

el cuento. Ella _____ en una silla en la sala y mis primos y yo _____ en el
                   7. (sentarse)   *8.* (sentarse)

piso frente a su silla. Ella siempre _____ el cuento con la misma introducción y nosotros
                                        9. (comenzar)

_____. Ninguno de mis primos _____ durante el cuento. Las tías nos
    10. (sonreír)   *11.* (dormirse)

_____ leche y galletas, y mis primos Héctor y Felipe siempre _____ más.
    12. (servir)   *13.* (pedir)

A veces los cuentos son cómicos y Felipe _____ muchísimo. Entonces mi abuela
                                            14. (reír)

le _____ porque él _____ terminar el cuento. Cuando ella termina el cuento,
     15. (reñir)   *16.*(impedir)

ella _____ de nosotros con estas palabras: «Yo lo _____ mucho, pero es el fin
        17. (despedirse)   *18.* (sentir)

del cuento.» Me gustan sus cuentos y yo se los _____ a mis amigos. Son cuentos alegres
                                                  19. (repetir)

porque nadie _____ en ellos.
                20. (morir)

◆ 3 ◆ VERBS ENDING IN *-IAR* AND *-UAR*

    a. Some verbs ending in *-iar* and *-uar* have a written accent mark on the *i* (*í*) or the *u* (*ú*) in all present-tense forms, except those for *nosotros* and *vosotros*.

	enviar *to send*	**continuar** *to continue*
yo	envío	continúo
tú	envías	continúas
Ud., él, ella	envía	continúa
nosotros, -as	enviamos	continuamos
vosotros, -as	enviáis	continuáis
Uds., ellos, ellas	envían	continúan

NOTES:

1. The verbs *anunciar, averiguar, cambiar, copiar, estudiar, iniciar, limpiar, odiar, principiar,* and *pronunciar* are exceptions and have no accents on the *i* or the *u*.

2. All *-iar* and *-uar* verbs that have an accent on the *i* or *u* are identified in the end vocabulary by (*í*) or (*ú*) after the verb.

b. Verbs like *enviar* and *continuar*

actuar *to act*	**resfriarse** *to catch a cold*
confiar (en) *to rely (on), to confide (in)*	**situar** *to place, to locate*
graduarse *to graduate*	**variar** *to vary*
guiar *to guide, to drive (a vehicle)*	

EXERCISE L. **Your friend Lenny's sister is away at school and it's her birthday. Tell what everyone sends her.**

EXAMPLE: su abuela / besos   Su abuela **le envía** besos.

1. yo / una tarjeta de cumpleaños _____

2. sus padres / dinero _____

3. su novio / flores _____

4. su hermana / globos _____

5. sus amigos / un correo electrónico _____

6. tú / un disco compacto _____

7. todo el mundo / felicitaciones _____

EXERCISE M. **June is a busy month for the Vargas family. Everyone seems to be graduating. Tell where they are graduating from.**

EXAMPLE: la hermana mayor / la universidad   La hermana mayor **se gradúa de** la universidad.

1. el hermano menor / la primaria _____

2. Elena y Rosa / la secundaria _____

3. la prima Olivia / el jardín de niños _____

4. la tía Raquel / la Facultad de Leyes _____

5. tú / la Facultad de Medicina _____

6. los primos Tony y Celso /
   la escuela vocacional _____

EXERCISE N.   **Answer the questions a Spanish–speaking exchange student asks you.**

1. ¿Guías el automóvil de tu familia?

_____

2. ¿Continúas las clases de español este año?

_____

3. ¿Te envían tus amigos regalos de cumpleaños?

_____

4. ¿Guían tus amigos su propio carro?

_____

5. ¿Te resfrías fácilmente?

_____

6. ¿Varías tu horario a menudo?

_____

7. ¿Actúan tus amigos y tú en las obras de teatro de la escuela?

_____

8. ¿Te gradúas de la secundaria este año?

_____

◆4◆ VERBS ENDING IN -UIR

a. Verbs ending in *-uir* (but not *-guir*) insert a *y* in the stem before the present–tense endings.

huir *to flee*			
yo	huyo	nosotros, (-as)	huimos
tú	huyes	vosotros, (-as)	huís
Ud., él ,ella	huye	Uds., ellos, ellas	huyen

NOTE: All verbs ending in *-uir* that add a *y* are identified in the end vocabulary by (*y*) after the infinitive.

b. Frequently Used Verbs Ending in *-UIR*

concluir *to conclude*	**destruir** *to destroy*	**influir** *to influence*
construir *to construct, to build*	**distribuir** *to distribute*	**sustituir** *to substitute*
contribuir *to contribute*		

EXERCISE O. One of the clubs in your school is sponsoring a toy drive for charity. Tell what each person contributes.

EXAMPLE: Roger / una pelota   Roger **contribuye** una pelota.

1. el señor Olmeda / un rompecabezas _____

2. Franco / un juguete _____

3. Lisa y Janet / dos animales de peluche _____

4. yo / un guante de béisbol _____

5. tú / una pelota de voleibol _____

6. mi hermano y yo / un juego de damas _____

EXERCISE P. The following observations are made at a public town-hall meeting. Complete each one with the appropriate form of the verb in parentheses.

1. Los políticos (*influir*) _____ mucho en la vida del pueblo.

2. Los perros (*destruir*) _____ las plantas y las flores de los parques.

3. Mi vecino (*construir*) _____ una fuente grande entre las dos casas.

4. Lázaro y yo (*distribuir*) _____ muchos folletos a favor de la conservación.

5. Muchas veces tú (*sustituir*) _____ una idea por otra.

6. Los comerciantes (*contribuir*) _____ mucho dinero a las obras públicas.

7. La reunión (*concluir*) _____ con muchos aplausos.

MASTERY EXERCISES

EXERCISE Q. Tell who does the following things.

preferir ver una telenovela	servir el café	graduarse de la escuela
pensar viajar en el verano	guiar el carro	no resfriarse
acostarse temprano	resolver el problema	actuar en una película
morder un hueso		

1. Mi hermano mayor _____.

2. El bebé _____.

3. Los matemáticos _____.

4. Yo _____.

5. La actriz _____.

6. El perro _____.

7. Tú _____

8. Mi mamá _____.

9. El mesero _____.

10. Los médicos _____.

EXERCISE R.   Match the situation in column A with an appropriate reaction in column B. Then, using that reaction, write what these people do.

EXAMPLE: Papá está muy cansado.   dormir la siesta
Papá **duerme** la siesta.

A

Yo recuerdo que es el cumpleaños de mi novia.
Alicia tiene que llegar a la escuela a las 7:30.
Mi mamá quiere comprar una alfombra nueva.
Los niños están muy contentos.
El arquitecto necesita una casa más grande.
A Susana le gustan los deportes.
Tú compras dos regalos pero necesitas tres.

B

a. jugar al tenis y al voleibol
b. reír mucho
c. volver a la tienda
d. enviar una tarjeta
e. medir el cuarto
f. despertarse temprano
g. construir una casa grande

1. _____

2. _____

3. _____

4. _____

5. _____

6. _____

7. _____

EXERCISE S.   Use the cues provided to answer the questions a friend asks you.

1. ¿Cuántas horas duermes cada noche? (*ocho*)

_____

2. ¿Cuándo te acuestas? (*tarde*)

_____

3. ¿Cuándo te despiertas? (*temprano*)

_____

4. ¿Dónde almuerzan tus amigos y tú? (*la cafetería de la escuela*)

_____

5. ¿Cuánto cuesta el almuerzo? (*tres dólares*)

_____

6. ¿Cuándo sonríes? (*estoy contento*)

_____

7. ¿Qué trabajo tienes los sábados? (*distribuir folletos*)

_____

> **EXERCISE T.**   **You are participating in a Habitat for Humanity project during your summer vacation. Write a description in your Spanish journal about this experience. You may wish to include the following:**

- You are participating in a summer project in another city.

- You meet a lot of people.

- You and other teenagers are constructing houses.

- The people ask for large rooms.

- The architects include several large rooms in the plan.

- Each room costs a different amount.

- They begin the construction in the spring.

- We do not work when it rains.

- If the weather is bad, we lose a lot of time.

- You are able to help them only during vacation.

- They intend to finish on time.

- Sometimes a few teenagers quarrel with other teenagers.

- They usually laugh a lot also.

- The project relies a lot on young volunteers like you.

⟨ A C T I V I D A D E S ⟩

You are traveling in Spain with your family. Write an email in Spanish to a friend at home, in which you relate the people you meet on the trip, what you want to do during the trip, how you are managing in a Spanish-speaking country, the foods you are trying, and other interesting details. Try to use as many of the verbs as you can from this chapter.

Verbs with Spelling Changes in the Present Tense

◆1◆ VERBS ENDING IN -*CER* AND -*CIR*

a. Most verbs whose infinitives end in -*cer* and -*cir* have the ending -*zco* in the first-person singular of the present tense. This pattern occurs only if a vowel precedes the *c* in the infinitive.

	ofrecer *to offer*	**producir** *to produce*
yo	ofrezco	produzco
tú	ofreces	produces
Ud., él, ella	ofrece	produces
nosotros, -as	ofrecemos	producimos
vosotros, -as	ofrecéis	producís
Uds., ellos, ellas	ofrecen	producen

b. If a consonant precedes the *c* in the infinitive, the ending -*zo* is used in the first–person singular of the present tense.

vencer	*to conquer, defeat*		
yo	venzo	nosotros, -as	vencemos
tú	vences	vosotros, -as	vencéis
Ud., él, ella	vence	Uds., ellos, ellas	vencen

NOTE: Verbs with these spelling changes are identified in the glossary by (*z*) or (*zc*) after the infinitive.

c. Frequently Used Verbs with Spelling Changes

    1. -*CER* Verbs (like *ofrecer*)

agradecer *to thank (for)*	**nacer** *to be born*	**parecer** *to seem*
aparecer *to appear*	**obedecer** *to obey*	**permanecer** *to remain*
conocer *to know (a person)*	**ofrecer** *to offer*	**pertenecer** *to belong*
desaparecer *to disappear*	**padecer** *to suffer*	**reconocer** *to recognize*
merecer *to deserve*		

    2. -*CER* Verbs (like *vencer*)

convencer *to convince*	**vencer** *to conquer, to defeat*
ejercer *to exert, to practice (a profession)*	

    3. -*CIR* Verbs

conducir *to lead, to drive*	**reducir** *to reduce*
producir *to produce*	**traducir** *to translate*

NOTE: The verbs *hacer* and *decir* are exceptions.

EXERCISE A.   **Tell who obeys and who follows rules.**

EXAMPLE: los soldados / el toque de queda   Los soldados **obedecen** el toque de queda.

1. el chofer / el semáforo rojo _____

2. el perro / a su dueño _____

3. los ciudadanos / las leyes _____

4. yo / a mis padres _____

5. tú / al entrenador del equipo _____

6. Sabrina y yo / las reglas del juego _____

EXERCISE B.   **The president of the freshman class is mentioning the places in the school with which each of them is already familiar.**

EXAMPLE: Humberto / la biblioteca   Humberto **ya conoce** la biblioteca.

1. Sarita y Mercedes / el teatro _____

2. Felipe / la cafetería _____

3. Ralph y yo / el gimnasio _____

4. tú / la piscina _____

5. yo / los laboratorios _____

6. Miguel / la oficina del director _____

EXERCISE C.   **The Spanish Club is planning for a visit by Spanish-speaking exchange students to their school. Tell what the members volunteer to translate for them.**

EXAMPLE: Ruth / el manual estudiantil   Ruth **traduce** el manual estudiantil.

1. yo / el menú de la cafetería

_____

2. Larry / los anuncios diarios

_____

3. Nilda e Inés / las reglas de seguridad

_____

4. Ana y yo / la tarea

_____

5. tú / un artículo del periódico estudiantil

_____

6. Bárbara / el horario de los partidos de fútbol

_____

EXERCISE D.   Using the suggestions, tell the profession each of these people practices.

SUGGESTIONS: actor   maestro   médico   entrenador personal
pintor   mecánico   mesero

EXAMPLE: Alfredo les enseña a las personas en el gimnasio.
Alfredo ejerce la profesión de **entrenador personal.**

1. Mi hermana le enseña a los alumnos.

_____

2. Mi madre cura a los enfermos.

_____

3. Mi tío arregla los carros.

_____

4. Yo trabajo en un restaurante y les sirvo a los clientes.

_____

5. Tú pintas muchos cuadros bonitos.

_____

6. Gladys y yo trabajamos en el teatro.

_____

EXERCISE E.   Complete with the appropriate form of the verbs indicated the letter that Gabriel wrote to Guy shortly after his arrival in Santander.

Querido Guy:

Yo _____ mucho toda tu ayuda antes de la hora del viaje. _____ que yo
   1. (agradecer)   *2.* (parecer)

_____ de la mala costumbre de dejarlo todo para el último momento. Tú _____
   3. (padecer)   *4.* (parecer)

ser mi único buen amigo. Mis otros amigos _____ cuando más los necesito. Esta ciudad
                                                                              5. (desaparecer)

_____ mucho para el turista. Hay museos, teatros, cines, parques, playa y restaurantes
   6. (ofrecer)

buenos. Yo ya _____ los restaurantes baratos y los cafés donde se reúnen los jóvenes.
                              7. (conocer)

El chofer del autobús en que viajamos _____ muy rápido y _____ que
                                                                      8. (conducir)   *9.* (parecer)

no _____ las señales de tránsito. El guía _____ todo y _____
       10. (obedecer)   *11.* (traducir)   *12.* (permanecer)

con el grupo todo el día. El _____ antes del desayuno y no _____ hasta después
                                          13. (aparecer)   *14.* (desaparecer)

de la cena. Yo _____ a un grupo de jóvenes divertidos y nosotros _____
                        15. (pertenecer)   *16.* (reconocer)

que tenemos los mismos intereses. Nos levantamos temprano cada día y corremos dos millas en el parque.

Ellos me _____ de permanecer en España por más tiempo. Es todo por ahora.
                  17.(convencer)

Hasta pronto, mi buen amigo.

Saludos de,

Gabriel

◆2◆ VERBS ENDING IN *-GER* AND *-GIR*

a. Most verbs whose infinitives end in *-ger* and *-gir* have the ending *-jo* in the first–person singular of the present tense.

b. This pattern occurs to preserve the original sound in accordance with the rules for Spanish pronunciation.

	proteger *to protect*	**dirigir** *to direct*
yo	prote**jo**	diri**jo**
tú	proteges	diriges
Ud., él, ella	protege	dirige
nosotros, -as	protegemos	dirigimos
vosotros, -as	protegéis	dirigís
Uds., ellos, ellas	protegen	dirigen

NOTE: Verbs with these spelling changes are identified in the end vocabulary by (*j*) after the infinitive.

c. Frequently Used *-GER* and *-GIR* Verbs

coger *to seize, to catch*	**recoger** *to pick up, to gather*	**dirigirse** *to make one's way toward, to address*
escoger *to choose*	**corregir (i)** *to correct*	
proteger *to protect*	**dirigir** *to direct*	**elegir (i)** *to elect*

EXERCISE F. Everyone is helping to pick up after the party. Tell what each person picks up.

EXAMPLE: Gina / vasos   Gina **recoge** los vasos.

1. Anthony / platos sucios _____

2. Javier y Joan / discos compactos _____

3. yo / decoraciones _____

4. Frida y yo / botellas vacías _____

5. tú / papeles _____

6. Alice / velas _____

EXERCISE G. At summer camp everyone has to choose a sport. Tell which sport each person chooses.

SUGGESTIONS: el béisbol   el fútbol   la natación
                la equitación   el golf   el voleibol

EXAMPLE: A Carlos le gusta jugar con una o dos personas.   Carlos **escoge el tenis.**

1. A mí me gusta ir a la playa cuando hace mucho calor.

Yo _____ .

2. A Robert le gusta correr y patear una pelota.

Robert _____ .

3. A Manny y a José les gusta caminar mucho y meter una pelota en un hoyo.

Manny y José _____ .

4. A ti te gusta montar a caballo.

Tú _____ .

5. A Pablo y a mí nos gusta batear pelotas.

Pablo y yo _____ .

6. A Daniel le gusta pasar una pelota de un lado de la red a otro.

Daniel _____ .

(EXERCISE H.)   **Use the cues provided to tell who directs what activity.**

EXAMPLE: el policía / dirigir el tránsito   El policía **dirige** el tránsito.

1. Susana / dirigir una orquesta   _____

2. Enrique /dirigir a los actores   _____

3. tú / dirigir una banda   _____

4. yo / dirigir a los mecánicos   _____

5. mis padres / dirigir a los jardineros   _____

6. Carol y yo / dirigir al perro   _____

◆3◆ Verbs Ending in -*GUIR*

a. Most verbs whose infinitives end in -*guir* have the ending -*go* in the first-person singular of the present tense.

b. This pattern occurs to preserve the original sound in accordance with the rules for Spanish pronunciation.

distinguir *to distinguish*			
yo	distingo	nosotros, -as	distinguimos
tú	distingues	vosotros, -as	distinguís
Ud., él, ella	distingue	Uds., ellos, ellas	distinguen

NOTE: Verbs with these spelling changes are identified in the end vocabulary by (*g*) after the infinitive.

c. Frequently Used -*GUIR* Verbs

conseguir (i)   *to get, to obtain, to succeed in*   perseguir (i)   *to pursue*

distinguir   *to distinguish*   seguir (i)   *to follow, to continue*

extinguir   *to extinguish*

EXERCISE I.   **Complete each statement with an appropriate form of *distinguir* to explain each person's doubt.**

1. Los padres de Héctor siempre lo castigan. Héctor no _____ entre lo bueno y lo malo.

2. ¿Es una corbata verde o azul? Yo no _____ los colores.

3. El gato duerme todo el día y quiere jugar por la noche. El gato no _____ entre el día y la noche.

4. ¿Es un mango o una papaya? Nosotros no _____ los sabores.

5. ¿Es un teatro o una iglesia? Tú no _____ bien los edificios.

6. ¿Es un diamante o una esmeralda? La señora no _____ las piedras preciosas.

EXERCISE J.   **Combine the words in the two columns to tell who does what (use the verb *seguir*).**

yo	los consejos de los profesores
el atleta	la misma carrera que nuestro padre
la señora	las instrucciones del médico
los enfermos	la misma ruta a la ciudad
tú	una dieta muy estricta
mis hermanos y yo	un régimen de ejercicios
el chofer	la receta

EXAMPLE: tú / la receta   Tú **sigues** la receta.

1. _____

2. _____

3. _____

4. _____

5. _____

6. _____

MASTERY EXERCISES

EXERCISE K.   **Beto's little brother always wants to be the center of attention. He contradicts everything he hears. Tell what he says.**

EXAMPLE: El policía persigue al ladrón.   ¡No! **Yo persigo** al ladrón.

1. Elena sigue el plano de la ciudad.

_____

2. Rogelio y yo escogemos la película.

_____

3. El profesor corrige la frase.

_____

4. Mamá conoce a los nuevos vecinos.

_____

5. El niño explorador merece una medalla.

_____

6. Geraldo y Larry nunca obedecen las señales de tránsito.

_____

7. Tú nunca recoges las hojas en el jardín.

_____

8. Los bomberos extinguen el fuego.

_____

9. Susan escoge una bicicleta azul.

_____

10. Aniluz consigue un boleto para el concierto.

_____

11. El perro siempre desaparece cuando hay un problema.

_____

12. José convence a sus padres fácilmente.

_____

EXERCISE L.   **Answer the questions your new friend asks you.**

1. ¿Escoges con cuidado a tus amigos ?

_____

2. ¿Les agradeces a tus amigos los favores que ellos te hacen?

_____

3. ¿Distingues entre la realidad y el sueño?

_____

4. ¿Corriges tus faltas?

_____

5. ¿Vences a tus rivales?

_____

6. ¿Proteges a tus hermanos?

_____

7. ¿Conoces a tus vecinos?

_____

8. ¿Ofreces ayuda en casa?

_____

9. ¿Desapareces cuando hay algo que hacer?

_____

10. ¿Consigues buenas notas en todas las clases?

_____

11. ¿Obedeces a tus padres?

_____

12. ¿Conduces un automóvil?

_____

13. ¿Recoges tus libros antes de salir de casa?

_____

14. ¿Sigues las noticias todos los días?

_____

15. ¿Padeces de dolor de cabeza?

_____

EXERCISE M. **Manuel attends a bilingual school and is running for president of the student government. Help him express what he plans to say at the election assembly in Spanish.**

- when the students elect the president of the student government

- the term of office

- the structure of the election, for example, the number of candidates

- what the president leads

- what he offers to the position

- why he deserves the support of the students

- what results his efforts will produce

- the principles he follows

- how the election is determined (the candidate with the most votes wins)

- why he deserves to win

◁ A C T I V I D A D E S ▷

1. Imagine that you are at a summer camp. Email your Spanish-speaking pen pal and describe your experience there. Write at least ten sentences in Spanish, using as many verbs from this chapter as possible.

You may use the following:

Salutation: **Querido(-a) _____:**
Closing: **Tu amigo(-a),**

2. Find ten pictures in a magazine, newspaper, or Web site that reflect the action of ten of the verbs presented in this chapter. Paste each picture on a sheet of paper and write a sentence below each one to describe it.

4

Verbs Irregular in the Present Tense

◆ 1 ◆ VERBS WITH IRREGULAR *YO* FORMS

a. In the present tense, the following verbs have irregular *yo* forms:

caber *to fit*	*quepo,* cabes, cabe, cabemos, cabéis, caben
dar *to give*	*doy,* das, da, damos, dais, dan
hacer *to make, to do*	*hago,* haces, hace, hacemos, hacéis, hacen
poner *to put, to place*	*pongo,* pones, pone, ponemos, ponéis, ponen
saber *to know*	*sé,* sabes, sabe, sabemos, sabéis, saben
salir *to go out*	*salgo,* sales, sale, salimos, salís, salen
valer *to be worth*	*valgo,* vales, vale, valemos, valéis, valen
ver *to see, to watch*	*veo,* ves, ve, vemos, veis, ven

b. The *yo* form of *caer* (to fall) and *traer* (to bring) has an *i* between the stem and the first-person singular ending (*-go*). Their other forms are regular.

caer *to fall*	*caigo,* caes, cae, caemos, caéis, caen
traer *to bring*	*traigo,* traes, trae, traemos, traéis, traen

EXERCISE A.   **Your friend Edgar is telling his parents all the things he can now do after attending camp for the first time. Follow the example and express what he says.**

EXAMPLE: hacer la cama   Yo **sé** hacer la cama.

1. trabajar en la computadora   _____

2. patinar en monopatín   _____

3. montar a caballo   _____

4. jugar al voleibol   _____

5. tocar el violín   _____

6. identificar las estrellas   _____

EXERCISE B.   **A group of young people are telling what they do after school. Express what each one says.**

EXAMPLE: Silvia / hacer la tarea   Yo **hago** la tarea.

1. Humberto / hacer ejercicios   _____

2. Amelia / ver mi programa favorito   _____

3. Peter / salir con mis amigos   _____

4. Virginia / poner las cosas en su lugar   _____

5. Alejandro / dar de comer a los gatos   _____

EXERCISE C. Your sister received an e-mail message from a friend who lives in Madrid, but the communication wasn't clear. Help her decipher the message by filling in the missing words.

Querida amiga:

Todos los días yo _____ planes diferentes para pasar las vacaciones de verano. Aquí
                    1. (hacer)

te _____ el plan más reciente. _____ de Madrid el 10 de julio en el vuelo
       2. (poner)   3. (salir)

400 de Iberia. Te _____ el número de teléfono de mi tía: 892 61 12. Yo te _____
                  4. (dar)   5. (ver)

pronto. Saludos.

                                        Emilio

EXERCISE D. Jeremy is trying to decorate and organize his room but things aren't going well for him. Describe what's happening.

EXAMPLE: el reloj / al suelo   El reloj **cae** al suelo.

1. la tarea / en la cesta de basura   _____

2. los discos / detrás del mueble   _____

3. las cortinas / de las ventanas   _____

4. el balón de fútbol / debajo de la cama   _____

5. los carteles / de la pared   _____

6. el refresco / al suelo   _____

EXERCISE E. Guillermo is organizing a party to celebrate the end of the school year. Tell what his friends bring to the party.

EXAMPLE: Gerardo / las papitas   Gerardo **trae** las papitas.

1. tú / los refrescos   _____

2. Marisol / las palomitas   _____

3. Alicia y yo / los sándwiches   _____

4. yo / el estéreo   _____

5. Kenji / los adornos   _____

6. Tony y Yolanda / los platos   _____

◆2◆ VERBS WITH IRREGULAR PRESENT-TENSE FORMS

The following verbs are irregular in the present tense:

decir *to say, to tell*	digo, dices, dice, decimos, decís, dicen
estar *to be*	estoy, estás, está, estamos, estáis, están
ir to go	voy, vas, va, vamos, váis, van

oír *to hear*	oigo, oyes, oye, oímos, oís, oyen
ser *to be*	soy, eres, es, somos, sois, son
tener *to have*	tengo, tienes, tiene, tenemos, tenéis, tienen
venir *to come*	vengo, vienes, viene, venimos, venís, vienen

EXERCISE F. It's the first day of summer vacation. Tell where the following people go.

EXAMPLE: Margarita / al centro comercial   Margarita **va** al centro comercial.

1. Luis / a la playa   _____

2. mis hermanos / al parque   _____

3. Gloria / al cine   _____

4. yo / al centro   _____

5. Esteban y José / al museo   _____

6. Migdalia y yo / al restaurante   _____

EXERCISE G. You are showing a friend some photographs of your trip to Mexico. Tell where each person is in the photos.

EXAMPLE: Lina y Beatriz están delante de la iglesia.

1. Ernesto y Lorenzo _____

_____ .

3. Mis padres _____

_____ .

2. Yo _____

_____ .

4. Ruthie _____

_____ .

5. Roberto y yo _____   **6.** Yo _____
_____ .   _____ .

EXERCISE H.   **Tell when each of the following people comes to school.**

EXAMPLE: los profesores / 7:00   Los profesores **vienen** a las siete.

1. yo / 8:15   _____

2. el director / 7:30   _____

3. mis amigos / 8:30   _____

4. tú / 8:00   _____

5. Armando y yo / 7:45   _____

6. Elena / 9:00   _____

EXERCISE I.   **Tell each person's profession, according to the job description.**

EXAMPLE: La señora Ramos da clases.   La señora Ramos **es maestra.**

1. La señorita Mateo cuida a los enfermos en su consultorio.

La señorita Mateo _____ .

2. Pablo vende cosas en un almacén grande.

Pablo _____ .

3. Tú apagas incendios.

Tú _____ .

4. Felipe y yo asistimos a la universidad.

Felipe y yo _____ .

5. Los señores Alba diseñan edificios.

Los señores Alba _____ .

6. Yo cuido a los nadadores en la playa en el verano.

Yo _____ .

EXERCISE J.   **You and several friends are hiking in the woods. Tell what each one hears.**

EXAMPLE: Gabriel **oye** el canto de los pájaros.

1. Yo _____ el ruido de un helicóptero.

2. Ralph y Ted _____ los pasos de otros excursionistas.

3. Tú _____ el zumbido de las abejas.

4. Susan _____ el sonido de un teléfono.

5. Elias y yo _____ el viento en las hojas.

EXERCISE K. Use the phrases below to tell what each person says in the following situations.

Gracias.	Buen provecho.	Adiós.	Buenos días.
Mucho gusto.	Igualmente.	Hola.	Salud.

EXAMPLE: Lola sale de la casa.   Lola dice **adiós.**

1. Entras en la casa de un amigo. Su familia cena.

Yo _____ .

2. Ricardo acaba de conocer a Carlos y a Jaime.

Él _____ y Carlos y Jaime _____ .

3. Tú acabas de estornudar.

Tu mamá _____ .

4. Antonia contesta el teléfono.

Ella _____ .

5. Tus padres ven a un vecino.

Ellos _____ .

6. Tú y tu hermano reciben un regalo de sus abuelos.

Ustedes _____ .

EXERCISE L. Describe each picture below using an expression with *tener*.

EXAMPLE: Ricky **tiene miedo.**

1. Las chicas _____

_____ .

2. Alberto _____

_____ .

3. Tú _____

_____ .

5. Yo _____

_____ .

4. Miriam _____

_____ .

6. Ellos_____

_____ .

EXERCISE M.   **Use the cues provided to answer your friend's questions.**

1. ¿Adónde vas mañana? (*a la playa*)   _____

2. ¿Sabes nadar bien? (*sí*)   _____

3. ¿A qué hora sales de la casa? (*7:30*)   _____

4. ¿Tienes que viajar en autobús a la
playa? (*sí*)   _____

5. ¿Haces ejercicios en la playa? (*sí*)   _____

6. ¿A quiénes ves allí? (*a mis amigos*)   _____

7. ¿Qué oyes en la playa?
(*los gritos de los niños*)   _____

8. ¿A qué hora vienes a la casa? (*3:30*)   _____

EXERCISE N.   **Complete the note that Marta leaves for her mother.**

Querida mamá:

_____ mediodía. Yo _____ muy contenta porque Arturo _____ a visitarme.
  1. (ser)   2. (estar)   3. (venir)

Él _____ de Costa Rica y _____ simpático. Nosotros _____ a ir al centro.
   4. (ser)   5. (ser)   6. (ir)

Yo _____ que comprar un libro para mi clase de inglés. Puesto que la librería _____
   7. (tener)   8. (estar)

cerca del cine, nosotros _____ a ver una película. Yo _____ a estar en casa a eso de las
                              9. (ir)   *10.* (ir)

cinco y media.

Nos vemos,

Marta

⟨ MASTERY EXERCISES ⟩

EXERCISE O.   **Migdalia describes her host family in Venezuela to a friend. Complete her account
with the appropriate form of the verbs in parentheses.**

Vivo con una familia muy agradable. _____ la familia Sagunto. Ellos _____
                                          1. (ser)   *2.* (ser)

de la Argentina pero ahora _____ en Caracas porque el señor Sagunto trabaja en la
                                3. (estar)

Embajada Argentina. La señora Sagunto _____ periodista. El periodismo _____
                                            4. (ser)   *5.* (ser)

una profesión muy interesante y divertida. Los Sagunto _____ tres hijos: Raúl
                                                              6. (tener)

_____ dieciséis años y Pilar e Hilda _____ catorce. Ellas
      7. (tener)   *8.* (tener)

_____ gemelas. Su casa _____ en una parte muy pintoresca de la ciudad.
      9. (ser)   *10.* (estar)

Desde la ventana de mi dormitorio yo _____ la salida del sol cada mañana porque el
                                           11. (ver)

dormitorio _____ al este. También _____ un parque que _____
            12. (dar)   *13.* (ver)   *14.* (tener)

muchos árboles. Nosotros _____ al parque a menudo, y a veces el perro
                              15. (ir)

_____ también. Coquito _____ un perro cómico y bien educado,
      16. (ir)   *17.* (ser)

pero a veces yo _____ sus ladridos a las seis de la mañana, cuando el vecino
                    18. (oír)

_____ del trabajo. A la familia le gusta pasar mucho tiempo juntos. Ellos _____
      19. (venir)   *20.* (ser)

aficionados al camping y los sábados, temprano por la mañana, ellos _____ todo el equipo
                                                                        21. (poner)

de acampar en su camioneta y _____ para las montañas o un lago. Yo _____
                                  22. (salir)   *23.* (ir)

con ellos y siempre _____ mi diccionario conmigo: _____ un amigo fiel
                        24. (traer)   *25.* (ser)

y útil. Nosotros apenas _____ en la camioneta porque nosotros _____
                            26. (caber)   *27.* (traer)

tantas cosas: el equipo de acampar, el equipo deportivo y la comida. Durante el fin de semana

nosotros _____ muchas cosas divertidas al aire libre. Ahora yo _____ planes
            28. (hacer)   *29.* (hacer)

de seguir esta rutina y _____ muy contenta.
                            30. (estar)

EXERCISE P. Select the appropriate reaction for each situation and express what you do.

darles un regalo

salir aprisa de la casa

ir a la fiesta

ver el horario de los estrenos

oír el pronóstico del tiempo

hacer la cama

ir al parque

tener que estudiar

poner la mesa

decir buenas noches

1. Hay una fiesta en casa de Elena.

Yo _____ .

2. Es el aniversario de mis abuelos

Yo _____ .

3. Pienso ir a la playa mañana.

Yo _____ .

4. Yo pienso ir al cine con mis amigos.

Yo _____ .

5. El autobús escolar pasa en un minuto.

Yo _____ .

6. Debo arreglar mi cuarto.

Yo _____ .

7. Ayudo a mi madre con los preparativos de la cena.

Yo _____ .

8. Quiero jugar al béisbol.

Yo _____ .

9. Es hora de acostarme.

Yo _____ .

10. Hay un examen mañana en la clase de historia.

Yo _____ .

EXERCISE Q. A friend stops by your house as you are getting ready to leave on a trip. Answer his questions using the cues provided.

1. ¿Quién es tu compañero de viaje? *(mi primo)*

_____

2. ¿Adónde van ustedes? *(España)*

_____

3. ¿Qué clase de vuelo tienen ustedes? *(directo)*

_____

4. ¿A qué hora salen ustedes de la casa? *(4:00)*

_____

5. ¿En cuántas maletas cabe la ropa? *(2)*

_____

6. ¿A qué hora llegan ustedes a España? *(no saber)*

_____

7. ¿Qué traes en la maleta de mano? *(el pasaporte y el dinero)*

_____

8. ¿Qué haces durante el vuelo? *(nada)*

_____

9. ¿Cuánto vale todo el viaje? *($1,500)*

_____

10. ¿Qué ves por la ventanilla del avión? *(las nubes)*

_____

EXERCISE R.   **You e-mail your Spanish pen pal to tell her your plans for next week. You may wish to include the following:**

- where you are going and when
- why you have chosen that destination
- how you become aware of which clothing to bring
- when you will be traveling
- what you bring with you
- why you include sneakers
- where you put your things to carry them
- who accompanies you sometimes
- some of the natural things you will see
- your appraisal of the experience
- why you generally enjoy it

CHAPTER

5

The Imperative

The imperative is the verb form used to give commands.

◆ 1 ◆ FORMAL COMMANDS

a. Formal commands (*Ud., Uds.*) are used with persons you would normally address with *usted* (strangers, adults).

b. The formal command is formed from the *yo* form of the present tense. The final *-o* is changed as follows:

-ar verbs: *-e* for *Ud.* (singular) and *-en* for *Uds.* (plural).

-er verbs: } *-a* for *Ud.* (singular) and *-an* for *Uds.* (plural).
-ir verbs:

INFINITIVE	PRESENT TENSE YO FORM	COMMAND FORMS SINGULAR	PLURAL	MEANING
caer	caigo	caiga	caigan	*fall*
comer	como	coma	coman	*eat*
decir	digo	diga	digan	*say*
escribir	escribo	escriba	escriban	*write*
hacer	hago	haga	hagan	*do, make*
huir	huyo	huya	huyan	*flee*
oír	oigo	oiga	oigan	*hear*
poner	pongo	ponga	pongan	*put*
salir	salgo	salga	salgan	*leave*
tener	tengo	tenga	tengan	*have*
tomar	tomo	tome	tomen	*take*
traducir	traduzco	traduzca	traduzcan	*translate*
traer	traigo	traiga	traigan	*bring*
venir	vengo	venga	vengan	*come*
ver	veo	vea	vean	*see*

NOTES:

1. The vowel of the endings of the command forms are the opposite of the vowel endings of the *él / ella / Ud.* form of the present tense: *-e* for *-ar* verbs, and *-a* for *-er* and *-ir* verbs.

2. *Ud.* and *Uds.* follow the verb, but are usually omitted.

3. In Spanish America, *Uds.* can be either formal or informal (familiar).

c. To form the negative command, place no before the verb.

No griten.   *Don't shout.*

No salga ahora.   *Don't leave now.*

d. Stem-changing Verbs

The formal command (*Ud.*) is formed from the yo form of the present tense. The final *o-* is changed as follows:

-ar verbs: *-e* for *Ud.* and *-en* for *Uds.*

-er verbs: ⎫
-ir verbs: ⎬ *-a* for *Ud.* and *-an* for *Uds.*

E TO IE VERBS	PRESENT TENSE YO FORM	COMMAND FORMS SINGULAR	PLURAL	MEANING
pensar	pienso	piense	piensen	*think*
defender	defiendo	defienda	defiendan	*defend*
referir	refiero	refiera	refieran	*tell*

E TO I VERBS	PRESENT TENSE YO FORM	COMMAND FORMS SINGULAR	PLURAL	MEANING
medir	mido	mida	midan	*measure*
pedir	pido	pida	pidan	*ask (for)*

O TO UE VERBS	PRESENT TENSE YO FORM	COMMAND FORMS SINGULAR	PLURAL	MEANING
contar	cuento	cuente	cuenten	*count*
mover	muevo	mueva	muevan	*move*
dormir	duermo	duerma	duerman	*sleep*

e. Verbs with Spelling Changes

Verbs that end in *-zar*, *-car*, and *-gar*, *-ger*, *-gir*, and *-guir* have spelling changes in the command forms. The spelling change in these verbs occurs to keep the original sound in the infinitive form.

INFINITIVE	PRESENT TENSE YO FORM	COMMAND FORMS SINGULAR	PLURAL	MEANING
comenzar	comienzo	comience	comiencen	*begin*
practicar	practico	practique	practiquen	*practice*
llegar	llego	llegue	lleguen	*arrive*
escoger	escojo	escoja	escojan	*choose*
corregir	corrijo	corrija	corrijan	*correct*
seguir	sigo	siga	sigan	*follow, continue*

EXERCISE A.   **You are preparing a recipe for a class cookbook. Complete the recipe by changing the infinitives to the appropriate command forms.**

EXAMPLE: sacar los ingredientes necesarios   **Saque** los ingredientes necesarios.

1. poner dos tazas de agua en un
     caldero de tamaño mediano   _____

2. hervir el agua   _____

3. añadir el arroz, una cucharada de aceite
de oliva o margarina y las especias   _____

4. revolver bien con un cucharón   _____

5. volver a hervir el arroz por un minuto   _____

6. cubrir el caldero bien   _____

7. reducir el fuego al mínimo   _____

8. cocinar por 25 minutos   _____

9. apagar el fuego   _____

10. servir en seguida con carne o pollo   _____

EXERCISE B.   **Your teacher is telling the class what they should do in preparation for a major examination. Complete each statement with the appropriate form of the verb infinitive.**

EXAMPLE: estudiar la noche anterior   **Estudien** la noche anterior.

1. llegar a tiempo   _____

2. traer un bolígrafo y un lápiz   _____

3. tomar el asiento asignado   _____

4. prestar atención al profesor   _____

5. no hablar con su vecino   _____

6. abrir el examen al recibir la señal   _____

7. leer todo con cuidado   _____

8. seguir las instrucciones   _____

9. trabajar diligente y rápidamente   _____

10. contestar todas las preguntas   _____

11. repasar sus respuestas   _____

12. no salir hasta la hora indicada   _____

EXERCISE C.   **In preparation for your first driving experience, the driver education teacher gives you the following instructions. Give the appropriate form of the infinitive.**

EXAMPLE: (*entrar*) _____ en el carro con cuidado.
            Entre en el carro con cuidado.

1. (*cerrar*)   _____ la puerta del carro.

2. (*ajustar*)   _____ el asiento y los espejos.

3. (*abrochar*) _____ el cinturón de seguridad.

4. (*poner*) _____ la llave en el motor.

5. (*arrancar*) _____ el motor.

6. (*mirar*) _____ los espejos antes de salir del estacionamiento.

7. (*acelerar*) _____ poco a poco.

8. (*usar*) _____ las señales de tránsito.

9. (*anticipar*) _____ cuando tiene que poner los frenos.

10. (*no mirar*) _____ al pasajero.

11. (*conducir*) _____ con cuidado.

EXERCISE D. You have been asked to prepare a radio announcement for the *Restaurante La Reja*. Base your radio announcement on the information contained in the newspaper ad shown below. Use the following verbs in your announcement: *bailar, celebrar, compartir, disfrutar, escuchar, llamar, pasar, pedir,* and *probar.*

Si quiere comer bien y pasar un rato agradable al mismo tiempo,

el *Restaurante La Reja* le ofrece:

- Comidas típicas
- Especialidades diarias
- Salón para fiestas privadas
- Ambiente intimo
- Música en vivo
- Pista de baile

Calle Mayor, 10   Reservaciones: 5-80-90-00

EXAMPLE: Llame al 5-80-90-00 para reservar una mesa.

_____
_____
_____
_____
_____
_____
_____

◆ 2 ◆ FORMAL COMMANDS OF IRREGULAR VERBS

a. The following verbs form the formal (polite) command irregularly:

INFINITIVE	PRESENT TENSE YO FORM	COMMAND FORMS SINGULAR	PLURAL	MEANING
dar	doy	dé	den	*give*
estar	estoy	esté	estén	*be*
ir	voy	vaya	vayan	*go*
saber	sé	sepa	sepan	*know*
ser	soy	sea	sean	*be*

NOTES:

1. *Dé* has an accent mark to distinguish it from *de* (of).

2. *Esté* and *estén* have accent marks to indicate that the stress falls on the last syllable.

b. To form the negative command, place *no* before the verb.

No sea descortés.   *Don't be impolite.*

No vayan allí.   *Don't go there.*

EXERCISE E.   **Write the instructions your parent gave when you and various friends went to the theater.**

EXAMPLE: comer antes de entrar en el teatro   **Coman** antes de entrar en el teatro.

1. saber la dirección del teatro   _____

2. ir al teatro en tren   _____

3. no perder los boletos   _____

4. ser puntuales   _____

5. estar allí a las siete y media   _____

6. dar los boletos al acomodador   _____

EXERCISE F.   **You just joined a tour in Lima, Peru. Write the instructions the tour guide gives to you.**

EXAMPLE: no ir solo al museo   No **vaya** solo al museo.

1. saber el número del autobús   _____

2. estar en el autobús a la hora indicada   _____

3. ir en grupos de cuatro   _____

4. no ser impaciente   _____

5. no volver tarde al autobús   _____

6. dar una propina al guía   _____

◆ 3 ◆ INFORMAL COMMANDS OF REGULAR VERBS

a. Use of informal commands

Informal commands are used with those people you normally address with the *tú* form (friends, classmates, parents, pets).

b. *Tú* commands

The *tú* command is the same as the *él, ella,* and *Ud.* form of the present tense.

c. *Vosotros* commands

The *vosotros* command is formed by changing the final *-r* of the infinitive to *-d*.

INFINITIVE	TÚ COMMAND	VOSOTROS COMMAND	MEANING
abrir	abre	abri**d**	*open*
cerrar	cierra	cerra**d**	*close*
dar	da	da**d**	*give*
hablar	habla	habla**d**	*speak*
leer	lee	lee**d**	*read*
perder	pierde	perde**d**	*lose*
servir	sirve	servi**d**	*serve*
ver	ve	ve**d**	*see*
volver	vuelve	volve**d**	*return*

NOTES:

1. Subject pronouns are usually omitted.

2. The *vosotros* command is rarely used in Spanish America. The *ustedes* (*Uds.*) command is used instead.

Lee el libro   *Read the book.*
Lean el libro.   *Read the book.*

d. All negative familiar commands are expressed by the present subjunctive.

| INFINITIVE | TÚ | | VOSOTROS | |
	AFFIRMATIVE	NEGATIVE	AFFIRMATIVE	NEGATIVE
abrir	abre	no abras	abrid	no abráis
cerrar	cierra	no cierres	cerrad	no cerréis
dar	da	no des	dad	no deis
hablar	habla	no hables	hablad	no habléis
leer	lee	no leas	leed	no leáis
perder	pierde	no pierdas	perded	no perdáis
servir	sirve	no sirvas	servid	no sirváis
ver	ve	no veas	ved	no veáis

EXERCISE G.   **Your friend Nora has decided to follow a rigorous exercise program. Express the advice you give to her.**

EXAMPLE: descansar después de hacer ejercicio   **Descansa** después de hacer ejercicio.

1. prometer ser seria   _____

2. correr una milla todos los días _____

3. tomar mucha agua _____

4. dejar de comer dulces _____

5. practicar un deporte _____

6. no dormir menos de ocho horas
   cada noche _____

7. seguir la misma rutina todos los días _____

8. prestar atención al entrenador _____

9. no comer en exceso _____

10. no perder la esperanza _____

EXERCISE H.   **You want everyone attending a party at your home to have a good time. You tell them to do the following:**

EXAMPLE: ¡Tomás, (*tomar*) más refresco!   ¡Tomás, **toma** más refresco!

1. ¡Juan, (*comer*) _____ otro pedazo de pastel!

2. ¡Grace, (*tocar*) _____ otra canción en la guitarra!

3. ¡Emilio, (*bailar*) _____ con Inés!

4. ¡Estelita, (*participar*) _____ en los juegos!

5. ¡Antonio, (*contar*) _____ un chiste!

6. ¡Ricky, (*abrir*) _____ tu regalo!

EXERCISE I.   **Several friends stayed after the party to help Gregorio clean up. Express what Gregorio told each one to do.**

EXAMPLE: Vinny / sacar la basura   ¡Vinny, **saca** la basura!

1. Lisa / guardar los discos _____

2. Pedro / recoger los vasos _____

3. Emilia / pasar la aspiradora _____

4. Paco / descolgar los adornos _____

5. Sonia / lavar los platos _____

6. Jack / ayudar a Paco _____

◆ 4 ◆ INFORMAL COMMANDS OF IRREGULAR VERBS

a. The following verbs have irregular *tú* commands:

INFINITIVE	TÚ COMMAND	VOSOTROS COMMAND	MEANING
decir	*di*	decid	*say, tell*
hacer	*haz*	haced	*do, make*
ir	*ve*	id	*go*
poner	*pon*	poned	*put*
salir	*sal*	salid	*leave, go out*
ser	*sé*	sed	*be*
tener	*ten*	tened	*have*
venir	*ven*	venid	*come*

NOTE:　The *vosotros* form of these verbs is regular.

EXERCISE J.　One of your friends is not doing well in school. After class you tell her what she should do to improve.

EXAMPLE:　hacer la tarea todos los días　　¡**Haz** la tarea todos los días!

1. poner más atención a los estudios　＿＿＿＿＿＿＿＿＿＿＿＿＿＿＿＿

2. tener paciencia　＿＿＿＿＿＿＿＿＿＿＿＿＿＿＿＿

3. ser más diligente　＿＿＿＿＿＿＿＿＿＿＿＿＿＿＿＿

4. ir a la biblioteca con más frecuencia　＿＿＿＿＿＿＿＿＿＿＿＿＿＿＿＿

5. venir a mi casa para estudiar juntos(-as)　＿＿＿＿＿＿＿＿＿＿＿＿＿＿＿＿

6. decirles la verdad a tus padres　＿＿＿＿＿＿＿＿＿＿＿＿＿＿＿＿

b. The negative familiar command of the following verbs is expressed by the present subjunctive.

INFINITIVE	TÚ AFFIRMATIVE	TÚ NEGATIVE	VOSOTROS AFFIRMATIVE	VOSOTROS NEGATIVE
decir	di	no digas	decid	no digáis
hacer	haz	no hagas	haced	no hagáis
ir	ve	no vayas	id	no vayáis
poner	pon	no pongas	poned	no pongáis
salir	sal	no salgas	salid	no salgáis
ser	sé	no seas	sed	no seáis
tener	ten	no tengas	tened	no tengáis
venir	ven	no vengas	venid	no vengáis

EXERCISE K.　Jenny is going to visit her pen pal Christina in San José, Costa Rica. Express what Jenny's mother tells her not to do.

EXAMPLE:　no tener miedo　　No **tengas** miedo.

1. no estar nerviosa　＿＿＿＿＿＿＿＿＿＿＿＿＿＿＿＿

2. no ponerse de mal humor _____

3. no decir cosas absurdas _____

4. no hacer más trabajo para la mamá
de Cristina _____

5. no salir sola por la noche _____

6. no ir de compras todos los días _____

7. no ser descortés _____

◆ 5 ◆ COMMANDS WITH OBJECT PRONOUNS

a. Object pronouns (including reflexive pronouns) are attached to the affirmative command. A written accent mark is generally required on the vowel that is stressed.

Dígale la verdad.	_Tell him the truth._
Escríbanles pronto.	_Write to them soon._
Siéntate.	_Sit down._
Lávense las manos.	_Wash your hands._

b. In negative commands, the object pronoun precedes the verb.

No le diga la verdad.	_Don't tell him/her the truth._
No les escriban pronto.	_Don't write to them soon._
No te sientes.	_Don't sit down._
No se laven las manos.	_Don't wash your hands._

EXERCISE L.   **Ricky has a new puppy and is trying to train him. Use the familiar command of the verbs in parentheses to express the commands Ricky gives the puppy.**

EXAMPLE: (_venir_)   ¡_____ aquí!   ¡**Ven** aquí!

1. (_sentarse_)   ¡_____!

2. (_darme la pata_)   ¡_____ la pata!

3. (_traerme la pelota_)   ¡_____ la pelota!

4. (_buscar el hueso_)   ¡_____ el hueso!

5. (_quedarse_)   ¡_____!

6. (_caminar despacio_)   ¡_____ despacio!

7. (_prestar atención_)   ¡_____ atención!

8. (_mover la cola_)   ¡_____ la cola!

9. (_ladrar_)   ¡_____!

10. (_ponerse de pie_)   ¡_____ de pie!

EXERCISE M. Ricky's brother likes to hassle Ricky by telling the dog not to do what he is told. Express what he says by making the commands in Exercise L negative.

EXAMPLE: *(venir)* ¡ _____ aquí! ¡**No vengas** aquí!

1. _____
2. _____
3. _____
4. _____
5. _____
6. _____
7. _____
8. _____
9. _____
10. _____

EXERCISE N. Eileen is babysitting her younger brother. Express in Spanish what her mother tells her to do while she babysits.

EXAMPLE: Si Víctor tiene sed, *(darle jugo)*, *(no darle refresco)*.
Si Víctor tiene sed, **dale** jugo, **no le des** refresco.

1. Si Víctor tiene sueño, *(acostarlo) en la cuna, (no dejarlo) en el sofá.*

    _____

2. Si él tiene frío, *(ponerle) un suéter, (no ponerle) una chamarra.*

    _____

3. Si él tiene hambre, *(darle) una galleta, (no darle) chocolates.*

    _____

4. Si él empieza a llorar, *(abrazarlo), (no gritarle).*

    _____

5. Si él quiere salir, *(decirle) que no puede, (no sacarlo) a la calle.*

    _____

⟨⟨ MASTERY EXERCISES ⟩⟩

EXERCISE O. You are helping your sister prepare for a trip. Use the cues to give her some good suggestions.

EXAMPLE: no olvidar tu pasaporte   ¡No **olvides** tu pasaporte!

1. comprar cheques de viajero   _____

2. hacer las maletas con anticipación   _____

3. lavar la ropa que vas a llevar   _____

4. no esperar hasta el último momento   _____

5. terminar tu trabajo   _____

6. no perder el boleto de avión   _____

7. decir adiós a tus abuelos   _____

8. escoger revistas para leer durante
el vuelo   _____

EXERCISE P.   **You give advice to your friends. Use the expression in parentheses to tell them what you say.**

EXAMPLE: ALAN: Acabo de recibir mi licencia de conducir.
    TÚ: (*no conducir rápidamente*)   **No conduzcas** rápidamente.

1.   GISELA: Quiero comprar los aretes que vimos en la joyería.

   TÚ: (*decírselo a tus padres y esperar tu cumpleaños*)

   _____

2.   GREG: Saqué una buena nota en el último examen.

   TÚ: (*seguir estudiando y hacerlo otra vez en el próximo examen*)

   _____

3.   LISA: Mañana es la carrera y quiero ganar.

   TÚ: (*tener confianza y no estar nerviosa*)

   _____

4.   RAÚL: Está lloviendo y no quiero mojarme.

   TÚ: (*no salir; quedarse en casa*) _____

5.   VANESSA: Toda mi familia está enferma.

   TÚ: (*no venir a mi casa esta tarde*) _____

6.   ANTONIO: Elena no puede acompañarme a la fiesta.

   TÚ: (*no preocuparse; ir solo*) _____

7.   MARISSA: Salgo en un viaje mañana por la mañana.

   TÚ: (*hacer la maleta ahora*) _____

8.   ALEX: Jane nos invitó a Tom y a mí a un baile pero tenemos otro compromiso.

   TÚ: (*decirle la verdad*) _____

EXERCISE Q.   **A Spanish-speaking friend just received the same cell phone that you have as a gift. She has texted you a message asking how to do a particular function on the phone (such as sending a photo, checking the weather, or opening a new App). Text her the instructions needed to do this function. Include all the steps, as well as things she should not do.**

ACTIVIDADES

1. Using commands, make a list of ten things your classmates should do and should not do to demonstrate school spirit.

2. The Spanish Club is soliciting ads for its magazine. Prepare an ad for two local merchants to be placed in the magazine, e.g., a restaurant, or a florist.

3. It's safety month in your school. Prepare a list of what students should do or not do in case of a fire, if they witness an accident, etc.

CHAPTER 6

Preterit Tense of Regular Verbs

74/100

The preterit tense is used to narrate an action or event in the past.

◆ 1 ◆ REGULAR -AR VERBS

a. The preterit tense of regular -*ar* verbs is formed by dropping the infinitive ending -*ar* and adding the personal endings -*é, -aste, -ó, -amos, -asteis,* and -*aron.*

	bailar *to dance*	**contar** *to count*
yo	bailé	conté
tú	bailaste	contaste
Ud., él, ella	bailó	contó
nosotros, -as	bailamos	contamos
vosotros, -as	bailasteis	contasteis
Uds., ellos, ellas	bailaron	contaron

NOTE: The preterit tense has the following meanings in English:

Ud. bailó   *you danced, you did dance*
Yo conté   *I counted, I did count*

b. In the preterit, the *nosotros* ending (-*amos*) is the same as in the present tense: *regresamos* (we return, we returned).

c. Most verbs that are stem-changing (*o* to *ue; e* to *ie*) do not change the stem in the preterit tense:
(contar)   cuento (present)   conté (preterit)

d. Verbs that end in -*car,* -*gar,* and -*zar* have a spelling change in the *yo* form. In -*car* and -*gar* verbs, this change occurs to keep the original sound of the *c* and *g,* respectively. The change occurs in -*zar* verbs because *z* rarely precedes *e* or *i* in Spanish.

tocar   yo toqué
llegar   yo llegué
comenzar   yo comencé

◆ 2 ◆ FREQUENTLY USED -AR VERBS IN THE PRETERIT

aceptar *to accept*
acompañar *to accompany*
acostarse *to go to bed*
admirar *to admire*
asar *to roast*
cerrar *to close*
cobrar *to collect*
cocinar *to cook*

colgar *to hang*
comprar *to buy*
contar *to count*
conversar *to converse*
copiar *to copy*
cortar *to cut*
desayunarse *to have breakfast*
elevar *to raise, to lift*

encontrar *to find, to meet*
enviar *to send*
espantar *to frighten, to scare*
estudiar *to study*
examinar *to examine*
hablar *to speak*
inflar *to inflate*
jugar *to play (a sport, game)*

54

lavar *to wash*	**planchar** *to iron*	**sacar** *to take out*
llorar *to cry, to weep*	**preparar** *to prepare*	**tocar** *to play (an instrument)*
mirar *to look at*	**prestar** *to lend*	**trabajar** *to work*
pasar *to pass, to spend time*	**pronunciar** *to pronounce*	**visitar** *to visit*
pensar *to think, to intend*	**robar** *to rob*	

EXERCISE A. Lucy is describing what everyone did in preparation for the party. Use the cues to express what she says.

EXAMPLE: mi mamá / preparar la comida   Mi mamá **preparó** la comida.

1. Gabriel / comprar los refrescos _Gabriel compró los refrescos_

2. Susie y Glenda / limpiar la sala _Limpiaron la sala_

3. yo / colgar las decoraciones _colgé las decoraciones_

4. Ricky y yo / inflar los globos _inflamos los globos_

5. tú / lavar los vasos _tu lavaste los vasos_

6. Miriam y Silvia / enviar las invitaciones _Enviaron las invitaciones_

EXERCISE B. On the first day of school, some friends are talking about what they and other students did during the summer. Follow the example and express what they say.

EXAMPLE: yo / trabajar en la oficina de un abogado   Yo **trabajé** en la oficina de un abogado.

1. Manuel / visitar a sus primos en Venezuela _visitó a sus primos in Venezuela_

2. Blanca y Virginia / estudiar en la universidad _Estudiaron en la universidad_

3. tú / viajar con tu familia _Viajaste con tu familia_

4. Alex y yo / cantar en un coro _cantamos en un coro_

5. yo / comenzar a estudiar el violín _comenzué estudiar el violín_

6. Efraín / jugar en un equipo de béisbol _Jugué en un equipo de beisbol_

EXERCISE C. You and a group of friends are in a restaurant. One of your friends is helping you figure out the check. Answer her questions.

1. ¿Quién ordenó hamburguesas y papas fritas? (*Milton y Jaime*) _Ellos ordenaron h y pf_

2. ¿Quién tomó dos tés helados? (*Laura*) _Laura tomó dos helados_

3. ¿Quién desayunó huevos fritos y tocino? (*tú*) _tu desayunaste huevos fritos y tocino_

4. ¿Quién probó el plato especial del día? (*Carlos y yo*)

Nosotros probuma el plato especial

5. ¿Quién pagó la cuenta? (*yo*)

yo pagué la cuenta

EXERCISE D.   **Tell what these people did in each of these circumstances. Use the suggestions provided.**

SUGGESTIONS: estudiar mucho   cortar las flores   tocar la trompeta
                lavar el carro   pagar la cuenta   llorar mucho
                tomar un refresco

EXAMPLE: Hay un examen en mi clase de matemáticas.
            Estudié mucho.

1. La niña no encontró a su mamá en la tienda.
Ella _lloró mucho._

2. Tenía sed.
Yo _tomé un refresco_

3. El carro de mi papá se llenó de lodo.
Mi papá _lavó el carro_

4. Había muchas flores en el jardín de mi abuela.
Mi abuela _cortó las flores_

5. Compré una raqueta de tenis.
Yo _pagué la cuenta_

6. Había un concierto en mi clase de música.
Yo _toqué la trompeta_

EXERCISE E.   **You could not attend the latest family function. Your little sister tells you in her usual non-stop fashion what happened there. Complete her monologue with the appropriate form of the verbs indicated.**

Nosotros _llegamos_ a la fiesta temprano. Yo _ayudé_ a mi tía a poner la mesa.
    1. (llegar)   2. (ayudar)

Cuando mis primos _llegaron_, yo _empezué_ a jugar con ellos pero yo no
                    3. (llegar)   4. (empezar)

jugué con ellos por mucho tiempo porque yo _acompañó_ a mi tío al supermercado.
    5. (jugar)   6. (acompañar)

Nosotros _viajamos_ en motocicleta y _pasamos_ mucho tiempo allí. Mi tío
            7. (viajar)   8. (pasar)

pagó con su tarjeta de crédito. Nosotros _regresamos_ a la casa en la motocicleta y Felipe
    9. (pagar)   10. (regresar)

sacó una fotografía de cuando _entré_ en la casa con las manos llenas
    11. (sacar)   12. (entrar)

de paquetes. Sarita _tocó_ el piano cuando Pablo _cantó_ «Cumpleaños
                    13. (tocar)   14. (cantar)

feliz» a Mirta. Nosotros ___*admiramos*___ sus regalos pero a ella no le ___*gustó*___ todos. Yo
15. (admirar)   16. (gustar)

___*jugué*___ con el perro del vecino, hasta que (él) me ___*espantó*___ con sus ladridos y yo
17. (jugar)   18. (espantar)

___*grité*___ .
19. *(gritar)*

Toda la familia ___*cenó*___ a las cinco porque ___*comenzó*___ a llover. Yo ___*regresé*___
20. (cenar)   21. (comenzar)   22. (regresar)

a casa en el carro de Pablo. Yo ___*pasé*___ un buen rato hoy. Y tú, ¿cómo ___*pasé*___
23. (pasar)   24. (pasar)

el día?

◆ 3 ◆ REGULAR -ER AND -IR VERBS

a. The preterit tense of regular *-er* and *-ir* verbs is formed by dropping the infinitive ending and adding the personal; endings *-í*, *-iste*, *-ió*, *-imos*, *-isteis*, and *-ieron*.

	romper *to break*	**recibir** *to receive*
yo	romp*í*	recib*í*
tú	romp*iste*	recib*iste*
Ud., él, ella	romp*ió*	recib*ió*
nosotros, -as	romp*imos*	recib*imos*
vosotros, -as	romp*isteis*	recib*isteis*
Uds., ellos, ellas	romp*ieron*	recib*ieron*

b. The preterit endings are the same for *-er* and *-ir* verbs.

c. In *-ir* verbs, the *nosotros* ending (*-imos*) is the same as in the present tense. In *-er* verbs, however, the endings are different.

d. The accent mark is omitted over the following forms of *ver: vi, vio.*

e. Stem-changing verbs ending in *-er* do not change the stem vowel in the preterit tense. Stem-changing verbs ending in *-ir* have special stem changes in the preterit and are discussed in Chapter 7.

◆ 4 ◆ FREQUENTLY USED -ER AND -IR VERBS IN THE PRETERIT

-ER Verbs

aparecer *to appear*	**escoger** *to choose*	**prometer** *to promise*
aprender *to learn*	**establecer** *to establish*	**reconocer** *to recognize*
conocer *to know (a person)*	**meter** *to put in*	**romper** *to break*
convencer *to convince*	**mover** *to move*	**vender** *to sell*
devolver *to return, to give back*	**nacer** *to be born*	**ver** *to see*
envolver *to wrap*	**perder** *to lose*	**volver** *to return*

-IR Verbs

abrir *to open*	**decidir** *to decide*	**salir** *to go out, leave*
aplaudir *to applaud*	**interrumpir** *to interrupt*	**sufrir** *to suffer*
asistir *to attend*	**recibir** *to receive*	**vivir** *to live*

EXERCISE F.   **Everyone is having a bad day. Tell what happened to each person.**

EXAMPLE: el chofer / no ver el otro carro   El chofer no **vio** el otro carro.

1. tú / perder las llaves de la casa

   tú perdiste las llaves

2. el vendedor / no vender nada

   El vendedor no vendió nada

3. los miembros del coro / no aprender la canción

   los miembros no aprendió la can

4. yo / recibir una mala nota en la clase de historia

   yo recibí una mala nada en la clase de

5. la clase / no reconocer al nuevo maestro de español

   La clase no reconocieron al nuevo maestro

6. Javier y yo / romper unos platos

   Javier y yo rompieron unos platos

7. una tormenta / interrumpir el concierto al aire libre

   Una tormenta interrumpió el concierto

EXERCISE G.   **Tell what you and your family decided to do during the weekend.**

EXAMPLE: Alicia y Felicia / nadar / piscina   Alicia y Felicia **decidieron** nadar en la piscina.

1. Bobby y yo / bailar   _decidimos bailar... bailamos_

2. mis padres / ir / cine   _decidieron ir... Mis padres fueron al cine_

3. mi hermano / jugar / voleibol   _El jugó al voleibol_

4. tú / comprar / suéter   _tú compraste suéter_

5. yo / limpiar / dormitorio   _yo limpié mi dormitorio_

6. toda la familia / ir / restaurante   _toda la familia fuimos al restaurant_

EXERCISE H.   **Complete the text message that Raquel sent to a friend after missing a concert. Give the appropriate form of the verbs indicated.**

Querida amiga:

Yo _____prometí_____ escribirte después de asistir al concierto de nuestro grupo favorito. La verdad es
        1. (prometer)

que yo no _____asistí_____. Ema y yo _____compramos_____ los boletos hace mucho tiempo pero a
        2. (asistir)   3. (comprar)

última hora ella _____decidió_____ ir con su familia a las montañas y _____vendió_____ su
        4. (decidir)   5. (vender)

boleto. Ella se lo _____vendió_____ a su prima Imelda. Imelda y yo _____decidimos_____ ir juntas. Yo
        6. (vender)   7. (decidir)

_____salió_____ de la casa con bastante tiempo pero _____tomé_____ el autobús equivocado
   8. (salir)   9. (tomar)

y _____*llegué*_____ tarde a su casa. Yo _____*(buscé)*_____ un taxi pero no _____*encontré*_____
      10. (llegar)   11. (buscar)   12. (encontrar)

ninguno. El padre de Imelda nos _____*llevamos*_____ al concierto en su carro pero no _____*llegamos*_____
                                              13. (llevar)   14. (llegar)

a tiempo. Yo me _____*perdí*_____ todo el concierto e Imelda _____*se enojó*_____ conmigo.
                    15. (perder)   16. (enojarse)

Nosotras _____*Volvimos*_____ a casa muy tristes.
               17. (volver)

Hasta luego,

Raquel

EXERCISE I.   **Answer the questions a reporter from the school newspaper asks you. Use the cues provided.**

(-2)

1. ¿Cuándo decidiste participar en la excavación arqueológica? *(el año pasado)*
   _____*el año pasado yo lo decidí* ok *participar...*_____

2. ¿Cuántas personas asistieron? *(20)*
   _____*20 personas asistieron.*_____

3. ¿Sufriste muchas inconveniencias? *(sí)* *yo...*
   _____*Sí, muchas problemas sufrió.*_____

4. ¿Cuándo salieron Uds. del país? *(el primero de julio)*
   _____*Salimos el primero de julio.*_____

5. ¿Dónde viviste durante la excavación? *(tiendas de campo)*
   _____*Yo vivimos en tiendas de campo.*_____

6. ¿Encontraron Uds. cosas interesantes? *(sí)*
   _____*Sí, encontramos cosas interesante.*_____

7. ¿Qué hallaste tú? *(una olla)*
   _____*yo Hallé una olla*_____

8. ¿Quién examinó la olla? *(el arqueólogo principal)*
   _____*el arqueólogo principal examinó la olla.*_____

9. ¿Cuánto tiempo pasaste allí? *(un mes)*
   _____*yo pasé un mes aya.*_____

10. ¿Aprendiste mucho? *(sí)*
    _____*Sí, Aprendio mucho.*_____

⇔ MASTERY EXERCISES ⇔

(-5)

EXERCISE J.   **Janet always answers for her sister as well as for herself. Complete the questions and Janet's responses to her mother's questions. Use the verbs indicated.**

EXAMPLE: *(terminar)* ¿Terminaste la tarea?
           Sí, yo **terminé** la tarea, pero Gloria no la **terminó**.

1. (lavar/secar) ¿ _Lavaste_ tú los platos y los _secó_ Gloria?
   Sí, yo _Lavé_ los platos y Gloria los _secó_.

2. (practicar) ¿ _practican_ Uds. el yoga?
   Sí, yo _practiqué_ el yoga, pero Gloria no lo _practicó_.

3. (escribir) ¿ _escribisteis_ Uds. una carta a su tía?
   Sí, yo _escribí_ una carta, pero Gloria no la _escribió_.

4. (romper) ¿ _rompiste_ tú algo en la cocina?
   No, yo no _rompí_ nada, pero Gloria _rompió_ un vaso.

5. (devolver) ¿ _devolvisteis_ Uds. los libros a la biblioteca?
   Sí, yo los _devolví_, pero Gloria no los _devolvió_.

6. (convencer) ¿ _convenciste_ tú a tu padre?
   Sí, nosotras le _convencimos_.

7. (asistir) ¿ _asistieron_ Uds. a la clase de baile?
   Sí, yo _asistí_ a la clase, pero Gloria no _asistió_.

8. (meter) ¿Quién _metió_ los refrescos en el refrigerador?
   Nosotras _metimos_ los refrescos en el refrigerador.

9. (jugar) ¿ _jugaron_ Uds. al tenis?
   Sí, yo _jugué_ al tenis, pero Gloria _jugó_ al voleibol.

10. (reconocer) ¿ _reconociste_ tú al hijo de mi amiga?
    Sí, yo lo _reconocí_, pero Gloria no lo _reconoció_.

You can't use a "vosotros" conjugation with an "Uds" subject

EXERCISE K.   **Tell who did what activities during the weekend.**

mi hermano	cortar el césped
mi padre	lavar el carro
mi madre	perder el número de teléfono
mis padres	asistir a un concierto
yo	ver una película
tú	recibir muchos regalos
mis amigos y yo	sacar una novela de la biblioteca
la Sra. Ortiz	empezar a trabajar
	llegar tarde al teatro
	correr en el parque

1. _Mi hermano cortó el césped_
2. _Mi padre lavó el carro_
3. _Mi madre perdió el número de teléfono_
4. _Mis padres asistieron a un concierto._
5. _yo vi una película_

6. *tú recibiste muchos regalos*
7. *Mis amigos y yo sacamos una novela de biblioteca*
8. *La Sra. Ortiz, empezó a trabajar*
9. *yo llego tarde al teatro*
10. *Nosotros corremos en el parque*

EXERCISE L. You participated in a trip to a city in a Spanish-speaking country during spring break, which also coincided with the celebration of Holy Week (Semana Santa). Prepare an entry in your Spanish journal in which you describe the trip. You may wish to include the following.

- the city or cities you visited
- the length of the trip
- where you stayed
- something about the flight
- some of the places you visited
- your impression of the food
- an outstanding/memorable event during the trip
- what you enjoyed the least
- an amusing detail about the trip

ACTIVIDADES

1. The school's online newspaper has asked you to do a study of how students spent the summer vacation. Prepare a series of questions in Spanish for your study.

2. You are doing a social experiment on cause and effect. For each of the statements below, indicate what you think the people did to accomplish the result they achieved.
   a. El cuarto de Alicia está limpio y ordenado.
   b. Raúl sacó una nota alta en el examen final de química.
   c. Ruth se ve muy bien; no es ni delgada ni gorda, y tiene mucha energía.
   d. Jack y Miguel tienen mucho dinero en el banco.
   e. Ahora yo uso la computadora para todo.

3. Prepare an entry for your journal in which you describe the activities in which you participated last week. Use as many of the verbs you have learned in the preterit tense as you can.

CHAPTER 7

Preterit Tense of Stem-Changing and Irregular Verbs

◆ 1 ◆ VERBS THAT CHANGE *I* TO *Y* IN THE PRETERIT

a. In the preterit, *-er* and *-ir* verbs whose stems end in a vowel change the endings of the third-person singular and plural forms from *-ió* to *-yó* and *-ieron* to *-yeron*, respectively. The *i* has an accent in all the other forms.

	caer *to fall*	**creer** *to believe*	**leer** *to read*	**oír** *to hear*
yo	caí	creí	leí	oí
tú	caíste	creíste	leíste	oíste
Ud., él, ella	cayó	creyó	leyó	oyó
nosotros, -as	caímos	creímos	leímos	oímos
vosotros, -as	caísteis	creísteis	leísteis	oísteis
Uds, ellos, ellas	cayeron	creyeron	leyeron	oyeron

b. Other verbs

caer *to fall*   huir *to flee*   oír *to hear*

construir *to construct, to build*   incluir *to include*   poseer *to possess, to own*

creer *to believe*   leer *to read*

distribuir *to distribute*

NOTES:

1. Exceptions are *traer*, *atraer*, and all verbs ending in *-guir*.

2. Verbs that end in *-uir* do not have an accent in the endings *-uiste*, *-uimos*, and *-uisteis*.

EXERCISE A.   Tell from what or whom the following people fled.

EXAMPLE: el ladrón / la policía   El ladrón **huyó** de la policía.

1. los ciudadanos / las inundaciones

   los ciudadanos huyeron las inundaciones

2. los inmigrantes / la pobreza

   los inmigrantes huyeron la pobreza

3. yo / la muchedumbre

   yo huí de la muchedumbre

4. el chofer / el accidente

   el chofer huyo el accidente

5. tú / las olas fuertes del mar

   tú huiste las olas fuertes del mar

6. Rebeca y yo / el ruido fuerte del estéreo

   Nosotros huimos el ruido del
   estéro

EXERCISE B. Everyone in school is trying to earn community service credit. Follow the example and tell what the following students did.

EXAMPLE: Otto / el periódico escolar   Otto **distribuyó** el periódico escolar.

1. yo / los recados a los profesores

_____ Yo reples los recados a los profesores _____

2. Emilio / los exámenes en la clase de español

_____ Emilio distribuyó los exámenes a la clase de español. _____

3. tú / los libros

_____ tú leíste los libros _____

4. Edgar y José / los premios al terminar el juego

_____ Edgar y José poseyeron los premios al terminar el juego _____

5. Gabi / los boletos para la obra de teatro

_____ Gabi distribuyó los boletos de la obra de teatro. _____

6. Roberta y yo / el jugo a los niños de primer año

_____ Roberto y yo distrib distribuimos. _____

EXERCISE C. Some students are telling what they read last night in celebration of the reading month. Tell what each one read based on what you know about them. Use the suggestions below.

SUGGESTIONS:
la crítica de una película
un drama
un libro de recetas
una guía turística
una revista deportiva
la sección de anuncios del periódico
las tiras cómicas

EXAMPLE: Alfredo quiere ser cocinero y dueño de un restaurante.
Alfredo **leyó** un libro de recetas.

1. A Gino le gustan los deportes. Practica el fútbol, el tenis y la natación.

Gino _____ leyó una revista deportiva _____ .

2. Yo pienso visitar a mis primos en Montevideo la semana que viene.

Yo _____ leí una guía turística _____ .

3. Nicolás quiere ser actor. Siempre va al teatro.

Nicolás _____ leyó un drama _____ .

4. Tú no eres seria. No te gustan los libros grandes ni largos.

Tú _____ leíste las tiras cómicas _____ .

5. Patricia y yo vamos al cine con mucha frecuencia.

Nosotros _____ leímos la crítica de una película _____ .

6. Arnaldo busca un trabajo.

Arnaldo _____ leyó la sección de anuncios del periódico _____

♦2♦ STEM-CHANGING -*IR* VERBS IN THE PRETERIT

a. Stem-changing verbs ending in -*ir* change the stem vowel from *e* to *i* and *o* to *u* in the third-person singular and plural of the preterit.

	pedir *to ask for*	**dormir** *to sleep*
yo	ped**í**	dorm**í**
tú	pediste	dormiste
Ud., él, ella	pid**ió**	durm**ió**
nosotros, -as	pedimos	dormimos
vosotros, -as	pedisteis	dormisteis
Uds., ellos, ellas	pid**ieron**	durm**ieron**

b. Other verbs that change *e* to *i* are:

medir *to measure*	**referir** *to tell*	**sentir** *to feel*
pedir *to ask for*	**reñir** *to argue*	**servir** *to serve*
preferir *to prefer*	**repetir** *to repeat*	**vestir** *to dress*

c. Other verbs that change *o* to *u* are:

morir *to die*	**podrir** *to rot*

d. Stem-changing verbs ending in -*ar* or -*er* do not change the stress vowel in the preterit tense.

	cerrar *to close*	**mover** *to move*
yo	cerré	moví
tú	cerraste	moviste
Ud., él, ella	cerró	movió
nosotros, -as	cerramos	movimos
vosotros, -as	cerrasteis	movisteis
Uds., ellos, ellas	cerraron	movieron

NOTE: -*Ir* verbs that have *ñ* directly before the ending (*gruñir, reñir*) drop the *i* of the ending in the third-person singular and plural (*riñó, riñeron*). The sound of the ending is still regular because of the *ñ*.

EXERCISE D. One of your friends doesn't remember what everyone ordered in the restaurant last night. Tell her what each person ordered.

EXAMPLE: Harry **pidió** una pizza.

1. Annette y Andy ___pidieron___ hamburguesas y papas fritas.

2. Yo ___pedí___ una ensalada de atún.

3. Pablo ___pidió___ un sándwich de jamón y queso.

4. Irma y yo ___pidió___ té helado.

5. Vicki ___pidió___ una ensalada de frutas frescas.

6. Tú ___pediste___ un helado de chocolate y fresa.

EXERCISE E.   **Your mother is telling a friend where all her guests slept when they visited. Follow the example and complete her statements.**

EXAMPLE: Beatriz **durmió** en la cama de la abuela.

1. Los hijos de mi hermano ___durmieron___ en bolsas de dormir.

2. Mi hermano y su esposa ___durmieron___ en el sofá cama.

3. Mi esposo y yo ___dormimos___ en nuestra cama.

4. Antonio ___durmió___ en un colchón de aire.

5. El bebé ___durmió___ en la habitación con sus padres.

6. Tú ___dormiste___ en tu propia casa.

7. Yo ___dormí___ en mi dormitorio.

EXERCISE F.   **Tell who did these different things. Use the suggestions below.**

SUGGESTIONS:

medir el cuarto

pedir más postre

referir cuentos de su juventud

vestir una muñeca

preferir ver la televisión

sentirse mal

repetir la misma frase muchas veces

dormir una siesta

servir la cena

reñir al perro

1. Mi papá ___se sintió mal___.

2. La abuela ___vistió una muñeca___.

3. El carpintero ___midió el cuarto___.

4. Los niños ___prefieren ver la televisión___.

5. Yo ___dormí una siesta___.

6. Mi tía ___sirvió la cena___.

7. Tú y yo ___pedimos más postres___.

8. Los vecinos ___riñieron al perro___.

9. Mi mamá ___repite la misma frase muchas veces___.

10. Mis hermanos ___refirieron cuentos de sus juventud___.

◆3◆ VERBS IRREGULAR IN THE PRETERIT

a. *I*-stem Verbs in the Preterit

The following verbs have irregular stems and endings:

	hacer *to do, to make* hic-	querer *to want, to love* quis-	venir *to come* vin-
yo	hice	quise	vine
tú	hiciste	quisiste	viniste
Ud., él, ella	hizo	quiso	vino
nosotros, -as	hicimos	quisimos	vinimos
vosotros, -as	hicisteis	quisisteis	vinisteis
Uds., ellos, ellas	hicieron	quisieron	vinieron

NOTES:

1. The preterit endings of -*i*-stem verbs do not have accent marks.

2. In the third-person singular of *hacer,* the *c* changes to *z* to preserve the original sound.

EXERCISE G.   Everyone in the family is very disappointed because their weekend plans didn't work out. Tell what each person wanted to do.

EXAMPLE: Gregorio **quiso** ver el partido de fútbol.

1. Papá _____ ir a pescar.

2. Mis hermanos _____ nadar en la piscina.

3. Mamá _____ ir de compras.

4. Yo _____ ver una película.

5. Tú _____ ir a un restaurante japonés.

6. Mis primos y yo _____ jugar al tenis.

EXERCISE H.   It's your mother's birthday and everyone in your family wants to surprise her. Complete the statements with the appropriate form of *hacer,* as she tries to learn who did what.

EXAMPLE: Pepe, ¿hiciste el desayuno?   No, yo no **hice** el desayuno. Gloria lo hizo.

1. Gloria, ¿_____ tú la limpieza de la casa?

   No, yo no _____ la limpieza; Pepe y Adela la _____.

2. Adela, ¡qué bonito pastel _____ tú!

   Yo no _____ el pastel; mi abuela lo _____.

3. ¿Quién _____ el arreglo de flores?

   Gloria y yo _____ el arreglo.

4. Daniel, ¿_____ tú el paquete de mi regalo?

No, yo no _____ el paquete. El dependiente de la tienda lo _____.

5. ¿Quién _____ la reservación en el restaurante?

Mi papá _____ la reservación.

EXERCISE I. Joaquín broke his leg skiing. While visiting him at the hospital, you and a friend are trying to find out who came to see Joaquín and when.

EXAMPLE: Carmela **vino** a las ocho y media de la mañana.

1. Yo _____ antes de ir a la escuela.

2. El médico _____ por la mañana.

3. Tú _____ al mediodía.

4. Edgar y Mauricio _____ después de las clases.

5. Raúl y yo _____ antes de cenar.

6. La maestra de español _____ a las siete de la noche.

EXERCISE J. Use the cues to answer the questions your grandmother asks you about a party that was held in your house.

1. ¿Cuándo hiciste la fiesta? *(el sábado pasado)*

_____

2. ¿Cuántos amigos vinieron a la fiesta? *(10)*

_____

3. ¿Quisiste invitar a más amigos? *(no)*

_____

4. ¿Cómo vinieron a la casa? *(en autobús)*

_____

5. ¿Qué hizo tu mamá para la fiesta? *(sándwiches)*

_____

6. ¿Hicieron Uds. adornos? *(sí)*

_____

7. ¿Cuál de tus amigos no quiso asistir? *(Pablo y Renée)*

_____

8. ¿Quién no quiso bailar? *(Elena)*

_____

b. *U*-stem Verbs in the Preterit

The following verbs have irregular stems and endings:

INFINITIVE	STEM	PRETERIT FORMS
andar	anduv	anduve, anduviste, anduvo, anduvimos, anduvisteis, anduvieron
estar	estuv	estuve, estuviste, estuvo, estuvimos, estuvisteis, estuvieron
poder	pud	pude, pudiste, pudo, pudimos, pudisteis, pudieron
poner	pus	puse, pusiste, puso, pusimos, pusisteis, pusieron
saber	sup	supe, supiste, supo, supimos, supisteis, supieron
tener	tuv	tuve, tuviste, tuvo, tuvimos, tuvisteis, tuvieron
traer	traj	traje, trajiste, trajo, trajimos, trajisteis, trajeron
decir	dij	dije, dijiste, dijo, dijimos, dijisteis, dijeron
traducir	traduj	traduje, tradujiste, tradujo, tradujimos, tradujisteis, tradujeron

NOTES:

1. The preterit endings of *u*-stem verbs do not have accent marks.

2. All verbs ending in *-ducir* are conjugated like *traducir*.

	conducir *to drive, to lead*	producir *to produce*
yo	conduje	produje
tú	condujiste	produjiste
Ud., él, ella	condujo	produjo
nosotros, -as	condujimos	produjimos
vosotros, -as	condujisteis	produjisteis
Uds., ellos, ellas	condujeron	produjeron

EXERCISE K. Albert is writing a paragraph about something he and a friend did when they were in Madrid. Complete his paragraph with the appropriate verb forms.

Cuando Héctor y yo _____ en Madrid visitamos el Museo del Prado. Nosotros
           1. (estar)

_____ por todos los salones del museo. Héctor _____ mucho de la
2. (andar)   *3. (saber)*

pintura española, pero yo _____ que comprar un libro en la tienda del museo. Yo
                          4. (tener)

no _____ llevar mi cámara conmigo por el museo; por eso la _____ en mi
   5. (poder)   *6. (poner)*

mochila en el guardarropa del museo. Héctor visitó el museo el mes pasado y él _____
                                                                                7. (poder)

visitar un salón especial. Este día el salón _____ cerrado al público. Héctor y yo
                                              8. (estar)

_____ regresar al museo dos veces, pero yo nunca _____ ver el salón especial.
9. (poder)   *10. (poder)*

EXERCISE L.   Jack and some friends spent a day at a new amusement park. Use the following phrases to tell what each person was able to do there.

montar a caballo
subir en los aparatos
comer palomitas
nadar en una piscina grandísima

jugar muchos juegos
ganar muchos premios
conducir un carro eléctrico

EXAMPLE: Manny **pudo** montar a caballo.

1. Jack _____ .

2. Raquel y Leslie _____ .

3. Yo _____ .

4. Alex _____ .

5. Tú _____ .

6. Jack y yo _____ .

EXERCISE M.   Tell why you and none of your friends went to the football game on Saturday.

EXAMPLE: Elvira **tuvo** que ir de compras.

1. Gabriela y María _____ visitar a sus abuelos.

2. Yo _____ trabajar.

3. Tú _____ estudiar para un examen.

4. Ricky y Eddy _____ ayudar en casa.

5. Maddy y yo _____ ir al centro.

6. Javier _____ llevar el perro al veterinario.

EXERCISE N.   Danny is telling his parents where his friends hid an object during a game they played. Tell where each person put the object. Use the suggestions.

en la cocina   en la cama del perro   dentro de un cajón
debajo del sofá   detrás de un libro

EXAMPLE: Emilio lo **puso** en el patio de la casa.

1. Yo _____ .

2. Rogelio _____ .

3. Carmen y yo _____ .

4. Tú _____ .

5. Andrés y Pilar _____ .

6. Víctor _____ .

EXERCISE O.   In preparation for a student trip to Mexico, a group is practicing some polite expressions in Spanish. Use the following phrases to express what each person said in various situations.

SUGGESTIONS: buenos días   con permiso   gracias
                buenas tardes   salud   por favor
                buenas noches   buen provecho   hasta luego

EXAMPLE: Cuando Hugo entró en la casa por la tarde, él dijo «**buenas tardes**».

1. Cuando Esteban estornudó, todo el mundo _____.

2. Cuando Adela y Luz pasaron entre dos personas, ellas _____.

3. Cuando yo saludé a la familia por la mañana, yo _____.

4. Cuando pediste un refresco en el café, tú _____.

5. Cuando el mesero nos sirvió la cena a Beto y a mí, nosotros _____.

6. Cuando Gerardo salió de la casa, él _____.

7. Al servir la comida la señora _____.

c. The Verbs *dar, ir,* and *ser* in the Preterit

Dar, ir, and *ser* are also irregular. *Dar* takes the endings of regular *-er* and *-ir* verbs, but without a written accent in the first- and third-person singular forms. *Ir* and *ser* have the same forms.

	dar *to give*	**ir** *to go* **ser** *to be*
yo	di	fui
tú	diste	fuiste
Ud., él, ella	dio	fue
nosotros, -as	dimos	fuimos
vosotros, -as	disteis	fuisteis
Uds., ellos, ellas	dieron	fueron

◆4◆ USES OF THE PRETERIT TENSE

a. The preterit tense is used to narrate an action or event that occurred in the past. It may indicate the beginning or end of the action, or the completed action or event begun and finished in the past.

(1) Beginning or End of an Action

Empezamos a bailar.   *We began to dance.*

Cerraron la puerta.   *They closed the door.*

(2) Completed Action

Fui al cine anoche.   *I went to the movies last night.*

b. Some expressions often used with the preterit are:

anoche *last night*   el año pasado *last year*

ayer *yesterday*   el mes pasado *last month*

anteayer *the day before yesterday*   la semana pasada *last week*

EXERCISE P. Before shutting off the computer for the night, you look at your calendar to check that you did everything in your list of things to do. Tell what you did today.

1. ESTUDIAR PARA UN EXAMEN

2. ESCUCHAR LAS NOTICIAS DEL DÍA

3. TERMINAR LA TAREA

4. DEVOLVER DOS LIBROS A LA BIBLIOTECA

5. VISITAR A MIS ABUELOS

6. CUIDAR A MI HERMANO MENOR

7. ESCRIBIRLE UNA CARTA A MI PRIMA

8. SALIR CON MI PADRE

9. LEER UN ARTÍCULO

1. _____

2. _____

3. _____

4. _____

5. _____

6. _____

7. _____

8. _____

9. _____

10. _____

EXERCISE Q. Upon returning to school in September, various students are discussing the summer vacation. Tell where each student went.

EXAMPLE: Virginia **fue a** España.

1. Pedro _____ Puerto Rico.

2. Yo _____ la granja de mis abuelos.

3. Donald _____ Canadá.

4. Los hermanos _____ un campamento de tenis.

5. Tú _____ acampar en las montañas.

6. Anita y yo _____ un congreso sobre el medio ambiente.

EXERCISE R. A friend was absent from school yesterday. Answer the questions she asks you.

1. ¿Estuvo ausente otro alumno?

_____

2. ¿Fue la clase de historia a escuchar el debate?

_____

3. ¿Viniste a tiempo a la escuela?

_____

4. ¿Trajiste muchos libros a la escuela hoy?

_____

5. ¿Hiciste el trabajo para hoy?

_____

6. ¿Pusiste todos los nombres en el trabajo?

_____

7. ¿Leyeron Uds. muchos artículos del periódico?

_____

8. ¿Anduviste por la calle Moya después de las clases?

_____

9. ¿Diste el trabajo al maestro?

_____

10. ¿Tradujeron Uds. los anuncios al español?

_____

EXERCISE S.   A friend is trying to help you remember when you did different things. Using the information provided, tell what he asks and give your response.

EXAMPLE: conducir el carro / anoche / el domingo pasado

¿**Condujiste** el carro anoche?
No, **conduje** el carro el domingo pasado.

1. ir al cine / la semana pasada / anteayer

¿ _____ ?

_____

2. dar un paseo por el parque / el mes pasado / ayer

¿ _____ ?

_____

3. jugar al tenis / esta mañana / el mes pasado

¿ _____ ?

_____

4. pescar en el lago / el domingo pasado / el verano pasado

¿ _____ ?

_____

5. estar en el centro / anteayer / anoche

¿ _____ ?

_____

⟨ M A S T E R Y   E X E R C I S E S ⟩

EXERCISE T.   You just realized that you misplaced your wallet/purse. Write a series of ten sentences in Spanish in which you retrace your activities during the day to help you locate the wallet.

EXAMPLE: Almorcé en un café y pagué la cuenta. Luego fui a la biblioteca y pasé dos horas allí. Conduje el carro de mi mamá. . .

_____

_____

_____

_____

_____

_____

EXERCISE U.   You and your friend Gladys go to a school dance. Gladys isn't very happy. Read the description of the dance and then rewrite it, changing the verbs to the preterit.

Mi amiga Gladys y yo vamos a un baile de la escuela. El baile tiene lugar en el gimnasio del colegio. Ella quiere ir al baile pero Shawn no la invita. En el baile, Gladys ve a Shawn y quiere bailar con él, pero Shawn prefiere bailar con otras chicas. Hay un concurso de baile y Gladys no puede participar en él. Busca una pareja pero no tiene suerte. Durante un intermedio, ve a Shawn. Él va hacia ella. Ella se pone muy contenta porque cree que Shawn toma otra decisión. Shawn anda rápidamente y nos pasa sin mirarnos. Va al bar y pide un refresco. Gladys se da cuenta de esto y huye del gimnasio. Yo la sigo y tomamos un taxi de regreso a casa.

_____

_____

_____

_____

EXERCISE V.   Last night there was a natural disaster in your area. Write a description in your Spanish journal of what happened and how it affected you, your family, neighbors, and friends. You may wish to include the following:

- what took place

- what you could not do

- what caused the disaster

- what you heard and/or saw

- how it affected your family members

- what you did to ensure safety

- a specific incident that occurred

- what you did when it was over

◀ A C T I V I D A D E S ▶

1. Prepare an entry for your journal, in which you describe what you did yesterday. Divide your entry into what you did in the morning, the afternoon, and last night. Provide at least four different activities for each time period.

2. A famous alumnus is coming to your school to talk to the student body. You are going to interview him for the school newspaper. Prepare ten questions you will ask him. Use the suggestions provided.

    EXAMPLE: ¿Quiénes influyeron su interés por la música?

    SUGGESTIONS:

cuándo	qué	(a) quién(es)	dónde	adónde
por qué	cuánto(s)	andar	conocer	empezar
estar	hacer	influir	ir	poder
poner	querer	saber	tener	venir

3. Role-play the interview with a classmate. Take notes on his answers and then write the article for the Spanish section of the school newspaper.

CHAPTER

8

Imperfect Tense

◆1◆ THE IMPERFECT TENSE OF REGULAR VERBS

a. The imperfect tense of regular verbs is formed by dropping the ending (*-ar, -er, -ir*), and adding the following endings:

	pensar *to think*	**querer** *to return*	**venir** *to suffer*
yo	pens*aba*	volv*ía*	sufr*ía*
tú	pens*abas*	volv*ías*	sufr*ías*
Ud., él, ella	pens*aba*	volv*ía*	sufr*ía*
nosotros, -as	pens*ábamos*	volv*íamos*	sufr*íamos*
vosotros, -as	pens*abais*	volv*íais*	sufr*íais*
Uds., ellos, ellas	pens*aban*	volv*ían*	sufr*ían*

b. Verbs that are stem changing in the present tense do not change the stem vowel in the imperfect.

c. In the imperfect, *yo, Ud., él* and *ella* have the same form. Subject pronouns are used if necessary to clarify the meaning of the verb.

EXERCISE A.   Tell where each person used to walk to.

EXAMPLE: El señor **andaba** al tren.

1. Jimmy_____

_____ .

2. Los amigos _____

_____ .

3. Yo _____

_____ .

5. Mi hermano _____

_____ .

4. Tú _____

_____ .

6. Mi mamá y yo _____

_____ .

EXERCISE B. **Tell who used to drink these beverages.**

EXAMPLE: Dora / agua   Dora **bebía** agua.

1. el bebé / leche   _____

2. las señoras / té helado   _____

3. tú / té caliente con limón   _____

4. Andy y yo / chocolate   _____

5. yo / batidos de frutas   _____

6. Irma e Hilda / refrescos dietéticos   _____

EXERCISE C. **A group of friends are talking about things they used to write. Tell what they wrote.**

EXAMPLE: Genaro / canciones   Genaro **escribía** canciones.

1. yo / versos   _____

2. Elena y su hermana / cuentos infantiles   _____

3. Richie / cartas a su amigo   _____

4. tú / reglas para juegos nuevos   _____

5. Yoko y yo / refranes   _____

6. Marta y Rosa / chistes   _____

EXERCISE D.   **A friend is asking you what you used to do in different situations. Answer her questions using the responses provided.**

EXAMPLE: ¿Qué hacías cuando no tenías tarea? (*ver la televisión*)
　　　　　Cuando no tenía tarea yo **veía** la televisión.

1.   ¿Qué hacías cuando tus padres salían? (*invitar a mis amigos*)

_____

2.   ¿Qué hacías cuando estabas enfermo? (*guardar cama*)

_____

3.   ¿Qué hacías cuando no querías hablar con un amigo por teléfono? (*no contestar el teléfono*)

_____

4.   ¿Qué hacías cuando tus padres te preguntaban adónde ibas? (*decir la verdad*)

_____

5.   ¿Qué hacías cuando perdías un partido? (*felicitar al ganador*)

_____

6.   ¿Qué hacías cuando no hacía buen tiempo? (*no salir de la casa*)

_____

EXERCISE E.   **Some people are talented and did two things simultaneously. Tell what the following people were doing at the same time.**

EXAMPLE: escuchar la radio / estudiar
　　　　　Felipe **escuchaba** la radio mientras **estudiaba**.

1.   silbar / trabajar

El señor Perón_____.

2.   hablar por teléfono / cocinar

Mi mamá_____.

3.   cantar / bañarse

Yo _____.

4.   reír / pelear

Los niños_____.

5. dormir / estar en la clase de historia

Tú_____.

6. hablar / comer

Romi y yo_____ .

EXERCISE F.   You and some friends are remembering the part-time jobs you all had while going to school. Tell who did what.

Gary	distribuir folletos
Felipe y Juan	cortar el césped
Alicia	cuidar a los niños del vecino
yo	entregar pizza a domicilio
Mirta y yo	contestar el teléfono en una oficina
tú	lavar carros

EXAMPLE: Pedro **lavaba** platos todos los sábados.

1. _____

2. _____

3. _____

4. _____

5. _____

6. _____

EXERCISE G.   Tell how frequently these people did these activities.

EXAMPLE: Esteban / mirar la televisión / todos los días
Esteban **miraba** la televisión todos los días.

1. Miriam / enviar tarjetas a sus amigos / siempre

_____

2. José y Clemente / jugar al fútbol / todos los sábados

_____

3. yo / telefonear a mi mejor amiga / cada noche

_____

4. Estela y yo / visitar las tiendas / de vez en cuando

_____

5. mi familia / comer en un restaurante / con frecuencia

_____

6. tú / escribir poemas / a veces

_____

◆ 2 ◆ VERBS IRREGULAR IN THE IMPERFECT TENSE

There are three irregular verbs in the imperfect tense: *ir, ser,* and *ver.*

	ir *to go*	**ser** *to be*	**ver** *to see*
yo	iba	era	veía
tú	ibas	eras	veías
Ud., él, ella	iba	era	veía
nosotros, -as	íbamos	éramos	veíamos
vosotros, -as	ibais	erais	veíais
Uds., ellos, ellas	iban	eran	veían

EXERCISE H. Tell where these people used to go. Include an expression to indicate with what frequency they did this.

EXAMPLE: Eduardo / la piscina   Eduardo **iba** a la piscina **cada tarde.**

1. Martina / el centro comercial _____

2. yo / el gimnasio _____

3. Hugo y Vicente / el salón de videojuegos _____

4. tú / el parque de diversiones _____

5. Joan y Joyce / el café _____

6. Víctor y yo / el club de golf _____

EXERCISE I. Jacqueline and a friend are looking at a class photograph from elementary school. Tell what they say about different people they recognize in the photo.

EXAMPLE: Clara / cómico   Clara **era** cómica.

1. Roberto / guapo _____

2. Jeff y Ed / divertido _____

3. tú / muy serio _____

4. Lance / alto y fuerte _____

5. yo / tímido _____

6. Ginny y yo / buenos amigos _____

EXERCISE J. Tell what type of movies these people used to see.

EXAMPLE: Miguel / películas policíacas   Miguel **veía** películas policíacas.

1. mi mamá y mi tía / películas románticas

_____

2. Rigoberto y yo / películas de ciencia-ficción

_____

3. tú / películas de historia

_____

4. Angel / películas cómicas

_____

5. yo / películas dramáticas

_____

6. mi papá / películas antiguas

_____

(**EXERCISE K.**)   **Answer the questions a friend asks you about how you used to celebrate your birthday when you were younger.**

1. ¿Tenías una fiesta para celebrar tu cumpleaños?

_____

2. ¿Invitaba tu mamá a muchos niños a la fiesta?

_____

3. ¿Recibías muchos regalos?

_____

4. ¿Apagabas las velas del pastel fácilmente o necesitabas ayuda?

_____

5. ¿Jugaban Uds. muchos juegos?

_____

6. ¿Ibas al cine a veces?

_____

7. ¿Escogías tus propios regalos?

_____

8. ¿Te daban tus papás todo lo que pedías?

_____

9. ¿Rompían Uds. una piñata en la fiesta?

_____

10. ¿Eras feliz?

_____

Chapter 8

◆3◆ USES OF THE IMPERFECT TENSE

The imperfect tense is used:

a. to express what used to happen.

Ellas visitaban a los abuelos todos   *They used to visit the grandparents every*
   los domingos.   *Sunday.*

Yo jugaba al tenis.   *I played (used to play) tennis.*

b. to describe what was going on at a particular time.

Yo *leía* el periódico durante el   *I was reading the newspaper during*
   desayuno.   *breakfast.*

c. to describe simultaneous actions in the past. *Mientras* is usually used to connect the two actions.

Comía una manzana *mientras* hacía   *I was eating an apple while I did*
   la tarea.   *the assignment.*

d. to describe what was going on in the past (imperfect) when something else began or ended (preterit). *Cuando* usually links the two actions.

Yo *hablaba* por teléfono *cuando*   *I was speaking on the telephone when*
   Ana *tocó* a la puerta.   *Ana knocked on the door.*

e. to describe persons or things in the past.

Felipe *era* alto y fuerte.   *Philip was tall and strong.*

Los trenes *eran* modernos.   *The trains were modern.*

f. to express the time of day (the hour) in the past.

Eran las tres.   *It was three o'clock.*

EXERCISE L.   **Pilar asked her grandmother to send her an email describing what life was like when she was young and lived in a small town. The letter didn't arrive in very good shape. Help Pilar complete it by giving the imperfect tense of the verbs that are missing.**

Cuando yo _____ pequeña, mi familia y yo _____ en un pueblo
              1. (ser)   2. (vivir)

pequeño. Todas las tiendas _____ en una calle que _____ a la plaza principal.
                              3. (estar)   4. (dar)

Los viernes _____ un mercado al aire libre porque muchos campesinos _____
                5. (haber)   6. (venir)

al pueblo para vender sus productos. Yo siempre _____ a mi mamá cuando ella
                                                    7. (acompañar)

_____ de compras. Ella _____ una canasta y los vendedores
     8. (ir)   9. (llevar)

_____ las frutas y las legumbres que nosotros _____ en ella.
     10. (poner)   11. (comprar)

Me _____ mucho acompañarla. Cerca de la escuela _____ un parque
       12. (gustar)   13. (haber)

donde los niños _____. El parque _____ un subibaja y columpios. Mis
                    14. (jugar)   15. (tener)

hermanos y yo _____ allí todos los domingos. Como todavía no _____ la
                  16. (ir)   17. (existir)

televisión, mis hermanos y yo _____ la radio o _____ libros que
                                  18. (escuchar)   19. (leer)

_____ prestados a la biblioteca. Una vez al mes yo _____ al cine con mi
          20. (pedir)   21. (ir)

hermana mayor. Nos _____ las películas norteamericanas. Cada dos semanas toda la
                          22. (fascinar)

familia _____ en la casa de mis abuelos. Mi abuela siempre _____ los
              23. (reunirse)   24. (preparar)

platos favoritos de todos los nietos. Todo el mundo _____ que ayudar a mis abuelos. En
                                                                25. (tener)

cada reunión, mis primos y yo _____ mucho tiempo juntos. Nosotros _____
                                    26. (pasar)   27. (inventar)

juegos divertidos. La vida en mi pueblo no _____ aburrida.
                                                28. (ser)

EXERCISE M.   **A lot of activities were going on at the same time at the Hidalgo family reunion. Follow the example and express what was happening.**

EXAMPLE: los hombres / jugar al voleibol / las mujeres / charlar
            Mientras los hombres **jugaban** al voleibol, las mujeres **charlaban.**

1. Pedro y yo / pescar / Mauricio / nadar en el lago

_____

2. Cristina / practicar el baile / los niños / subir a los columpios

_____

3. Tim y Greg / practicar la lucha libre / todo el mundo / mirarlos

_____

4. mi tío / cocinar / mis tías / poner la mesa

_____

5. mi abuelo / dormir la siesta / mi abuela y yo / andar por el parque

_____

EXERCISE N.   **Something interrupted what these people were doing. Relate each pair of events in a complete sentence.**

EXAMPLE: Ana / preparar la tarea / el teléfono / sonar
            Ana **preparaba** la tarea cuando el teléfono **sonó.**

1. tú / regar el césped / los vecinos / llegar

_____

2. yo / trabajar en la computadora / la luz / apagarse

_____

3. la familia / comer en el bosque / un oso / aparecer

_____

4. el equipo / jugar al béisbol / una tormenta / caer

_____

5. mi padre / dormir la siesta / alguien / tocar a la puerta

_____

6. Elena y yo / nadar en la piscina / nosotros / ver un relámpago

_____

7. Javier / escuchar la radio / un locutor / interrumpir la emisión

_____

8. el chofer / conducir el taxi / el motor / dejar de funcionar

_____

MASTERY EXERCISES

EXERCISE O.   **Rewrite this entry from Eugenio's diary in the imperfect tense.**

Estoy en Venezuela y asisto a un programa especial de verano. Vivo con una familia venezolana. Tienen tres hijos. Dos de ellos son simpáticos y divertidos, pero el menor es muy travieso y a menudo, antipático. Le gusta salirse con la suya y no hay día en que no hace ninguna travesura. Siempre hay muchos gritos en la casa porque el hermano menor molesta mucho a sus hermanos mayores. No hace nada en la casa y sus padres lo consienten mucho. Cuando los amigos de sus hermanos vienen a la casa, él siempre quiere hacer lo que ellos hacen. Los sigue por todas partes. Muchas veces yo voy a su cuarto para hablar con él, pero él siempre cierra la puerta en mi cara. Es divertido ver que esta familia se parece mucho a la mía.

_____

_____

_____

_____

_____

_____

_____

_____

_____

_____

EXERCISE P.   **You are describing someone from your childhood. Include as many details about this person as you can. You may wish to include the following suggestions:**

- the person's name and relationship to you (friend, neighbor, etc.)

- where you lived and where this person lived

- the person's age in relation to your age

- the frequency which with you saw this person

- some personality characteristics of this person (activities, likes, dislikes, etc.)

- something special about this person

- what you enjoyed (or disliked) most about this person

ACTIVIDADES

1. Describe yourself when you were ten years old. Mention your physical and personality characteristics, the activities you enjoyed, and why you enjoyed them. Describe also your friends, your favorite possession, and your favorite pastime(s).

2. Who were your favorite teachers when you were in elementary school? Describe them, tell three things about them, and why you liked them.

Preterit and Imperfect Tenses Compared

1. The preterit is used to indicate the beginning or the end of an action or event occurring in the past. It may also indicate the complete event (both beginning and end).

Empezó a trabajar.	*He began to work.*
Cesó de llover.	*It stopped raining.*
Visité a María ayer.	*I visited Mary yesterday.*

2. The imperfect is used to indicate the continuance of a situation or event in the past. Neither the beginning nor the end is indicated. Thus, it is used:

a. To express what was happening, used to happen, or happened repeatedly in the past.

¿Qué *hacían* ellos mientras el niño dormía?	*What were they doing while the child slept (was sleeping)?*
Vivíamos en Madrid.	*We used to live in Madrid.* *We were living in Madrid.*
Yo lo *veía* a menudo.	*I used to see him often.*

b. To describe persons, things, or situations in the past.

María *tenía* los ojos azules.	*Mary had blue eyes.*
La imprenta *era* una máquina útil.	*The press was a useful machine.*

c. To express the time of day in the past.

Eran las ocho.	*It was eight o'clock.*

d. In the construction *hacía + time expression + que + imperfect,* to describe an action or event that began in the past and continued in the past. In questions, *how long?* is expressed by *¿cuánto tiempo hacía que . . .? + imperfect.*

Hacía una hora que estudiaban.	*They had been studying for an hour.*
¿Cuánto tiempo hacía que Ud. trabajaba?	*How long had you been working?*

e. With the preterit, to describe what was going on in tenses past (imperfect) when another action or event occurred, that is, began or ended (preterit).

Yo leía cuando mi hermano entró.	*I was reading when my brother entered.*

EXERCISE A. **In each selection the choice of the preterit or imperfect form of the verb is offered. Select the appropriate one.**

1. Cuando Emilio (*llegó, llegaba*) al aeropuerto, se (*dio, daba*) cuenta de que no (*tuvo, tenía*) su boleto. —«¿Dónde lo (*dejé, dejaba*)?»—, (*pensó, pensaba*) Emilio, mientras la agente de la aerolínea (*trató, trataba*) de ayudarlo. Sólo (*hubo, había*) una manera de resolver su problema. (*Tuvo, Tenía*) que comprar otro boleto. (*Buscó, Buscaba*) la cartera en el bolsillo pero no lo (*encontró, encontraba*). (*Fueron, Eran*) ya las dos y cuarto y el avión (*salió, salía*) a las dos y media.

2. (*Fue, Era*) una noche cálida de agosto. (*Fueron, Eran*) las diez de la noche y todavía (*hubo, había*) muchas personas en la playa. Estela (*estuvo, estaba*) en el balcón y desde allí (*pudo, podía*) ver que (*ardieron, ardían*) varias fogatas en la playa. La luz de las llamas de las fogatas (*iluminó, iluminaba*) la escena de la playa. Pero por la oscuridad de la noche no (*se distinguió, se distinguía*) dónde (*comenzó, comenzaba*) el mar y dónde (*terminó, terminaba*) la playa. Estela (*oyó, oía*) claramente las voces de las personas en la playa y el ruido de las olas que (*se rompieron, se rompían*) al tocar la orilla.

3. Lucy siempre (*pasó, pasaba*) muchas horas leyendo revistas de músicos contemporáneos. En una ocasión (*leyó, leía*) la historia de uno de sus cantantes favoritos. El artículo (*dijo, decía*) que el cantante nunca (*demostró, demostraba*) ningún interés discernible hacia la música. El (*asistió, asistía*) a la universidad y (*decidió, decidía*) estudiar leyes. Le (*gustaron, gustaban*) los deportes, especialmente el fútbol. (*Jugó, Jugaba*) con frecuencia y (*fue, era*) muy buen futbolista. Un día, mientras (*condujo, conducía*) su carro, (*tuvo, tenía*) un accidente automovilístico. (*Pasó, Pasaba*) dos meses en el hospital. Al volver a casa, (*comenzó, comenzaba*) a estudiar la guitarra y (*compuso, componía*) varias canciones. Cuando (*pudo, podía*) volver a la universidad, (*terminó, terminaba*) sus estudios y (*llegó, llegaba*) a ser abogado. (*Abandonó, Abandonaba*) la idea de ser abogado y (*grabó, grababa*) un disco de sus canciones. Y así (*se hizo, se hacía*) famoso este cantante.

EXERCISE B.   **Raúl never straightened up his room. His mother took a photograph of his room to show him what he wasn't doing. Then Raúl showed her a photo he took of the room. Using the first photo, tell what Raúl wasn't doing. Then, using the second photo, tell what he did. Use the suggestions below.**

EXAMPLE: Raúl no arreglaba su cuarto.   Raúl **arregló** su cuarto.

SUGGESTIONS: (no) colgar la ropa en el armario   (no) apagar el estéreo
                      (no) poner los libros en el librero   (no) guardar los zapatos en el armario
                      (no) hacer la cama   (no) arreglar su cuarto
                      (no) sacar la basura

EXERCISE C. **Complete the passage below with the appropriate form of the verbs indicated in the preterit or imperfect tenses.**

Él _____ a Mariana una sola vez, pero su imagen _____ profundamente
  1. (conocer)   *2.* (quedar)

grabada en su memoria. Ella _____ alta, esbelta y joven. _____ los ojos
                              3. (ser)   *4.* (tener)

claros y una sonrisa simpática. Ella y sus amigas _____ una semana en un hotel cerca de
                                                    5. (pasar)

donde él _____ un cuarto mientras _____ a la universidad. Sus
          6. (alquilar)   *7.* (asistir)

pasos _____ casi todos los días a la hora de la comida. Él _____ comer
        8. (cruzarse)   *9.* (soler)

en un restaurante pequeño cerca de la pensión y las jóvenes _____ allí cada día. ¡Qué
                                                              10. (desayunarse)

bonito _____ poder desayunar a la hora en que todo el mundo _____!
        11. (ser)   *12.* (almorzar)

_____ él. El joven _____ saber cómo ella _____, pero no
 13. (pensar)   *14.* (querer)   *15.* (llamarse)

_____ a acercarse a su mesa para presentarse. Un día le _____ el mo-
 16. (atreverse)   *17.* (llegar)

mento propicio. Él _____ a la caja para pagar la cuenta y ella _____
                     18. (ir)   *19.* (levantarse)

y _____ a la caja en el mismo momento. Por un instante, _____ inmóvil
   20. (acercarse)   *21.* (quedarse)

y _____ que su boca _____ muy seca. Ella le _____ y
   22. (sentir)   *23.* (ponerse)   *24.* (sonreír)

él _____ aprovecharse de la oportunidad. Él le _____ una señal de
    25. (decidir)   *26.* (hacer)

pasar primero a la caja y ella le _____ las gracias. Entonces, el joven _____
                                   27. (dar)   *28.* (tratar)

de decirle algo pero las palabras no _____ de su boca. Ella _____ un
                                       29. (salir)   *30.* (hacer)

comentario sobre el tiempo, pero él sólo _____ contestarle con un movimiento de la
                                          31. (poder)

cabeza. Ella _____ en los libros que él _____ y le _____
               32. (fijarse)   *33.* (traer)   *34.* (preguntar)

si _____ estudiante. Entonces _____ que si no le _____, la
    35. (ser)   *36.* (saber)   *37.* (responder)

oportunidad sería perdida para siempre.

EXERCISE D. **Antonio is interested in knowing how long his friends had been doing different activities. Prepare the questions he asks.**

EXAMPLE: Jaime / ser miembro del equipo de fútbol
           ¿Cuánto tiempo hacía que Jaime **era** miembro del equipo de fútbol?

1.   Renaldo / actuar en los dramas de la escuela

_____

2.   tus abuelos / pasar el invierno en la Florida

_____

3.   tú / competir en los concursos

_____

4. Angela y Gerardo / ser novios

_____

5. June y yo / jugar al boliche todos los viernes por la noche

_____

6. Uds. / asistir a los conciertos

_____

7. Vicente / montar a caballo

_____

EXERCISE E.   **Answer the questions in Exercise D using the information provided.**

EXAMPLE: _(dos años)_   **Hacía dos años que** Jaime **era** miembro del equipo de fútbol.

1. _(un año)_ _____

2. _(cinco años)_ _____

3. _(seis meses)_ _____

4. _(dos semanas)_ _____

5. _(cinco semanas)_ _____

6. _(tres meses)_ _____

7. _(diez años)_ _____

EXERCISE F.   **Your father wants to know why you didn't answer the telephone when he called. Answer the questions he asks.**

1. ¿Dónde estabas cuando sonó el teléfono?

_____

2. ¿Qué hacías?

_____

3. ¿Quiénes estaban contigo?

_____

4. ¿Tenían Uds. el estéreo puesto?

_____

5. ¿Oíste cuando el vecino llamó a la puerta?

_____

6. ¿Por qué no contestaste el teléfono cuando yo llamé?

_____

MASTERY EXERCISES

EXERCISE G. You are helping your younger brother write a report on a hero for his Spanish class. Complete his report by providing the appropriate form of the verb given in the preterit or imperfect tense.

El padre Miguel Hidalgo _____ un gran patriota mexicano. _____ el
          1. (ser)   2. (ser)

primer jefe de la lucha por la independencia. México _____ entonces una colonia
                                                              3. (ser)

española. Los mexicanos no _____ tomar parte en el gobierno. Los gobernadores
                                    4. (poder)

_____ todos españoles, nombrados por el rey de España. Muchos _____
      5. (ser)   6. (aceptar)

puestos solamente para hacerse ricos, a costa de los mexicanos. El deseo de liberar a su patria

_____ el corazón de Hidalgo, que _____ entonces sacerdote de la
      7. (inflamar)   8. (ser)

pequeña aldea de Dolores. En 1810 _____ un partido patriótico cuyo objeto
                                          9. (organizar)

_____ trabajar y luchar por la independencia. Ellos _____ un ejército
      10. (ser)   11. (formar)

y _____ hacia Guanajuato, una ciudad grande y rica, fortificada y defendida por los
      12. (avanzar)

españoles. Gracias al heroísmo de Hidalgo, los revolucionarios _____ vencer a los españoles.
                                                                      13. (poder)

Hidalgo _____ la ciudad y la _____ centro de la revolución. En seguida
          14. (fortificar)   15. (hacer)

_____ a llegar miles de mexicanos que _____ juntarse a las fuerzas
      16. (empezar)   17. (querer)

patrióticas. Con la ayuda de éstos, Hidalgo _____ continuar la lucha.
                                                    18. (poder)

EXERCISE H. Mrs. Duarte asks her son Joey many questions when he returns from school. Answer the questions she asks him.

1. ¿Diste la tarea a tu maestra?

_____

2. ¿Encontraste a muchos amigos esta mañana mientras ibas a la escuela?

_____

3. ¿A qué hora llegaste a la escuela?

_____

4. ¿Atravesaste muchas calles hoy para llegar a la escuela?

_____

5. ¿Cuando entraste en la casa ahora, colgaste tu abrigo en el armario?

_____

EXERCISE I.   Answer the questions a new friend asks you about what you were like when you were younger.

1. ¿Cuando eras niño(-a), soñabas con viajar?

_____

2. ¿Siempre obedecías a tu mamá?

_____

3. ¿Poseías una bicicleta?

_____

4. ¿Les tiraban piedras tú y tus amigos a los otros niños?

_____

5. ¿Interrumpías a tus padres cuando ellos hablaban?

_____

EXERCISE J.   A new student in your class has been asked to write a description of his first day in your school. Express what he said in Spanish.

1. I had been waiting on the corner for the bus for fifteen minutes.

_____

2. The bus finally arrived.

_____

3. There were so many students on the bus that I could not sit down.

_____

4. One student offered to share his seat with me.

_____

5. We began to speak.

_____

6. He told me that he had just come to the school also.

_____

7. He was from El Salvador.

_____

8. When I arrived at school, I went to the office.

_____

9. A very nice lady gave me my schedule.

_____

10. A student accompanied me to my first class.

_____

11. When I entered the room, the class was watching a movie.

_____

12. The teacher and I went into the hall, and she welcomed me.

_____

13. We returned to the classroom and she intoduced me to the other students.

_____

14. They were polite and friendly.

_____

15. I sat down and listened while the class discussed the movie.

_____

CHAPTER

10

The Future Tense

◆ 1 ◆ THE FUTURE TENSE OF REGULAR VERBS

The future tense is formed by adding to the infinitive the following endings:

	ayudar *to help*	**aprender** *to learn*	**abrir** *to open*
	I shall (will) help, you will help, etc.	*I shall (will) learn, you will learn, etc.*	*I shall (will) open, you will open, etc.*
yo	ayud**aré**	aprend**eré**	abr**iré**
tú	ayud**arás**	aprend**erás**	abr**irás**
Ud., él, ella	ayud**ará**	aprend**erá**	abr**irá**
nosotros, -as	ayud**aremos**	aprend**eremos**	abr**iremos**
vosotros, -as	ayud**aréis**	aprend**eréis**	abr**iréis**
Uds. ellos, ellas	ayud**arán**	aprend**erán**	abr**irán**

NOTES:

1. In English, the future tense is expressed by means of the helping verb *will* or *shall*.

    Estaré en la escuela mañana.   *I shall be in school tomorrow.*

    ¿Cenarás conmigo esta noche?   *Will you have dinner with me tonight?*

2. All the endings have an accent mark, except *-emos*.

EXERCISE A.   **Everyone is making plans for the following day. Tell what each person will do.**

EXAMPLE: Marta / visitar a una amiga   Marta **visitará** a una amiga.

1. yo / jugar al voleibol   _____

2. Felipe y Martín / remar en el lago   _____

3. mis padres / comer en un restaurante   _____

4. tú / ir de compras   _____

5. Uds. / ver una película   _____

6. Jimmy y yo / asistir a un concierto   _____

EXERCISE B.   **As one year ends and a new one is about to begin, several friends discuss their plans for the new year. Tell what each one will do.**

EXAMPLE: Andrés / buscar un trabajo   Andrés **buscará** un trabajo.

1. Vicki / terminar sus estudios   _____

2. Esteban y yo / viajar a México   _____

3. tú / aprender a conducir _____

4. yo / leer «El Quijote» _____

5. Ofelia y Arturo / correr en un maratón _____

6. Gisela / tocar en una orquesta _____

EXERCISE C. **Your father follows the same routine every day. Tell what he will do tomorrow.**

EXAMPLE: apagar el reloj despertador   Mi papá **apagará** el reloj despertador.

1. levantarse de la cama en seguida _____

2. bañarse y luego vestirse _____

3. comer el desayuno con mi mamá _____

4. ir al trabajo _____

5. conducir el carro _____

6. asistir a una reunión en su oficina _____

7. llamar a mi mamá a mediodía _____

8. volver a casa a las seis _____

9. cenar con toda la familia _____

10. sentarse en la sala _____

11. leer el periódico _____

12. oír las noticias _____

13. dormirse en el sillón _____

◆2◆ THE FUTURE TENSE OF IRREGULAR VERBS

Some verbs form the future tense by adding the future personal endings (*-é, -ás, -á, -emos, -éis, -án*) to an irregular stem.

a. The following verbs drop the *e* of the infinitive ending before adding the endings of the future:

caber *to fit*	cabré, cabrás, cabrá, cabremos, cabréis, cabrán
haber *to have* (*also an auxiliary verb*)	habré, habrás, habrá, habremos, habréis, habrán
poder *to be able*	podré, podrás, podrá, podremos, podréis, podrán
querer *to want, wish*	querré, querrás, querrá, querremos, querréis, querrán
saber *to know*	sabré, sabrás, sabrá, sabremos, sabréis, sabrán

EXERCISE D.   You and some friends are going on a school trip to Spain. Tell what each person will be able to do there. Use the verb *poder* in each sentence.

EXAMPLE: Ema / hablar español todo el día   Ema **podrá** hablar español todo el día.

1. Michael / ir a una corrida de toros   _____

2. Celia y Laura / visitar el museo del Prado   _____

3. Verónica y yo / comprar muchos recuerdos   _____

4. yo / comer paella   _____

5. tú / ver programas de televisión en español   _____

6. Uds. / conocer a muchos jóvenes españoles   _____

EXERCISE E.   You are organizing a school dance. Answer the questions some classmates ask you about it.

1.   ¿Cabrán todos los estudiantes en el gimnasio?

_____

2.   ¿Habrá mucha comida y bebidas?

_____

3.   ¿Cuándo sabrás cuántas personas asistirán al baile?

_____

4.   ¿Querrás nuestra ayuda la noche del baile?

_____

5.   ¿Podrán los músicos tocar nuestras canciones favoritas?

_____

b. The following verbs replace the *e* or *i* of the infinitive ending with a *d* before adding the endings of the future:

poner	*to put*	pondré, pondrás, pondrá, pondremos, pondréis, pondrán
salir	*to leave, go out*	saldré, saldrás, saldrá, saldremos, saldréis, saldrán
tener	*to have*	tendré, tendrás, tendrá, tendremos, tendréis, tendrán
valer	*to be worth*	valdré, valdrás, valdrá, valdremos, valdréis, valdrán
venir	*to come*	vendré, vendrás, vendrá, vendremos, vendréis, vendrán

c. The following verbs drop the *e* and *c* of the infinitive before adding the endings of the future:

| decir | *to say, tell* | diré, dirás, dirá, diremos, diréis, dirán |
| hacer | *to do, make* | haré, harás, hará, haremos, haréis, harán |

◆3◆ USES OF THE FUTURE TENSE

The future tense is used:

a. To express future time.

¿A qué hora *llegará* el tren?   *At what time will the train arrive?*

b. To express wonderment or probability in the present time.

¿Qué hora *será*?   *I wonder what time it is.*
Será la una.   *It is probably one o'clock.*

EXERCISE F.   **Before leaving for Costa Rica, you receive an e-mail message from a friend who was an exchange student in your school. Complete his message with the future tense of the verbs indicated.**

¡Por fin Uds. _____ a San José! Nosotros _____ juntos durante los días
               1. (venir)   2. (salir)

que Uds. _____ aquí. Yo _____ mucho gusto en mostrarles mi ciudad.
          3. (estar)   4. (tener)

Uds. _____ regresar a San José durante las próximas vacaciones. Mi papá
      5. (querer)

_____ un carro a sus órdenes. Nosotros _____ hablar de las semanas que
  6. (poner)   7. (poder)

pasé en su escuela y también _____ un viaje a la playa. ¡Ya _____ Uds. qué
                               8. (hacer)   9. (decir)

bonito es mi país! Es un viaje largo pero _____ la pena. Hasta pronto.
                                           10. (valer)

EXERCISE G.   **Tell what these people will do when something happens to change their plans.**

EXAMPLE: Tú y un amigo piensan ir al cine, pero él está enfermo. *(ir solo al cine)*
             Yo **iré** solo al cine.

1. Manuel quiere correr en el parque, pero hace mucho calor. *(nadar en la piscina)*

Él _____ .

2. Sara piensa ir de compras con una amiga, pero ella dice que no tiene dinero. *(prestarle dinero)*

Su amiga _____ .

3. Dos amigos van al cine para ver una película, pero el teatro cambió la película. *(ver otra película)*

Ellos _____ .

4. Vas a salir con tus amigos, pero tus padres no te prestan el carro. *(no salir)*

Yo _____ .

5. Tu hermana se durmió mientras preparaba un pastel. El pastel se quemó. *(hacer otro pastel)*

Ella _____ .

6. Inés iba a trabajar durante el verano, pero salió mal en una clase. *(tener que tomar la clase durante el verano)*

Ella _____ .

⟨⟨ MASTERY EXERCISES ⟩⟩

EXERCISE H.   Sam invited a group of friends to his house. His younger brother is very inquisitive and asks questions about everything Sam says. Write the questions his brother probably asks.

EXAMPLE: Unos amigos vienen a la casa esta noche. (*¿quiénes?*)
            ¿Quiénes **vendrán**?

1. Van a llegar a las ocho. *(llegar a tiempo)*

    _____

2. Voy a poner algunos discos compactos en la disquetera. *(¿qué?)*

    _____

3. Debo hacer algo de comer para ellos. *(¿qué?)*

    _____

4. Quiero atenderlos bien. *(¿por qué?)*

    _____

5. Puedo poner algunos adornos. *(¿dónde?)*

    _____

6. Alex viene con Diana. *(¿con quién?)*

    _____

EXERCISE I.   You and several friends are talking about the future. Answer their questions.

1. ¿Dónde vivirás en el futuro?   _____

2. ¿Qué clase de trabajo tendrás?   _____

3. ¿Ganarás mucho dinero?   _____

4. ¿Vendrás a ver a tus amigos a menudo?   _____

5. ¿Harás muchos viajes al extranjero?   _____

6. ¿Podrás ahorrar mucho dinero?   _____

7. ¿Pondrás el dinero en la Bolsa?   _____

8. ¿Sabrás hacer buenas inversiones con
    tu dinero?   _____

EXERCISE J.   Your mother is planning a large holiday celebration. Using the verbs indicated, tell what each family member will do to help.

1. Yo le _____ qué hacer a cada persona. *(decir)*

2. Todo el mundo _____ que arreglar su cuarto. *(tener)*

3. Alicia _____ la mesa. (*poner*)

4. El abuelo _____ ayudar con la limpieza. (*querer*)

5. Tú _____ los adornos. (*hacer*)

6. Víctor y su papá _____ al supermercado. (*salir*)

7. Los invitados _____ a las cuatro. (*venir*)

8. La abuela y yo _____ a qué hora poner todo en el horno. (*saber*)

9. Yo _____ descansar antes de la llegada de los invitados. (*poder*)

EXERCISE K.   **Answer the questions a friend asks you on the school bus in the morning.**

1. ¿A qué hora saldrás de la escuela hoy?

_____

2. ¿A qué hora estarás en casa esta tarde?

_____

3. ¿Podrás ir al cine esta noche?

_____

4. ¿Tendrás que estudiar para un examen mañana?

_____

5. ¿Qué harás mañana después de las clases?

_____

6. ¿Podrás ir al centro conmigo?

_____

7. ¿Sabrás si Gus podrá ir al centro también?

_____

8. ¿Dónde pasarás el fin de semana?

_____

9. ¿En qué fecha vendrán tus primos a verte?

_____

10. ¿Te gustará tomar un refresco conmigo en el café?

_____

EXERCISE L.   You school has a sister-school in Quito, Ecuador. A group of students from the sister school is visiting your school and a bus trip around your city has been planned. You will be the guide and you prepare information you will give them in Spanish. You may wish to include the following suggestions:

- the time the bus will leave

- what your role will be

- a general overview of the day's activities

- the need to purchase tickets for admission to the museum

- the cost of the admission

- the need to leave cameras on the bus while at the museum

- who will remain on the bus

- the length of the museum visit

- other things they will see while riding on the bus

- when the tour will end

- other tours and activities that will take place on other days

- you will be happy to answer all their questions

ACTIVIDADES

1. What will the world be like in twenty-five years? How old will you be? What will you be doing? Will the same problems still exist: wars throughout the world, overpopulation, climate change, extinction of animal species, etc.? Write a paragraph in Spanish in which you tell what you think the world will be like in twenty-five years. Address as many of the topics listed above. Be sure to use the future tense of as many regular and irregular verbs as you can.

2. You have told your classmates in your Spanish class that your parents have promised you a trip to any place in the world as a graduation gift. However, they want to know why you selected the destination. Prepare a presentation to them in Spanish in which you include your desired destination, why you want to go there, what you will see, learn, and be able to do there, how long you will need to spend there, etc. You may wish to consult the Internet for information about your chosen destination that you can include in your presentation. Use the future tense as often as you can.

CHAPTER

11

The Conditional Tense

◆ 1 ◆ REGULAR VERBS

a. The conditional tense is formed by adding to the infinitive the following endings:

	viajar *to travel*	**comer** *to eat*	**permitir** *to permit*
yo	viaja**ría**	come**ría**	permiti**ría**
tú	viaja**rías**	come**rías**	permiti**rías**
Ud., él, ella,	viaja**ría**	come**ría**	permiti**ría**
nosotros, -as	viaja**ríamos**	come**ríamos**	permiti**ríamos**
vosotros, -as	viaja**ríais**	come**ríais**	permiti**ríais**
Uds., ellos, ellas	viaja**rían**	come**rían**	permiti**rían**

b. In English, the conditional tense is expressed by means of the helping verb *would*.

¿Adónde *viajarías*?	*Where would you travel to?*
Yo *viajaría* a la América del Sur.	*I would travel to South America.*

c. All the endings have an accent mark on the *i* of the ending.

EXERCISE A. Several friends are speculating about what they would do if they had unlimited funds. Tell what each one would do.

EXAMPLE: Pablo / comprar un carro de modelo deportivo
Pablo **compraría** un carro de modelo deportivo.

1. Virginia / dar dinero a los pobres _____

2. Eddie y Roger / vivir en una isla tropical _____

3. Dennis y yo / ayudar a nuestras familias _____

4. tú / ir de compras todos los días _____

5. yo / ser dueño de una compañía grande _____

6. Franco / no trabajar _____

EXERCISE B. You are a member of an ecology club in your school. Tell what everyone would do to protect the environment.

EXAMPLE: todo el mundo / reciclar la basura   Todo el mundo **reciclaría** la basura.

1. Jenny / conservar el agua

_____

2. yo / proteger las flores y las plantas del parque

_____

3. Enrique y yo / usar el transporte público

_____

4. tú / no tirar papeles en el piso

_____

5. Selene y Rocío / montar en bicicleta

_____

6. la comunidad / organizar un programa de reciclaje

_____

EXERCISE C.   **Tell what these people would do in this situations.**

EXAMPLE: Mi amiga no me llama. (*llamarla*)   Yo la **llamaría.**

1. El abuelo de Carlos está en el hospital. (*ir a visitarlo*)

Carlos _____ .

2. Es el cumpleaños de mi hermano. (*comprarle un regalo*)

Yo _____ .

3. Mi tía perdió un anillo muy caro. (*ofrecer una recompensa*)

Ella _____ .

4. El cajero les dio demasiado cambio a Vinny y a Tony. (*devolver el dinero*)

Ellos _____ .

5. Nosotros tenemos boletos para un concierto pero no podemos asistir. (*dar los boletos a unos amigos*)

Nosotros _____ .

6. Tu padre no puede pintar la casa solo. (*ayudarle a pintar la casa*)

Tú _____ .

◆ 2 ◆ VERBS IRREGULAR IN THE CONDITIONAL TENSE

Some verbs form the conditional tense by adding the conditional personal endings to an irregular stem.

a. The following verbs drop the *e* of the infinitive ending before adding the endings of the conditional:

caber	*to fit*	cabría, cabrías, cabría, cabríamos, cabríais, cabrían
haber	*to have (auxiliary verb)*	habría, habrías, habría, habríamos, habríais, habrían
poder	*to be able*	podría, podrías, podría, podríamos, podríais, podrían
querer	*to want, wish*	querría, querrías, querría, querríamos, querríais, querrían
saber	*to know*	sabría, sabrías, sabría, sabríamos, sabríais, sabrían

b. The following verbs replace the *e* (or *i*) of the infinitive ending with a *d* before adding the endings of the conditional:

poner	*to put*	pondría, pondrías, pondría, pondríamos, pondríais, pondrían
salir	*to leave, go out*	saldría, saldrías, saldría, saldríamos, saldríais, saldrían
tener	*to have*	tendría, tendrías, tendría, tendríamos, tendríais, tendrían
valer	*to be worth*	valdría, valdrías, valdría, valdríamos, valdríais, valdrían
venir	*to come*	vendría, vendrías, vendría, vendríamos, vendríais, vendrían

c. The following verbs drop the *e* and *c* of the infinitive before adding the endings of the conditional:

decir	*to say, tell*	diría, dirías, diría, diríamos, diríais, dirían
hacer	*to do, make*	haría, harías, haría, haríamos, haríais, harían

NOTE: When *would* is used in the sense of *used to,* it is expressed by the imperfect tense, not the conditional.

Siempre nos ayudaba.   *He always would (used to) help us.*

EXERCISE D. Janice and her friends have had a very busy school year. Follow the example and express what they would know how to do if they had had more time. Use the verb *saber* in your answers.

EXAMPLE: Janice / patinar en hielo   Janice **sabría** patinar en hielo.

1. Ralph y Perry / esquiar   _____

2. yo / conducir   _____

3. ellas / patinar en monopatín   _____

4. Felice y yo / jugar al tenis   _____

5. tú / navegar   _____

6. Mitch / montar a caballo   _____

EXERCISE E. You and your younger brother are waiting in the crowded dentist's office. To help distract him while you wait, you give him two lists. One contains the members of your family; the other contains activities they would prefer. Tell who would prefer what.

Papá	ir a la playa o a las montañas
Mamá	hacer un castillo en la arena o nadar en el mar
Sally	jugar al golf o al tenis
Richie	dar o recibir regalos
Tío Juan	pasar las vacaciones con la familia o con tus amigos
yo	comer en una cafetería o un restaurante elegante
tú y yo	poner el dinero en el banco o gastarlo
	visitar al dentista o ir a la heladería

EXAMPLE: Yo iría a la heladería.

1. _____

2. _____

3. _____

4. _____

5. _____

6. _____

7. _____

8. _____

EXERCISE F.   **You have been out of the country for over a month and haven't seen a local newspaper in all that time. Tell what you would know or do if you had a local newspaper. Use the suggestions.**

SUGGESTIONS: saber cuándo comienzan las baratas en las tiendas   ver los anuncios de las tiendas
poder seguir las tiras cómicas   enterarse de las noticias locales
hacer el crucigrama   saber los tantos de los equipos
leer las últimas noticias   de béisbol
hacer comentario sobre un suceso local

EXAMPLE: Yo **podría** seguir las tiras cómicas.

1. _____

2. _____

3. _____

4. _____

5. _____

6. _____

7. _____

EXERCISE G.   **You and your sister listened to a message your father left on your voicemail, but neither of you understood it. Express what you thought he said.**

EXAMPLE: él / llegar a casa en dos horas   El **llegaría** a casa en dos horas.

1. nosotros / deber esperarlo para cenar

_____

2. no haber trenes hasta la mañana debido a un accidente

_____

3. él / alquilar un carro

_____

4. tu mamá / poder buscarlo en la estación

_____

5. tú / no saber nada por dos horas

_____

6. él / tener que pasar la noche en un hotel

_____

7. él y un vecino / venir en autobús

_____

8. todo el mundo / no caber en el primer tren de la mañana

_____

9. los pasajeros / no salir del tren

_____

10. él / volver a llamar más tarde

_____

◆ 3 ◆ USES OF THE CONDITIONAL TENSE

The conditional is used:

a. To express what would or could happen in the future or to make a polite request.

Pagaría mucho por las joyas.	*I would pay a lot for the jewelry.*
Me gustaría ver una corbata de seda.	*I would like to see a silk tie.*

b. To express wonderment or probability in the past.

¿Qué hora sería?	*I wonder what time it was.*
Sería la una.	*It was probably one o'clock.*

NOTE: The future tense is commonly used in combination with the present or future tense; the conditional, with a past tense.

Dice que irá.	*He says he will go.*
Dijo que iría.	*He said he would go.*

EXERCISE H. **You are planning a trip with the travel agent. Answer her questions.**

1. ¿Adónde iría Ud.? _____

2. ¿Cuántas personas harían el viaje? _____

3. ¿Cuándo podrían Uds. salir? _____

4. ¿En qué fecha querrían regresar? _____

5. ¿Harían excursiones allí? _____

6. ¿Cuántas excursiones harían Uds.? _____

7. ¿Cuánto dinero querría Ud. gastar en el viaje? _____

8. ¿Tendría Ud. que alquilar un carro? _____

9. ¿Quién podría llevarlos al aeropuerto? _____

10. ¿Pagaría Ud. con un cheque personal
o con una tarjeta de crédito? _____

EXERCISE I. You are reading an ad for a health club. Tell five things you would do if you were a member.

El Gimnasio Universal
Especial de Verano

3 Meses Por $99

- Para hombres y mujeres
- Máquinas de entrenamiento
- Equipo cardiovascular
- Dietas para bajar de peso
- Piscina interior

- Clases de aeróbicos
- Pesas
- Entrenador personal
- Sauna

Abierto las 24 horas.   Llame al 522-07-29
Esta oferta vence el 31 de julio. Solamente para nuevos socios.

EXAMPLE: Yo **usaría** las máquinas de entrenamiento.

1. _____

2. _____

3. _____

4. _____

5. _____

MASTERY EXERCISES

EXERCISE J. You and a friend are going to Costa Rica to visit her family. You send her this e-mail. Complete the message with the appropriate form of the verbs indicated in the conditional.

El agente de viajes me dijo que el avión _____ a las siete de la noche. Nosotros
                                              1. (salir)

_____ que estar en el aeropuerto dos horas antes y me _____ estar allí a
   2. (tener)   **3.** (gustar)

la hora indicada. Así nosotras _____ los asientos con calma. También yo _____
                                  4. (escoger)   **5.** (querer)

comprar algo para tu familia en la tienda libre de impuestos. Entendí que tus padres te _____
6. (llevar)

al aeropuerto. ¿_____ Uds. pasar por mí camino al aeropuerto? Así yo no _____
7. (poder)   8. (tener)

que buscar un taxi y nosotras _____ juntas al aeropuerto.
9. (llegar)

Contéstame.

EXERCISE K.   **A friend calls you after school. Answer the questions.**

1. ¿Qué hora sería cuando te acostaste anoche?

   _____

2. ¿Cómo sabrías que el maestro estaría ausente?

   _____

3. ¿Sabías a qué universidad asistiría Pedro?

   _____

4. ¿Les aseguró el maestro que no recibirían un examen?

   _____

5. ¿Les prometiste a tus padres que estudiarías más?

   _____

6. ¿Les dijiste a tus amigos cuándo caería tu cumpleaños?

   _____

7. ¿Adónde querrías ir para celebrar tu cumpleaños?

   _____

8. ¿Escogiste los regalos que te gustaría recibir?

   _____

9. ¿Cuánto valdría un reloj como el que tenía Kyoko?

   _____

10. ¿Dónde pondrías un reloj tan caro cuando jugabas al tenis?

   _____

EXERCISE L.   **Your summer vacation is over and it feels as if it passed very quickly. Tell five things you would do differently next vacation.**

EXAMPLE: **No me acostaría** tan tarde cada noche.

1. _____

2. _____

3. _____

4. _____

5. _____

⬛ **EXERCISE M.**   A Spanish-speaking friend of your father is coming to your house for dinner. He owns a company and you would like to work there during the summer vacation. Plan what you will say and ask him in Spanish. You may wish to include the following:

• your promise to earn money during the summer

• your use of Spanish in the job

• the type of job and responsibilities you would like

• your work schedule (days and hours)

• your salary requirement

• other job recommendations or suggestions

⬅ A C T I V I D A D E S ➡

1. You are planning to study in a Spanish-speaking country during the summer. Write a letter to the director of a special program for foreigners in which you request information concerning the program. In your letter, provide information concerning your plans and goals. Also, obtain information concerning the program (duration, requirements, cost, etc.), living accommodations, travel options, etc. Write at least ten sentences in Spanish, using the conditional.

For your convenience, use the following:

Dateline: **2 de junio de** _____

Salutation: **Estimado(-a)** _____ :

Closing: **Atentamente,**

2. Tell what you would do in the situations shown in the pictures below.

For each situation write at least three sentences in Spanish using the conditional.

1. _____   *2.* _____

_____   _____

_____   _____

3. _____

_____

_____

4. _____

_____

_____

5. _____

_____

_____

The Gerund and the Progressive Tenses

In Spanish, the gerund (*el gerundio*) is generally equivalent to the English present participle, or *-ing* verb form.

◆ s ◆ THE GERUND OF REGULAR VERBS

Regular verbs form the gerund by dropping the infinitive endings and adding *-ando* (*-ar* verbs) and *-iendo* (*-er* and *-ir* verbs).

trabajar:	trabajando	*working*		vivir:	viviendo	*living*
aprender:	aprendiendo	*learning*				

◆ 2 ◆ GERUNDS ENDING IN *-YENDO*

Irregular *-er* and *-ir* verbs with stems ending in a vowel form their gerunds by adding *-yendo*.

caer:	cayendo	*falling*		ir:	yendo	*going*
construir:	construyendo	*constructing*		leer:	leyendo	*reading*
creer:	creyendo	*believing*		oír:	oyendo	*hearing*
destruir:	destruyendo	*destroying*		traer:	trayendo	*bringing*
huir:	huyendo	*fleeing*				

◆ 3 ◆ IRREGULAR GERUNDS

a. In the gerund, stem-changing *-ir* verbs change their stem vowel from *e* to *i* and from *o* to *u*.

decir:	diciendo	*saying, telling*		pedir:	pidiendo	*asking for*
dormir:	durmiendo	*sleeping*		sentir:	sintiendo	*feeling, regretting*
morir:	muriendo	*dying*		venir:	viniendo	*coming*

b. Other verbs of this type are:

conseguir:	consiguiendo	*obtaining*		repetir:	repitiendo	*repeating*
corregir:	corrigiendo	*correcting*		servir:	sirviendo	*serving*
mentir:	mintiendo	*lying*		vestir:	vistiendo	*dressing*

c. The gerund of the verb *poder* is *pudiendo.*

◆ 4 ◆ USES OF THE GERUND

The gerund is often the equivalent of *by + present participle.*

Trabajando, se gana dinero.	*By working, one earns money.*
Estudiando, aprendes mucho.	*By studying, you learn a lot.*

EXERCISE A. Beto is describing what he did last night. Complete each statement with the gerund of the verb indicated.

EXAMPLE: (*mirar*) _____ la televisión, me dormí.
Mirando la televisión, me dormí.

1. (*tener*) No _____ nada que hacer, yo fui al cine.

2. (*regresar*) _____ del cine, fui a casa de Pablo.

3. (*estar*) _____ en casa de Pablo, conocí a su primo.

4. (*saber*) _____ que era tarde, decidí irme.

5. (*dar*) _____ las gracias, pedí permiso y salí.

6. (*pasar*) _____ pasando frente al parque, Beto vio varios corredores.

EXERCISE B. Complete each statement with the gerund of the verb indicated.

1. (*construir*) _____ casas, el señor Paván se hizo rico.

2. (*leer*) _____ libros, Elsa conoció otras culturas.

3. (*oír*) _____ la noticia, llamé a mi tío.

4. (*creer*) _____ el chisme, Alicia lo contó a sus amigas.

5. (*decir*) _____ eso, se acabó la entrevista.

6. (*dormir*) _____ por ocho horas, Alex se sintió mejor.

7. (*repetir*) _____ el poema varias veces, la niña lo aprendió de memoria.

8. (*pedir*) _____ ayuda, yo aprendí a usar la computadora.

9. (*huir*) _____ del perro, el cartero se cayó.

10. (*traer*) _____ su traje de baño, Gregorio pudo nadar en la piscina.

◆ 5 ◆ PROGRESSIVE TENSES

The progressive tenses are used to talk about an action that is (was or will be) in progress or is continuing at the moment indicated. The gerund is used with forms of the verbs *estar, seguir,* and *continuar,* and with verbs of motion.

Los niños **están llorando.**	*The children are crying.*
Él **estaba leyendo.**	*He was reading.*
Siguen escribiendo.	*They continue writing.*
Continuaban hablando.	*They continued speaking.*
Entró gritando.	*He entered shouting.*

NOTE: The present participles of *estar, ir,* and *venir* are not usually used to form the progressive tenses. Instead, the simple tenses are used.

Ella **viene** aquí.	*She is coming here.*
Rosa **iba** al parque.	*Rosa was going to the park.*

EXERCISE C. Your school is celebrating a physical fitness day. Tell what each person is doing.

EXAMPLE: Enrique / levantar pesas   Enrique **está levantando** pesas.

1. Carmen / montar en bicicleta _____

2. Felipe y Rosa / correr en la pista _____

3. yo / hacer ejercicios _____

4. Imelda y yo / nadar en la piscina _____

5. Ruth / practicar yoga _____

6. todos los muchachos / jugar al
   voleibol _____

EXERCISE D. It's seven o'clock in the evening. Tell which member of your family is doing these activities.

EXAMPLE: lavar los platos   Mi hermano **está lavando** los platos.

1. sacar al perro _____

2. leer el periódico _____

3. mirar la televisión _____

4. jugar a las damas _____

5. hacer la tarea _____

6. oír la radio _____

7. tocar el piano _____

8. escribir cheques _____

EXERCISE E. The Spanish club in your school is having a dinner to celebrate *"El Día de la Raza."* Tell what everyone is busy doing.

EXAMPLE: colgar los adornos / Ricky y Guillermo
           Ricky y Guillermo **están colgando** los adornos.

1. poner las mesas / John y Lucy _____

2. calentar el arroz con pollo / Sofía _____

3. enfriar los refrescos / Lázaro _____

4. arreglar las flores / yo _____

5. escoger la música / tú _____

6. traer más sillas / Mirta y yo _____

EXERCISE F.   **You are working in a day care center. Tell what everyone is doing.**

EXAMPLE: Arturito / decir su primera palabra
Arturito **está diciendo** su primera palabra.

1. el bebé / dormir la siesta   _____

2. Sarita / vestir una muñeca   _____

3. tres niños / repetir el alfabeto   _____

4. yo / pedir ayuda   _____

5. Frances y yo / servir jugo a los niños   _____

6. los padres / venir por sus hijos   _____

EXERCISE G.   **You want to know what different people were doing at nine o'clock last night. Answer the questions using the cues in parentheses.**

EXAMPLE: ¿Qué estaba haciendo Nelson? (*leer una novela*)
Nelson **estaba leyendo** una novela.

1. ¿Qué estaba haciendo Andrés? (*mirar la television*)

   _____

2. ¿Qué estaban haciendo Joan y Joyce? (*dormir*)

   _____

3. ¿Qué estaba haciendo su mamá? (*despedirse de los invitados*)

   _____

4. ¿Qué estabas haciendo? (*trabajar en la cafetería*)

   _____

5. ¿Qué estaba haciendo Tía Pilar? (*vestir al bebé*)

   _____

EXERCISE H.   **You are telling your mother about your visit to the circus with some friends. Tell how each one left the circus.**

EXAMPLE: tú / reír   Tú saliste **riendo.**

1. Ana / llorar   _____

2. Tomás y Pedro / gritar   _____

3. yo / temblar   _____

4. Irma y yo / correr   _____

5. tú / decir chistes   _____

6. Michelle y Ema / brincar   _____

EXERCISE I.   You are going to a camp reunion. Prepare the questions you will ask your friends about themselves and other campers who are not present.

EXAMPLE: correr en el maratón / tú   ¿Sigues **corriendo** en el maratón?

1. coleccionar insectos / Gustavo   _____

2. tomar clases de baile / tú y
   tu hermana   _____

3. construir aviones en miniatura /
   Perry   _____

4. aprender a hablar español / tú   _____

5. ser buenos amigos / Ralph y
   Vicente   _____

6. pedir más comida / tú   _____

7. oír ruidos / la señorita Tess   _____

⟨⟩ MASTERY EXERCISES ⟨⟩

EXERCISE J.   A friend sent you an e-mail in which she describes her visit to her grandparents' home. Complete her message with the appropriate form of the verbs provided.

Cuando llegué a casa de mis abuelos, todo el mundo estaba _____ algo. Mi abuelo estaba
                                                              1. (hacer)

_____ el césped y continuó _____ en el jardín hasta la hora de la
    2. (cortar)   3. (trabajar)

comida. Mi abuela estaba _____ y siguió _____ muchos platillos para
                             4. (cocinar)   5. (preparar)

la comida. Tía Isabel estaba _____ flores en el jardín y pasó una hora y media
                                  6. (cortar)

_____ las flores por toda la casa. Mis primos estaban _____ en el patio y
    7. (poner)   8. (jugar)

nosotros seguimos _____ un buen rato allí hasta que llegó Marcela. Ella es mi prima,
                       9. (pasar)

pero le gusta molestar a sus primos mayores mientras ellos tratan de divertirse. Mi primo José estaba

_____ el carro de mi abuelo y pasó media hora _____ el limpiaparabrisas.
    10. (revisar)   11. (reparar)

Cuando llegué, el perro estaba _____ debajo de una mesa pero pasó toda la tarde
                                    12. (dormir)

_____ y _____ comida a todo el mundo. Todavía me duele la cabeza.
    13. (ladrar)   14. (pedir)

EXERCISE K.   You arrive late to a party at one of your friend's home. Tell what you saw when you arrived. Write at least five sentences.

EXAMPLE: Antonio **estaba tocando** la guitarra. Fred **estaba bailando** con Irma.

El perro **estaba durmiendo** en un rincón de la sala.

_____

_____

_____

_____

_____

EXERCISE L. Complete the letter that James wrote to a friend shortly after moving into the college dormitory. Write the gerund of the verb that is needed to complete each statement.

caer	dormir	leer	poner
cambiar	escribir	llover	terminar
construir	hacer	mentir	trabajar
decir	hacer	oír	vivir

Querido Rafael:

Estoy _____ esta carta en vez de estar _____ las mil cosas que debo estar

_____. Cuando llegué aquí ayer estaba _____. Pasé la tarde

_____ un estante para mis libros. Mientras estaba _____ yo estaba

_____ la radio. El locutor estaba _____ que las estaciones están

_____ porque las hojas ya están _____ de los árboles. No estoy

_____ cuando te digo que _____ solo no es fácil. Cada día continuaré

_____ más cosas en su lugar. Pasaré esta tarde _____

y _____. ¿Qué estás _____ en este momento?

EXERCISE M. As part of a hotel industry job fair, you are narrating a series of job photos to a group of Spanish-speaking attendees. Express what the following people are doing in the hotel.

1. las telefonistas

_____

2. los cocineros

_____

3. los meseros

_____

4. el portero

_____

5. el conserje

_____

6. el agente de reservaciones

_____

7. las camareras

_____

8. los guías

_____

9. los administradores

_____

10. los mecánicos

_____

11. los guardas

_____

12. los botones

_____

ACTIVIDADES

1. Using a picture from a magazine or the Internet that contains several people doing different things, make a list of what each person in the picture is doing at that moment. Use the present progressive.

2. Write a message to a friend in which you describe what you will be doing during the forthcoming summer. Use the present progressive and the verbs _continuar_ and _seguir_ in the letter.

The Past Participle; Compound Tenses

◆1◆ THE PAST PARTICIPLE

a. Past Participles of Regular Verbs

The past participle of regular verbs is formed by dropping the infinitive ending and adding *-ado* or *-ido:*

INFINITIVE	PAST PARTICIPLE	MEANING
visitar	visit*ado*	*visited*
aprender	aprend*ido*	*learned*
vivir	viv*ido*	*lived*

b. Past Participles Ending in *-ído*

The past participles of *-er* and *-ir* verbs with stems ending in a vowel have an accent mark.

INFINITIVE	PAST PARTICIPLE	MEANING
caer	ca*ído*	*fallen*
creer	cre*ído*	*believed*
leer	le*ído*	*read*
oír	o*ído*	*heard*
reír	re*ído*	*laughed*
traer	tra*ído*	*brought*

c. Irregular Past Participles Ending in *-to*

The following verbs have irregular past participles ending in *-to.*

INFINITIVE	PAST PARTICIPLE	MEANING
abrir	abier*to*	*opened*
cubrir	cubier*to*	*covered*
descubrir	descubier*to*	*discovered*
escribir	escri*to*	*written*
morir	muer*to*	*died*
poner	pues*to*	*put*
romper	ro*to*	*broken*
ver	vis*to*	*seen*
volver	vuel*to*	*returned*

The following verbs have irregular past participles ending in *-cho.*

INFINITIVE	PAST PARTICIPLE	MEANING
decir	di*cho*	*said*
hacer	he*cho*	*done, made*

EXERCISE A. Gladys leaves a note for her parents. Complete the note with the appropriate past participles of the verbs indicated.

Ricky yo yo hemos ___salido___. Hemos ___decido___ ver una película y nos
    1. (salir)   2. (decidir)

hemos ___ido___ al cine. He ___dado___ de comer al gato y ya lo ha
    3. (ir)   4. (dar)

___comido___ todo. Hemos ___seguido___ todas sus instrucciones: hemos ___sacado___
    5. (comer)   6. (seguir)   7. (sacar)

la basura, hemos ___apergado___ todas las luces, hemos ___cerrado___ las ventanas.
              8. (apagar)   9. (cerrar)

He ___sacado___ la carne del congelador y la he ___dejado___ en la mesa de la co-
    10. (sacar)   11. (dejar)

cina. También he ___barrido___ el piso. Y no hemos ___roto___ nada. ¡Hemos
                  12. (barrer)   13. (romper)

___sido___ muy buenos!
    14. (ser)

EXERCISE B. You are planning to call the Spanish-speaking exchange student who is ill at home. Complete the questions you will ask with the past participle of the verbs indicated.

1. ¿Has ___tomado___ la medicina? (*tomar*)

2. ¿Has ___bebido___ mucho jugo de naranja? (*beber*)

3. ¿Has ___comido___ sopa de pollo? (*comer*)

4. ¿Has ___permanecido___ en cama todo el día? (*permanecer*)

5. ¿Has ___dormido___ la siesta? (*dormir*)

6. ¿Has ___hablado___ con otros amigos? (*hablar*)

7. ¿Has ___recibido___ la tarea de matemáticas? (*recibir*)

8. ¿Ya has ___hecho___ la tarea? (*hacer*)

9. ¿Has ___leído___ el periódico de hoy? (*leer*)

10. ¿Has ___vuelto___ a ver al médico? (*volver*)

11. ¿Qué ha ___dicho___ el médico? (*decir*)

12. ¿Qué restricciones te ha ___puesto___ el médico? (*poner*)

◆ 2 ◆ THE PRESENT PERFECT TENSE

a. The present perfect tense is formed by the present tense of the verb *haber* (to have) and a past participle.

yo	he
tú	has
él, ella, Ud.	ha
nosotros, -as	hemos
vosotros, -as	habéis
ellos, ellas, Uds.	han

} visitado/aprendido/vivido

b. To make a verb in the perfect tenses negative, place *no* before the verb *haber*. To make a verb interrogative, place the subject after the past participle.

No han vivido allí.	*They haven't lived there.*
¿**Ha** visto Ud. la película?	*Have you seen the film?*
Yo **no** me he bañado todavía.	*I haven't bathed myself yet.*

NOTE: Nothing comes between the verb *haber* and the past participle. Pronouns (reflexive and object) come before the verb *haber*.

c. The present perfect tense is used to describe an action that began in the past and continues up to the present or an action that took place in the past but is connected with the present.

EXERCISE C.   Tell who has done the following things.

EXAMPLE: Mario / viajar a Italia muchas veces   Mario **ha viajado** a Italia muchas veces.

1. Pierre / visitar a París   *Pierre ha visitado a París*

2. Yo / ir al circo cada año   *Yo he ido al circo cada año*

3. Raúl y Gregorio / nadar en el mar Caribe   *Ellos han nadado en el mar Caribe*

4. Mi familia y yo / salir en un crucero _____

5. Tú / volar en un avión supersónico _____

6. Amir / ver las pirámides de Egipto _____

EXERCISE D.   You and your family are going to a family wedding. Your mother wants to know how close to being ready everyone is. Tell who has or has not done the following preparations.

Use *ya* or *todavía no* in your statements.

mi papá	afeitarse
mi mamá	bañarse
mi hermana mayor	peinarse
mi hermano	ponerse el maquillaje
mi abuela	ponerse la corbata
yo	vestirse

1. _____

2. _____

3. _____

4. _____

5. _____

6. _____

EXERCISE E. You are looking at a family album with a cousin. Tell what has happened to the people in the photographs.

EXAMPLE: ¡Cuánto (Cómo) ha crecido Jerry!

1. _____ .

2. _____ .

3. _____ .

Jodie 6 meses   Jodie 3 años

4. _____ .

EXERCISE F.   **A friend is showing you some photos from her trip to Mexico. You know someone who has been there or done the things in the photos. Tell who has done these things or has been to these places.**

1. Ronnie / subir a la pirámide   _____

2. mis padres / visitar el castillo de
Chapultepec   _____

3. Celia y yo / comprar muchas cosas   _____

4. yo / nadar en las playas de Acapulco   _____

5. yo / volver a ese restaurante
muchas veces   _____

EXERCISE G.   **Answer the questions a classmate asks you. Use the cues provided.**

1. ¿Has llegado temprano a la escuela? *(sí)*

_____

2. ¿Has estudiado para el examen de biología? *(todavía no)*

_____

3. ¿Has visto al maestro de español hoy? *(ya)*

_____

4. ¿Has hecho el experimento correctamente? *(sí)*

_____

5. ¿Han preparado Uds. la tarea para la clase de historia? *(no)*

_____

6. ¿Has leído los capítulos asignados? *(ya)*

_____

◆ 3 ◆ THE PLUPERFECT TENSE

a. The pluperfect tense is formed by the imperfect tense of the verb *haber* (to have) and a past participle.

yo	había
tú	habías
él, ella, Ud.	había
nosotros, –as	habíamos
vosotros, –as	habíais
ellos, ellas, Uds.	habían

visitado/aprendido/vivido

b. The pluperfect tense is used to describe an action that was completed in the past before another action took place.

Yo los había visitado antes.　　*I had visited them before.*

Nunca le habían escrito.　　*They had never written to her.*

EXERCISE H.　　Tell what the Valera children had done before their parents returned from vacation.

EXAMPLE:　Alicia / lavar la ropa　　Alicia **había lavado** la ropa.

1. Guillermo / cortar el césped　　_____

2. Alicia y Guillermo / arreglar la casa　　_____

3. tú / pasar la aspiradora　　_____

4. Inés y yo / hacer un pastel　　_____

5. yo / poner flores en la sala　　_____

6. todos los hijos / ir al supermercado　　_____

EXERCISE I.　　You are attending a local civic ceremony in which several community members are being honored. Tell what each one had done to merit the award.

EXAMPLE:　el alcalde / bajar los impuestos　　El alcalde **había bajado** los impuestos.

1. Juan Gálvez / organizar un programa de reciclaje

_____

2. un bombero / salvar a una familia en un incendio

_____

3. la señora Bustelo / abrir un centro para ancianos

_____

4. el director de la escuela / poner un semáforo en la esquina de la escuela

_____

5. el jefe de la policía / disminuir el número de crímenes

_____

EXERCISE J. Nothing ever seems to go right for Silvia. Tell what already happened in each of these situations that relate to her nephew's birthday party.

EXAMPLE: Ella llegó a la estación del metro a las ocho y cuarto.
el tren / salir a las ocho y doce
El tren **ya había salido** a las ocho y doce.

1. Silvia llegó tarde a la fiesta de cumpleaños de su sobrino.

   los invitados / cantar «Feliz cumpleaños»

   _____

2. No pudo entrar en la juguetería.

   los empleados / cerrar la tienda

   _____

3. Sacó el pastel del horno.

   el pastel / quemarse

   _____

4. Iba a colgar una piñata.

   los niños / romper otra piñata

   _____

5. Le dio un regalo a su sobrino.

   el sobrino / abrir todos los regalos

   _____

6. Quería leerle un cuento a su sobrino.

   el sobrino / leer ese cuento

   _____

MASTERY EXERCISES

EXERCISE K. Tell what you and a friend have done before going on a camping trip. Use the suggestions or be original.

SUGGESTIONS:

doblar la tienda	poner pilas nuevas en la linterna
sacar la brújula	conseguir un mapa
empacar la mochila	pedir permiso a los padres
ir de compras	volver a empacar el equipo varias veces
hacer una reservación en el campamento	buscar la mejor ruta
confirmar la reservación	leer el pronóstico de tiempo en el periódico

1. _____

2. _____

3. _____

4. _____

5. _____

6. _____

7. _____

8. _____

9. _____

10. _____

EXERCISE L. You were left to babysit your mischievous younger brother and sister while your parents went to the movies. Your parents are furious with you because of how they found the house when they returned. Tell what you had done before you fell asleep.

1. darles de comer a los hermanos _____

2. poner los platos en el lavaplatos _____

3. sacar la basura _____

4. apagar las luces y el televisor _____

5. acostar a los hermanos _____

6. hacer la tarea _____

7. cerrar la puerta _____

EXERCISE M. You are writing a letter to a friend in which you describe a visit you made to your old neighborhood. Express the following in Spanish.

1. Finally, I have returned to my old neighborhood.

_____

2. I hadn't been there in a long time.

_____

3. They have made many changes.

_____

4. They have closed the elementary school that I had attended for six years.

_____

5. They have built a very large and modern elementary school.

_____

6. They have also planted many trees and plants in the park where I had played with my friends.

7. Shortly before I moved, they had closed the factory.

_____

8. My friends and I had broken many windows in the factory.

_____

9. The factory had contaminated the air.

_____

10. In its place they have opened a large shopping mall.

_____

11. I hadn't thought about my days in the elementary school for a long time.

_____

ACTIVIDADES

1. You are applying to an exchange program in Costa Rica and have to describe the things you have done in school in addition to your studies. Write a paragraph in Spanish in which you describe the extra-curricular activities, community service, and/or sports activities in which you have participated.

2. For each of the newspaper article headlines below, tell what the people involved had done to deserve a spot in the news.

   a. Camacho ofrece concierto de violín en el Teatro de Bellas Artes.
   b. Joven devuelve dinero encontrado en el parque.
   c. Joven de 16 años gana el maratón de San Pedro.
   d. El presidente y 3.000 jóvenes se reúnen hoy en la capital.
   e. Escasez de aceite y azúcar en los supermercados.
   f. Harán simposio referido a temas de derecho de familia.
   g. Se inauguran 5 nuevas escuelas primarias.
   h. ¡Adictas al ejercicio!
   i. Peligro: vida sedentaria.
   j. Habrá acuerdo con camioneros.

CHAPTER

14

Ser and Estar

In Spanish, *ser* and *estar*, both correspond to the English verb "to be." They are not interchangeable and their use depends on the context.

◆ 1 ◆ USES OF *SER*

Ser is used:

a. to express a characteristic, a description, or an identification.

El pastel **es bueno**.	*The cake is good.*
La maestra **es estricta**.	*The teacher is strict.*
El alumno **es inteligente**.	*The student is intelligent.*
La señora Romero **es rica**.	*Mrs. Romero is rich.*
¿Quién es? Es Pablo.	*Who is it? It's Pablo.*

b. to express occupation or nationality.

Elvira **es abogada**.	*Elvira is a lawyer.*
Mis hermanos **son vendedores**.	*My brothers are salesmen.*
Julio **es español**.	*Julio is Spanish.*
Melinda **es argentina**.	*Melinda is Argentinian.*

c. to express time and dates.

Son las ocho.	*It is eight o'clock.*	**Es el veinte de octubre.**	*It's October 20.*
Es mediodía.	*It's noon.*	**Es el primero de enero.**	*It's January 1.*

d. with *de*, to express origin, possession, or material.

Sus padres **son de Venezuela**.	*His parents are from Venezuela.*
El aceite de oliva **es de España**.	*The olive oil is from Spain.*
Es el reloj **de Lucy**.	*It's Lucy's watch.*
Ese carro **es de mi abuelo**.	*That car is my grandfather's.*
La camisa **es de algodón**.	*The shirt is made of cotton.*
La pulsera **es de plata**.	*The bracelet is made of silver.*

NOTES:

1. Adjectives used with *ser* must agree with the subject in number and gender.

Las naranjas **son sabrosas**.	*The oranges are flavorful.*
El edificio **es muy alto**.	*The building is very tall.*

2. In questions, adjectives usually follow the verb.

¿Son nuevos los zapatos?	*Are the shoes new?*

3. The adjective *feliz* is generally used with *ser*.

El bebé **es feliz**.　　　　*The baby is happy.*

4. The forms of *ser* are summarized in the section on irregular verbs in the Appendix, page 442.

EXERCISE A. You are the president of the Spanish club in your school. After the first meeting, you and a friend are talking about the new members. Tell what you say about them using the correct form of *ser* and the suggested adjectives below.

SUGGESTIONS:

aburrido	celoso	guapo	responsable
antipático	divertido	independiente	simpático
bonito	gracioso	inteligente	tímido

EXAMPLE: Felipe **es** guapo y responsable.

1. Gladys _____

2. Ramón y Tom _____

3. Milton y Celia _____

4. Donald _____

5. Dennis y Raquel _____

6. Rita _____

7. Andrea y Elena _____

8. Joseph _____

EXERCISE B. Jeff is attending a youth conference. After introducing himself and telling his nationality, he presents the other people in the group. Use the cues to tell what Jeff says.

EXAMPLE: yo / el Canadá　　　Yo **soy del** Canadá. **Soy** canadiense.

1. Migdalia / Puerto Rico _____

2. Ricardo y Jaime / Colombia _____

3. Sarita / España _____

4. Claire y Marc / Francia _____

5. Elena y María / la Argentina _____

6. tú (Roberto) / Guatemala _____

EXERCISE C. George is going to a formal family function and has laid out the clothing he will wear. Tell what each article of clothing is made of.

EXAMPLE: pañuelo / seda　　　El pañuelo **es de** seda.

1. traje / lana _____

2. camisa / algodón _____

3. corbata / seda _____

4. zapatos, cinturón / cuero _____

5. reloj / oro _____

6. anillo / plata _____

EXERCISE D. You are cleaning up after a party in your house and find some things that your friends left behind. Tell to whom each of the things belong.

EXAMPLE: el disco compacto / Álvaro   El disco compacto **es de** Álvaro.

1. las llaves / Graciela _____

2. la mochila / Hugo _____

3. las fotos / los hermanos Ramos _____

4. el celular / Isabel _____

5. la chaqueta / Esteban _____

6. la bolsa / Virginia _____

EXERCISE E. While the Garza family was away on vacation all the clocks in their house stopped at different times. Express what time it is on each clock.

EXAMPLE: **Son las seis y media.**

1. _____

3. _____

2. _____

4. _____

5. _____

6. _____

EXERCISE F.   **You have just met someone in line at the post office. Answer the questions you are asked.**

1. ¿Cuál es su nombre?   _____

2. ¿De dónde es usted?   _____

3. ¿Cuál es su nacionalidad?   _____

4. ¿Cómo es usted?   _____

5. ¿Cuál es su color favorito?   _____

6. ¿De qué es la gorra que usa Ud.?   _____

7. ¿Es Ud. aficionado(-a) a un equipo o un grupo musical?   _____

8. ¿Quién es su actor/actriz favorito(-a)?   _____

9. ¿Cómo es su escuela?   _____

10. ¿Cómo son sus amigos?   _____

11. ¿Cuáles son sus pasatiempos favoritos?   _____

12. ¿Qué día es hoy?   _____

13. ¿Cuál es la fecha de hoy?   _____

14. ¿Qué hora es?   _____

15. ¿Cuál es la marca de la computadora que usa Ud.?   _____

◆ 2 ◆ USES OF *ESTAR*

Estar is used:

a. to express location or position.

Buenos Aires **está en la Argentina.**	*Buenos Aires is in Argentina.*
Mi padre **está en la oficina.**	*My father is in the office.*
Los platos **están en la mesa.**	*The dishes are on the table.*
¿Dónde **está la farmacia?**	*Where is the drugstore?*

b. to express a condition or state.

El horno **está muy caliente.**	*The oven is very hot.*
Los hombres **están sentados.**	*The men are seated.*
Gladys **está triste.**	*Gladys is sad.*
¿Cómo **estás? Estoy bien.**	*How are you? I'm fine.*
Las ventanas **están cerradas.**	*The windows are closed.*

c. to form the progressive tenses with the present participle.

Los niños **están jugando** al tenis.	*The children are playing tennis.*
Jorge **estaba trabajando.**	*Jorge was working.*

NOTES:

1. Adjectives used with *estar* agree with the subject in number and gender.

La madre **está preocupada.**	*The mother is worried.*
Los padres **están preocupados.**	*The parents are worried.*

2. In questions, the adjective usually follows the verb.

¿**Está preocupada** la madre?	*Is the mother worried?*
¿**Están preocupados** los padres?	*Are the parents worried?*

3. Some adjectives may be used with either *ser* or *estar*, but differ in meaning.

Alberto **es bueno (malo).**	*Albert is good (bad).*	Alberto **es listo.**	*Albert is clever.*
Alberto **está bueno (malo).**	*Albert is well (ill).*	Alberto **está listo.**	*Albert is ready.*

4. The forms of *estar* are summarized in the section on irregular verbs in the Appendix, page 439.

EXERCISE G.   Your younger brother wants to know where various people are. Write the questions he asks and your responses.

EXAMPLE: el actor / el teatro
¿Dónde **está** el actor?   El actor **está** en el teatro.

1. los payasos / el circo

_____

2. el médico / el hospital

_____

3. los estudiantes / el colegio

_____

4. el cocinero / la cocina

_____

5. el astronauta / el espacio

_____

6. los policías / la calle

_____

7. los pilotos / los aviones

_____

EXERCISE H.   The tournament results are in. Tell how the players feel.

EXAMPLE: Víctor / contento   Víctor **está** contento.

1. Felipe y José / preocupado _____

2. Antonio / desilusionado _____

3. Linda y Elena / nervioso _____

4. Ingrid / sorprendido _____

5. Doris y Ema / triste _____

6. el entrenador / orgulloso _____

EXERCISE I.   You received this flyer while attending a world youth conference in Buenos Aires. Answer the questions that a hotel guest asks you about the conference.

Bienvenidos al
XX^mo Congreso Mundial de Jóvenes

Tema:	La juventud moderna
Lugar:	el Gran Hotel, Buenos Aires
Fecha:	del 2 al 5 de julio
Reuniones:	Cada día a las 10, 12, 4 y 6
Salones:	Primavera, Verano, Otoño, Invierno

Comidas:	Desayuno:	8:00-10:00 -Salón Amanecer
	Comida:	2:00-4:00 -Salón Principal
	Cena:	8:00-10:00 -Salón Medianoche

Enfermería:	Segundo piso del hotel

1. ¿Cuándo es el congreso? _____

2. ¿En qué hotel está el congreso? _____

3. ¿A qué hora es la primera
reunión del día? _____

4. ¿A qué hora es la última reunión
cada día? _____

5. ¿En qué salones estarán los
congresistas? _____

6. ¿A qué hora es el desayuno?   _____

7. ¿A qué hora es la comida?   _____

8. ¿A qué hora es la cena?   _____

9. ¿Dónde está la enfermería?   _____

10. ¿Cuál es el tema del congreso?   _____

EXERCISE J.   **Julio is telling a friend what the members of his family were doing when his father returned home.**

EXAMPLE: Mi mamá **estaba cocinando**.

1. Elena _____

_____ .

4. Mi abuelo _____

_____ .

2. Alex y Enrique _____

_____ .

5. Yo _____

_____ .

3. Mi abuela _____

_____ .

MASTERY EXERCISES

EXERCISE K. **You received a letter from a friend who is spending a year studying in Argentina. Complete it with the appropriate forms of *ser* or *estar*.**

Querida amiga:

No puedo creer que yo _____ 1. en la Argentina. Hay quince jóvenes en el grupo y

nosotros _____ 2. estudiando en un colegio muy bueno. _____ 3. una escuela

antigua y la arquitectura de la escuela _____ 4. de estilo clásico. Vivo con una familia muy

simpática. Los miembros de la familia _____ 5. los señores Rivas y sus tres hijos. Los

nombres de los hijos _____ 6. Rafael, Hilda y Verónica. Rafael _____ 7. el

mayor. El señor Rivas _____ 8. arquitecto y la señora _____ 9. doctora. Su casa

_____ 10. amplia y _____ 11. situada en las afueras de Buenos Aires.

Tampoco puedo creer que _____ 12. el 10 de enero y hace calor. Ya sabes que la Argentina

_____ 13. en el hemisferio sur y cuando _____ 14. invierno en los Estados Unidos

_____ 15. verano en el hemisferio sur. _____ 16. un clima ideal porque no hace

muchísimo calor.

Los jóvenes del grupo _____ 17. muy agradables y divertidos. Cada uno

_____ 18. viviendo en casa de una familia porteña (así se llaman las personas que viven

en Buenos Aires). Solamente hay un joven que _____ 19. desilusionado en el grupo.

_____ 20. un joven bastante aplicado pero _____ 21. un poco frustrado porque no

habla bien el español. Las familias _____ 22. muy atentas y cariñosas pero hacen muchas preguntas.

Ya _____ 23. las siete de la noche y debo despedirme de ti. Yo _____ 24. muy

ocupada todos los días porque la vida de un estudiante aquí _____ 25. muy exigente. Escríbeme

pronto.

Tu amiga,

Lucinda

EXERCISE L. You overhear the following statements in the school cafeteria. Complete them with the appropriate form of *ser* or *estar*.

1. Susana no _____ en la escuela hoy porque _____ enferma.

2. La señora Galván _____ rica porque sus joyas _____ de oro.

3. Mi clase de física _____ a las diez y cuarto. ¿Qué hora _____ ?

4. El helado de fresa _____ más sabroso que el helado de chocolate.

5. Mi mamá no tiene tiempo para descansar. Siempre _____ muy ocupada.

6. Hoy _____ el tres de julio. Mañana _____ día de fiesta.

7. El maestro de matemáticas va a devolver los exámenes. Todos los alumnos _____ preocupados.

8. La familia de Amir _____ turca, pero ninguno de sus parientes _____ actualmente en Turquía.

9. Esta blusa no _____ mía, _____ de mi hermana mayor.

10. ¿Cuál _____ la fecha de tu cumpleaños? La mía _____ el 20 de marzo.

11. Mis abuelos _____ jubilados. Nunca _____ en casa.

12. El libro que tú _____ leyendo es fabuloso y el fin _____ algo que nunca esperabas.

13. Mi hermano _____ en la universidad también pero no _____ un estudiante diligente.

14. Hace frío aquí porque las puertas _____ abiertas.

15. En esta cafetería la comida que debe _____ caliente siempre _____ fría.

EXERCISE M. Describe your day in school in your journal. You may want to include the following:

- the day, date, and time

- the weather

- which class you are in at this time

- something about the class (interesting, easy, difficult, etc.)

- something about the teacher's personality and performance in class

- other students who are in the class with you

- how you feel about the class today

- what the teacher is doing right now

- what some other students are doing

- why your friend is not in class today

- where your books are

- where you would prefer to be at this moment

- why you are worried right now

$\Leftarrow\!\!\!\!\!\Leftarrow$ **A C T I V I D A D E S** $\Rightarrow\!\!\!\!\!\Rightarrow$

1. Select an interesting object or person and write a description of it that will enable the reader to guess what or who it is. Use *ser* and *estar* as often as possible in your description.

2. a. You are interviewing a new exchange student in school. Prepare ten questions you will ask him/her to find out as much as you can about him/her. Use *ser* and/or *estar* in your questions.

b. Answer these questions as if you were the exchange student.

C H A P T E R

15

Reflexive Verbs

◆ 1 ◆ REFLEXIVE VERBS IN SIMPLE TENSES

a. A reflexive verb requires a reflexive pronoun (*me, te, se, nos, os, se*) that refers the action of the verb back to the subject.

| Yo me baño. | *I bathe (myself).* |
| Ellos se lavan. | *They wash (themselves).* |

b. Reflexive pronouns generally precede the verb in the simple tenses.

PRESENT TENSE	
yo me baño	nosotros, -as nos bañamos
tú te bañas	vosotros, -as os bañáis
Ud., él, ella se baña	Uds., ellos, ellas se bañan

PRETERIT TENSE	
yo me bañé	nosotros, -as nos bañamos
tú te bañaste	vosotros, -as os bañasteis
Ud., él, ella se bañó	Uds., ellos, ellas se bañaron

IMPERFECT TENSE	
yo me bañaba	nosotros, -as nos bañábamos
tú te bañabas	vosotros, -as os bañabais
Ud., él, ella se bañaba	Uds., ellos, ellas se bañaban

FUTURE TENSE	
yo me bañaré	nosotros, -as nos bañaremos
tú te bañarás	vosotros, -as os bañaréis
Ud., él, ella se bañará	Uds., ellos, ellas se bañarán

CONDITIONAL TENSE	
yo me bañaría	nosotros, -as nos bañaríamos
tú te bañarías	vosotros, -as os bañaríais
Ud., él, ella se bañaría	Ud., ellos, ellas se bañarían

NOTE: When the statement is negative, *no* comes before the reflexive pronoun.

Yo no me bañé. *I didn't bathe.*

c. When a reflexive verb is used as an infinitive, the reflexive pronoun is attached to the end of the infinitive or placed before the conjugated verb. Both forms are accepted.

Voy a lavarme.
Me voy a lavar. } *I'm going to wash (myself).*

Queremos acostar**nos** ahora.
Nos queremos acostar ahora. } *We want to go to bed*

d. When a reflexive verb is used in a progressive tense, the reflexive pronoun is attached to the end of the present participle (gerund) or placed before the conjugated verb. When it is attached to the gerund, an accent mark is required. Both forms are accepted.

Estoy lavándo**me** la cara.
Me estoy lavando la cara. } *I am washing my face*

e. Frequently used reflexive verbs:

acostarse (ue) *to go to bed*	**irse** *to leave, go away*
afeitarse *to shave*	**marcharse** *to leave, go away*
asustarse *to be frightened*	**lavarse** *to wash oneself*
bañarse *to take a bath, bathe*	**levantarse** *to get up*
callarse *to be silent, keep still*	**llamarse** *to be named, be called*
cepillarse *to brush (one's teeth, hair, clothes)*	**maquillarse** *to put on makeup*
desayunarse *to have breakfast*	**pasearse** *to take a walk*
despedirse *to say goodbye, take leave of*	**peinarse** *to comb one's hair*
despertarse (ie) *to wake up*	**ponerse** *to put on (clothing), become*
divertirse (ie) *to enjoy oneself, have a good time*	**quedarse** *to stay, remain*
dormirse (ue) *to fall asleep*	**quejarse** *to complain*
ducharse *to take a shower*	**quitarse** *to take off (clothing)*
enfadarse *to get angry*	**secarse** *to dry oneself*
enojarse *to get angry*	**sentarse (ie)** *to sit down*
equivocarse *to be mistaken*	**vestirse (i)** *to get dressed*

EXERCISE A. Use the cues to tell what each person is doing.

EXAMPLE: Pedro / peinarse   Pedro **se peina.**

1. Papá / afeitarse _____

2. Arturo e Inés / desayunarse _____

3. tú / vestirse _____

4. yo / cepillarse los dientes _____

5. Renee y yo / maquillarse _____

6. mis abuelos / pasearse en el parque _____

EXERCISE B. Use the cues provided to tell what different people did in different situations.

EXAMPLE: Gloria tuvo hambre a las 8:30 de la mañana. (*desayunarse*)   Gloria **se desayunó.**

1. Miguel tuvo frío en el patio de la escuela. (*ponerse un suéter*)

_____

2. Después Miguel tuvo calor. (*quitarse el suéter*)

_____

3. Yo escondí la mochila de Sally. (*enojarse*)

_____

4. No me gustó la comida que sirvieron. (*quejarse a la mesera*)

_____

5. Jerry y yo tiramos pintura en la mesa. (*lavarse las manos*)

_____

6. La maestra vio un ratoncito en el piso. (*asustarse*)

_____

7. Tú supiste que nuestro pez se había muerto. (*ponerse triste*)

_____

EXERCISE C. **You have just returned from camp and your grandmother is asking you about it. Answer her questions using the cues provided.**

EXAMPLE: ¿Te despertabas fácilmente todos los días? (*sí*)
            Sí, **me despertaba** fácilmente todos los días.

1. ¿Te levantabas de la cama en seguida? (*sí*)

_____

2. ¿Cuántas veces al día te cepillabas los dientes? (*3*)

_____

3. ¿Te peinabas todos los días? (*sí*)

_____

4. ¿Te dormías después de la comida? (*no*)

_____

5. ¿Te paseabas con tus amigos? (*sí*)

_____

6. ¿Cómo se llamaba el consejero de tu grupo? (*Pedro*)

_____

7. ¿Te quejabas a menudo? (*no*)

_____

8. ¿Qué te ponías cuando hacía frío? (*un suéter*)

_____

9. ¿Se sentaban Uds. alrededor de una fogata y cantaban canciones? (*sí*)

_____

10. ¿Te enojabas con tus amigos? (*no*)

_____

EXERCISE D. You and your family are preparing to go to a family reunion. Tell who wants to do or is going to do the activities listed below. Use the appropriate form of *querer* or *ir a* in your responses.

mi hermana	vestirse en cinco minutos
yo	afeitarse ahora
papá	secarse el pelo rápidamente
mamá	quedarse en casa
tú	enfadarse
tú y yo	ducharse primero
mis hermanos	maquillarse antes de vestirse
	desayunarse mientras vestirse

EXAMPLE: Mamá **va a** ducharse primero.

1. _____
2. _____
3. _____
4. _____
5. _____
6. _____
7. _____

EXERCISE E. Describe what each person is doing using the present progressive tense.

EXAMPLE: Ruth / lavarse el pelo   Ruth **se está lavando** el pelo.
                              OR   Ruth **está lavándose** el pelo.

1. Ernesto / ducharse   _____

2. la señora Barca / maquillarse   _____

3. Kim y yo / pasearse   _____

4. Papá / afeitarse   _____

5. Gloria / quedarse en la cama   _____

6. tú / vestirse   _____

7. los niños / divertirse   _____

◆ 2 ◆ REFLEXIVE VERBS IN COMPOUND TENSES

a. In compound tenses like the present perfect and pluperfect, for example, the reflexive pronoun comes before the conjugated form of the helping (auxiliary) verb *haber*.

PRESENT PERFECT	
yo me he bañado	nosotros, -as nos hemos bañado
tú te has bañado	vosotros, -as os habéis bañado
Ud., él, ella se ha bañado	Uds., ellos, ellas se han bañado

PLUPERFECT	
yo me había bañado	nosotros, -as nos habíamos bañado
tú te habías bañado	vosotros, -as os habéis bañado
Ud., él, ella se había bañado	Uds., ellos, ellas se habían bañado

b. If the statement is negative, *no* is placed before the reflexive pronoun.

Él **no** se ha lavado.   *He hasn't washed himself.*

EXERCISE F. **Imelda is working in a day care center during the summer. She tells the person in charge what she and the children have already done or still haven't done. Tell what she says.**

EXAMPLE: Daniel / despertarse / no levantarse
Daniel ya **se ha despertado** pero todavía no **se ha levantado.**

1. Teresa / bañarse / no secarse

_____

2. Hugo y Felipe / vestirse / no ponerse los zapatos

_____

3. yo / desayunarse / no sentarse por un minuto

_____

4. los niños / lavarse las manos / no peinarse

_____

5. el bebé / asustarse / no callarse

_____

EXERCISE G. **Tell what the following people had done before they received a telephone call cancelling the party.**

EXAMPLE: Rogelio / afeitarse   Rogelio ya **se había afeitado.**

1. los niños / ponerse los disfraces   _____

2. Miriam / maquillarse   _____

3. yo / enfadarse   _____

4. tú / lavarse el pelo   _____

5. mi hermana y yo / despedirse
de nuestros padres   _____

◆ 3 ◆ COMMANDS WITH REFLEXIVE VERBS

In affirmative commands, reflexive pronouns follow the verb and are attached to it. In negative commands, reflexive pronouns precede the verb. Affirmative commands with more than two syllables have a written accent over the stressed vowel.

	AFFIRMATIVE COMMANDS	NEGATIVE COMMANDS
tú	¡Báñate!	¡No te bañes!
Ud.	¡Báñese!	¡No se bañe!
Uds.	¡Báñense!	¡No se bañen!

EXERCISE H. **You are going to spend the weekend at a friend's house. Tell what your mother tells you to do there.**

EXAMPLE: despertarse temprano   ¡**Despiértate** temprano!

1. levantarse en seguida _____

2. ducharse rápidamente _____

3. vestirse bien _____

4. desayunarse con la familia _____

5. lavarse las manos antes de comer _____

6. cepillarse los dientes después de comer _____

7. peinarse _____

8. callarse cuando otra persona hable _____

9. despedirse de la familia _____

10. divertirse mucho _____

EXERCISE I. **Your mother also tells you what you should not do at your friend's house.**

EXAMPLE: quejarse   ¡**No te quejes!**

1. acostarse tarde _____

2. levantarse a comer durante la noche _____

3. dormirse en el sofá o una silla _____

4. quitarse los zapatos en la sala _____

5. quedarse en la cama después de despertarse _____

6. peinarse en la mesa _____

7. enojarse con tu amigo _____

8. ponerse la gorra en la casa _____

9. irse sin dar las gracias _____

EXERCISE J. Janet is babysitting her cousins. Use the cues provided to express what she tells them to do.

EXAMPLE: sentarse en el piso **¡Siéntense** en el piso!

1. despedirse de sus padres _____

2. quedarse en la sala _____

3. callarse mientras miran la televisión _____

4. ponerse la pijama _____

5. cepillarse el pelo antes de acostarse _____

6. lavarse la cara y las manos _____

7. secarse bien las manos _____

8. acostarse a la hora indicada _____

EXERCISE K. Tell what the coach tells his team members they should not do before a big game.

EXAMPLE: desayunarse mucho **¡No se desayunen** mucho!

1. acostarse tarde _____

2. enojarse si cometen un error _____

3. despertarse tarde _____

4. ducharse con agua muy caliente _____

5. ponerse nerviosos _____

6. dormirse delante de la televisión _____

7. irse de la cancha sin pedir permiso _____

8. callarse cuando el equipo haga un gol _____

⟨ MASTERY EXERCISES ⟩

EXERCISE L. Complete this dialogue with the appropriate forms of the verbs indicated.

ALICIA: _____ , Emma. Tengo miedo. Cuando yo _____ hace cinco
            1. (despertarse)   2. (despertarse)

minutos, yo oí un ruido extraño y yo _____ mucho.
                                       3. (asustarse)

EMMA: _____ y _____ , ¿sabes qué hora es?
    4. (acostarse)   *5.* (dormirse)

ALICIA: _____ , por favor. Yo no puedo _____ .
    6. (levantarse)   *7.* (dormirse)

EMMA: Ay, yo no quiero _____ ahora. Nosotros _____ muy tarde y
        8. (levantarse)   *9.* (acostarse)

tengo mucho sueño. ¿Por qué _____ la bata?
         10. (ponerse)

ALICIA: Yo _____ la bata por dos razones: primero, tengo frío y segundo, podemos bajar a la
    11. ponerse

cocina a _____ .
    12. (desayunarse)

EMMA: Yo no _____ ni _____ a esta hora. Tú siempre
     13. (vestirse)   *14.* (desayunarse)

_____ de algo.
 15. (quejarse)

ALICIA: Yo no _____ de nada. Yo _____ cuando oí un ruido.
     16. (quejarse)   *17.* (espantarse)

Ahora yo _____ , _____ el pelo, _____ ,
    18. (bañarse)   *19.* (lavarse)   *20.* (peinarse)

_____ y _____ de ti.
 21. (vestirse)   *22.* (despedirse)

EMMA: ¿Adónde vas a esta hora?

ALICIA: Yo _____ . Regreso a mi propio dormitorio.
    23. (irse)

EXERCISE M. **You went on an overnight trip with some friends. Now you are telling another friend about it in an e-mail message. Use as many reflexive verbs as you can in your message. Include the name(s) of the friends with whom you travelled and some of their habits and personality traits.**

⟨ A C T I V I D A D E S ⟩

1. Write an entry in your journal in which you describe the activities you do everyday. Use as many reflexive verbs as you can.

2. a. Your parent has been hassling you about your daily routine—from the time you wake up in the morning until you go to bed at night. You believe that all people your age act the same way. Prepare a list of 10 questions in Spanish that you will ask several friends to learn if their daily routine is similar to yours.

b. Using the questions you prepared above, interview several friends and ask them the questions. Take notes of their responses. Then, write a summary of your survey in your Spanish journal in which you describe what several of your friends do.

CHAPTER

16

The Passive Voice

Spanish, like English, has an active and a passive voice. In the active voice, the subject generally performs some action. In the passive voice, the subject is acted upon.

ACTIVE: La madre **preparó** la comida.   *The mother prepared the meal.*
PASSIVE: La comida **fue preparada** por la madre. *The meal was prepared by the mother.*

◆ 1 ◆ THE PASSIVE VOICE IN SIMPLE SENTENCES

If the agent or doer of the action is mentioned or implied, the passive voice is formed by the subject + form of *ser* + past participle + *por* + agent or doer.

Este castillo **fue construido por** el rey.   *This castle was built by the king.*

Muchos árboles **fueron destruidos por** la tormenta.   *Many trees were destroyed by the storm.*

Jorge se encargó de las invitaciones; ésas **fueron mandadas** al día siguiente.   *Jorge took charge of the the invitations; these were (doer, Jorge, implied) sent on the following day.*

NOTES:

1. In the passive, the past participle is used like an adjective and agrees with the subject in gender and number.

2. The agent is usually preceded by *por.* If the past participle expresses feeling or emotion, rather than action, *por* may be replaced by *de.*

   Es **respetado** (estimado, amado) **de** todos.   *He is respected (esteemed, loved) by all.*

EXERCISE A.   The Spanish Club is publishing a yearbook. Tell what each person's role is, was, or will be.

EXAMPLE: Los estudiantes crearon un anuario.
              El anuario **fue creado por los estudiantes.**

1. Cindy saca las fotografías.   _____

2. Elvira y Jennifer escribirán los poemas.   _____

3. Gerardo venderá los anuncios.   _____

4. El profesor escribió el prólogo.   _____

5. Jack y Silvia hacen los dibujos.   _____

6. Gabriela y yo redactamos el anuario.   _____

7. Dawn diseñó el volumen.   _____

8. Mariluz coordinará la producción
   del anuario.

   _____

9. Todos los alumnos contribuirán una
   selección original.

   _____

10. El director de la escuela felicita a
    todos los alumnos.

    _____

EXERCISE B. **Tell who did each of the following:**

EXAMPLE: el restaurante / cerrar / el Departamento de Salubridad
        El restaurante **fue cerrado** por el Departamento de Salubridad.

1. las ventanas / abrir / el portero _____

2. los adornos / colgar / varios jóvenes _____

3. la nueva compañía / fundar /
   unos empleados

   _____

4. las calles / cerrar / la policía _____

5. el presidente / admirar / todos
   los ciudadanos

   _____

6. la música / oír / el público _____

7. los mayores / respetar / los menores _____

8. la carta / firmar / el alcalde _____

9. el cuadro / pintar / un gran artista _____

10. los árboles / plantar / un grupo de niños _____

◆ 2 ◆ THE PASSIVE VOICE IN COMPOUND TENSES

The passive voice in compound tenses is formed in the same way that it is formed in simple tenses: if the agent or doer of the action is mentioned or implied, the passive voice is formed by the subject + form of *ser* + past participle + *por* + agent or doer. However, the verb *ser* is used in its compound tenses (*ha sido, había sido, habrá sido,* etc.).

Las tiendas han sido abiertas por los dueños los domingos.	*The stores have been opened by the owners on Sundays.*
La mesa había sido puesta por el mesero.	*The table had been set by the waiter.*
Los gastos habrán sido pagados por la compañía.	*The expenses will have been paid by the company.*

NOTES:

1. In the passive, the past participle of the action verb is used like an adjective and agrees with the subject in gender and number.

2. The agent is usually preceded by *por*. If the past participle expresses feeling or emotion, rather than action, *por* may be replaced by *de*.

EXERCISE C. Complete this article that will appear in the local newspaper with the appropriate form of the verbs indicated. Use the present perfect, pluperfect, or conditional perfect.

Como resultado de la tormenta, muchos daños _____ por los ingenieros municipales. Un
                                          1. (descubrir)

aviso _____ por el alcalde veinticuatro horas antes de la llegada de la tormenta. En el aviso los
          2. (dar)

lugares que estaban en el ojo de la tormenta _____ por los ingenieros y los científicos.
                                                  3. (identificar)

Indicaron que si la información _____ en serio por los habitantes, mucha propiedad
                                     4. (tomar)

no _____ la tormenta. El alcalde _____ de los ingenieros por su acción de
       5. (destruir)   6. (alabar)

avisar a la población y prevenir mucho daño en el pueblo.

EXERCISE D. You are preparing headlines for several newspaper articles. Using the information provided, write a headline for each one.

EXAMPLE: la huelga de camioneros / resolver / el presidente

La huelga de camioneros **ha sido resuelta** por el presidente.

1. la fecha del maratón / posponer / las autoridades

_____

2. las clases universitarias / suspender / el decano

_____

3. el precio de la leche / aumentar / los lecheros

_____

4. el horario de charlas y debates / anunciar/ un grupo cívico

_____

5. los candidatos / nombrar / los partidos políticos

_____

◆ *3* ◆ THE PASSIVE VOICE WITH *SE*

If the agent or doer is not mentioned or implied and the subject is a thing, the reflexive construction (*se* + verb form for *Ud./él/ella* or *Uds./ellos/ellas*) is used in Spanish to express the passive voice. In such constructions, the subject usually follows the verb.

Aquí **se habla** español.	*Spanish is spoken here.*
Aquí **se hablan** español y alemán.	*Spanish and German are spoken here.*
¿A qué hora **se abren** las tiendas?	*At what time do the stores open?*
De hoy en adelante, **se ofrece** un descuento.	*From today on a discount is offered.*

EXERCISE E.   **Tell what happens in these stores.**

EXAMPLE: hacer/ Se hacen llaves.

1. hacer/ _____

_____ .

4. preparar/ _____

_____ .

2. vender/ _____

_____ .

5. cultivar/ _____

_____ .

3. reparar/ _____

_____ .

6. cambiar/ _____

_____ .

EXERCISE F.   **Complete the following recipe using the passive voice with *se*.**

1. (*necesitar*) _____ 2 pechugas de pollo deshuesadas, 3 cucharadas de aceite, 1/4 taza de salsa soya, 1/2 taza de caldo de pollo, 3 tazas de verduras picadas (zanahoria, habichuelas, coliflor, brócoli) y 1/2 libra de pasta corta.

2. (*cortar*) _____ las pechugas en tiras delegadas.

3. (*sofreír*) _____ las tiras de pechuga en el aceite.

4. (*sacar*) _____ las tiras doraditas de pechuga aparte.

5. (*sofreír*) _____ las verduras por 2 minutos en el aceite restante.

6. (*revolver*) _____ las verduras constantemente.

7. (*agregar*) _____ el pollo, la salsa soya y el caldo de pollo.

8. (*dejar*) _____ cocinar 5 minutos.

9. (*cocinar*) _____ la pasta al dente.

10. (*escurrir*) _____ la pasta.

11. (*mezclar*) _____ la pasta con la salsa.

12. (*servir*) _____ caliente.

EXERCISE G.   **Answer the questions that friend who is new to your city asks you. Use the cues provided.**

1. ¿Dónde se nada aquí? (*la piscina del Club Deportivo*)

   _____

2. ¿Cuándo se estrenará una nueva película en el cine? (*el jueves próximo*)

   _____

3. ¿Cuánto se cobra para ver una película? (*12 dólares*)

   _____

4. ¿Dónde se reparan bicicletas? (*la gasolinera*)

   _____

5. ¿Hasta qué hora se sirve la comida en el restaurante de la esquina? (*10:00*)

   _____

6. ¿Dónde se podrá conseguir un monopatín? (*la tienda de deportes*)

   _____

7. ¿Con qué frecuencia se recoge la basura? (*cada 2 días*)

   _____

8. ¿A qué hora se cierran las tiendas del centro? (*8:00*)

   _____

9. ¿Dónde se puede correr temprano por la mañana? (*el parque*)

   _____

10. ¿Qué fiestas se celebran aquí? (*patrióticas y religiosas*)

    _____

MASTERY EXERCISES

EXERCISE H.   **Víctor likes to repeat what he hears but he changes the way it was originally said. Tell what he repeats.**

EXAMPLE: Los hombres pintan las casas.   Las casas **son pintadas** por los hombres.

1. Su hermano cerró la puerta.   _____

2. Virginia no invitó a Gabriel.   _____

3. Los niños respetan a sus profesores.   _____

4. Pedro pagará la cuenta.   _____

5. Mi amigo ayudará a mis hermanas.   _____

6. Los padres aman a sus hijos.   _____

7. Los profesores estiman a esos alumnos. _____

8. El portero abrirá las puertas de las tiendas
   a las diez.   _____

9. El equipo ganó el trofeo.   _____

10. Yo prepararé la comida.   _____

EXERCISE I.   **Answer the questions a friend asks you as you roam through a new part of town. Use the cues provided.**

1. ¿Qué se fabrica en esa fábrica? (*juguetes*)

   _____

2. ¿Qué se exhibe en el museo hoy? (*obras de Goya*)

   _____

3. ¿Qué se cultiva en ese jardín? (*maíz*)

   _____

4. ¿Qué se anuncia en aquel letrero? (*un baile*)

   _____

5. ¿Qué se sirve en este café? (*pasteles franceses*)

   _____

6. ¿Cuándo se abrirá la nueva estación del metro? (*abril*)

   _____

7. ¿A qué hora se cierran las tiendas aquí? (*9:00*)

   _____

8. ¿Qué idioma se habla en la farmacia? (*español e inglés*)

_____

9. ¿Qué se cose allí? (*una bandera*)

_____

10. ¿Qué se vende en ese quiosco? (*refrescos*)

_____

EXERCISE J.   **You are working in a real-estate agency during the summer. Your boss has asked you to prepare in Spanish an information sheet that the agents will give to prospective Spanish-speaking buyers. You may wish to include the following, using the passive voice:**

• who developed this town

• something about this relationship with the inhabitants and the mayor

• information about services provided by the town (garbage collection, street cleaning, etc.)

• and their frequency

ACTIVIDADES

1. You are on the planning committee for homecoming in your school. Prepare a list that will serve as a directory and program for the day's events. For example:

Se dará un concierto en el auditorio a las cuatro.

List at least eight activities.

2. Your family received a letter that was mailed five years ago. The envelope of the letter contains postmarks and notes describing the curious journey of the letter. Write a paragraph in Spanish that describes this journey. Be sure to use the passive voice in your paragraph. You may wish to begin with:

Se echó la carta al buzón en . . .   **Fue mandado a Barcelona por el correo.**   **Luego. . . .**

CHAPTER 17

The Subjunctive Mood

Mood is a feature of verbs that allows speakers to express their attitude toward what they are saying. Chapters 1 through 16 deal with verb tenses in the indicative mood, which states facts and expresses certainty or reality.

The subjunctive mood, on the other hand, expresses uncertainty, doubt, wishes, desires, fears, conjecture, supposition, and conditions that are unreal or contrary-to-fact. It is also in secondary or dependent clauses. Its use is governed by the verb in the main clause or an uncertainty that is implied in some other way. The subjunctive mood occurs much more frequently in Spanish than in English.

In this and the next chapter, you will see how the subjunctive mood enables speakers of Spanish to express a variety of attitudes and feelings through the use of different verb forms and constructions.

◆ 1 ◆ THE PRESENT TENSE SUBJUNCTIVE

a. Regular Verbs

Most verbs form the present tense subjunctive by dropping the ending of the *yo* form of the present indicative (*-o*) and adding the corresponding endings.

	bailar (bail*o*)	vender (vend*o*)	recibir (recib*o*)
yo	bail*e*	vend*a*	recib*a*
tú	bail*es*	vend*as*	recib*as*
Ud., él, ella	bail*e*	vend*a*	recib*a*
nosotros, -as	bail*emos*	vend*amos*	recib*amos*
vosotros, -as	bail*éis*	vend*áis*	recib*áis*
Uds., ellos, ellas	bail*en*	vend*an*	recib*an*

b. Verbs with Irregular *yo* Forms

Verbs with irregular *yo* forms in the present tense indicative use the same irregular stem to form the present tense subjunctive.

caber:	*quepo,* quepa, quepas, quepa, quepamos, quepáis, quepan
coger:	*cojo,* coja, cojas, coja, cojamos, cojáis, cojan
conocer:	*conozco,* conozca, conozcas, conozca, conozcamos, conozcáis, conozcan
destruir:	*destruyo,* destruya, destruyas, destruya, destruyamos, destruyáis, destruyan
distinguir:	*distingo,* distinga, distingas, distinga, distingamos, distingáis, distingan
salir:	*salgo,* salga, salgas, salga, salgamos, salgáis, salgan
venir:	*vengo,* venga, vengas, venga, vengamos, vengáis, vengan

c. Stem-Changing Verbs

(1) Stem-changing *-ar* and *-er* verbs have the same stem changes in the present tense subjunctive as in the present tense indicative (*e* to *ie, o* to *ue*).

cerrar:	c*ie*rre, c*ie*rres, c*ie*rre, cerremos, cerréis, c*ie*rren
volver:	v*ue*lva, v*ue*lvas, v*ue*lva, volvamos, volváis, v*ue*lvan

(2) Stem-changing *-ir* verbs have the same stem changes in the present-tense subjunctive as in the present-tense indicative (*e* to *ie*, *o* to *ue*, *e* to *i*). In the *nosotros* and *vosotros* forms, the stem vowel *e* changes to *i* and the stem vowel *o* changes to *u*.

sentir: sienta, sientas, sienta, sintamos, sintáis, sientan

dormir: duerma, duermas, duerma, durmamos, durmáis, duerman

repetir: repita, repitas, repita, repitamos, repitáis, repitan

(3) Some verbs ending in *-iar* or *-uar* have an accent mark on the *i* or *u* (*í, ú*) in all forms except those for *nosotros* and *vosotros*.

enviar: envíe, envíes, envíe, enviemos, enviéis, envíen

continuar: continúe, continúes, continúe, continuemos, continuéis, continúen

d. Verbs with Spelling Changes

In the present subjunctive of verbs ending in *-car, -gar,* and *-zar, c* changes to *qu, g* to *gu,* and *z* to *c*. These spelling changes are the same as those that occur in the *yo* form of the preterit. (See page 435–437.)

	buscar (busqué)	pagar (pagué)	alzar (alcé)
yo	busque	pague	alce
tú	busques	pagues	alces
Ud., él, ella	busque	pague	alce
nosotros	busquemos	paguemos	alcemos
vosotros	busquéis	paguéis	alcéis
Uds., ellos, ellas	busquen	paguen	alcen

NOTE: To keep its original sound, the *u* in *averiguar* changes to *ü* before *e*. Otherwise, the *u* would be silent, as in *guerra*.

Preterit Tense Indicative: averigüé

Present Tense Subjunctive: averigüe

EXERCISE A. **At an orientation for freshmen, the counselor tells them what is important that they do. Express what she says, using the impersonal expression *"Es importante que"* in each statement.**

EXAMPLE: los estudiantes / entrar a tiempo a la escuela
Es importante que los estudiantes **entren** a tiempo a la escuela.

1. cada alumno / preparar la tarea cada día

_____

2. Uds. / estudiar para los exámenes

_____

3. los alumnos / traer los libros a la clase

_____

4. los alumnos y los profesores / comunicarse

_____

5. el alumno / no salir de la clase sin permiso

_____

6. Uds. y yo / hablar a menudo

_____

7. Uds. / aprovecharse de las facilidades que ofrece la escuela

_____

8. cada uno de Uds. / trabajar al máximo

_____

EXERCISE B. **You are babysitting for the first time. Before leaving, the children's mother gives you specific instructions. Express what she tells you, using** *Quiero que* . . .

EXAMPLE: Sally / terminar la tarea   Quiero que Sally **termine** la tarea.

1. los niños / acostarse a las nueve   _____

2. nadie / ver la televisión después
de las ocho   _____

3. Enrique y Andy / no pelear   _____

4. todos / tomar un vaso de leche   _____

5. Andy / cepillarse los dientes   _____

6. ellos / obedecerte   _____

7. tú / contestar el teléfono   _____

EXERCISE C. **The meteorologist's predictions are rarely accurate. Tell what is projected for the next five days, using** *"es probable que . . ."*

59°   ESTA NOCHE   MAÑANA   MARTES   MIÉRCOLES   JUEVES 90°   VIERNES

EXAMPLE: Es probable que **haga** fresco esta noche.

1. mañana   _____

2. martes   _____

3. miércoles   _____

4. jueves   _____

5. viernes   _____

EXERCISE D. This is Freddy's first year away at school. He calls home and tells his mother that many students in his dorm have the flu. Tell what his mother advises him, using *"espero que . . ."*

EXAMPLE: comer bien   Espero que tú **comas** bien.

1. acostarse temprano _____

2. dormir ocho horas _____

3. no visitar a los enfermos _____

4. tomar las vitaminas _____

5. consultar a un buen médico _____

6. tomar mucho jugo de naranja _____

7. descansar después de las clases _____

8. volver a llamarme mañana _____

EXERCISE E. You have a busy day ahead of you. Tell what you have to do, introducing each statement with *"Es necesario que . . ."*

estudiar para un examen   cuidar a mi hermano menor
escuchar las noticias del día   escribirle una carta a mi prima
terminar la tarea   salir con mis padres
devolver dos libros a la biblioteca leer un artículo
visitar a mis abuelos

EXAMPLE: Es necesario que yo **estudie** para un examen.

1. _____

2. _____

3. _____

4. _____

5. _____

6. _____

7. _____

8. _____

e. Present Tense Subjunctive of Irregular Verbs

The following verbs have irregular forms in the present subjunctive:

dar: dé, des, dé, demos, deis, den

estar: esté, estés, esté, estemos, estéis, estén

haber: haya, hayas, haya, hayamos, hayáis, hayan

ir:	vaya, vayas, vaya, vayamos, vayáis, vayan
saber:	sepa, sepas, sepa, sepamos, sepáis, sepan
ser:	sea, seas, sea, seamos, seáis, sean

EXERCISE F. Mrs. Salas is taking her twin sons to a play date. Tell what she tells them before they leave the house. Introduce each statement with "*Quiero que . . .*" or "*Espero que . . .*"

EXAMPLE: no gritar   Quiero (Espero) que Uds. **no griten.**

1. no pelear _____

2. compartir los juguetes con los otros niños _____

3. ser corteses _____

4. no dejar los juguetes en el piso _____

5. jugar bien con los otros niños _____

6. no ir a decir groserías _____

7. decir gracias cuando les ofrecen algo _____

8. estar tranquilos _____

9. saber portarse bien _____

10. no coger los juguetes de los otros niños _____

EXERCISE G. Javier intends to ask Lucy to marry him. Complete the letter he writes to a friend, in which he expresses his feelings.

Querido Paco:

Yo quiero que Lucy _____ conmigo. Espero que ella me _____ que sí
1. (casarse)   2. (decir)

porque le voy a hacer la pregunta esta noche. Yo no quiero que la boda _____ grande,
3. (ser)

pero dudo que Lucy _____ de acuerdo conmigo. Según ella, cuando dos personas
4. (estar)

se casan, es importante que todos los parientes y amigos _____ a la boda y que
5. (asistir)

_____ flores, comida, música y baile también. Ella quiere que todo el mundo
6. (haber)

_____ y que _____ ese momento. Es una lástima que nosotros no
7. (divertirse)   8. (compartir)

_____ escaparnos. Yo dudo que Lucy y yo _____ una casa en seguida.
9. (poder)   10. (comprar)

Será necesario que nosotros _____ trabajando y que _____ a ahorrar
11. (seguir)   12. (empezar)

mucho dinero. Es importante que nosotros _____ bastante dinero para comprar lo
                                              13. (tener)

necesario para amueblar un apartamento. Dudo que ella _____ vivir en la ciudad porque
                                                            14. (querer)

su mamá va a exigir que nosotros _____ cerca de ella. No me importa porque amo
                                      15. (vivir)

muchísimo a Lucy y sólo espero que nosotros _____ contentos.
                                                 16. (estar)

Saludos,

Javier

◆ 2 ◆ THE PRESENT-PERFECT SUBJUNCTIVE

a. The present-perfect subjunctive is formed by the present subjunctive of *haber* + the past participle of the verb in the dependent clause.

Esperamos que todo **haya salido** bien.   *We hope that everything went (has gone) well.*

b. The present-perfect subjunctive is used if the verb in the main clause is in the present tense and the dependent verbs refers to an event that has taken place.

Dudo que ellos **hayan escrito** la carta.   *I doubt that they have written (wrote) the letter*

EXERCISE H.   **Inclement weather has affected flight arrivals and departures at the airport. Express what Mr. Neblina says to other passengers.**

EXAMPLE: dudo / ningún avión / salir a tiempo hoy
           Dudo que ningún avión **haya salido** a tiempo hoy.

1. es probable / muchos vuelos / ser cancelados durante el día

_____

2. no me sorprende / los pronosticadores del tiempo / equivocarse otra vez

_____

3. me asombra / las colas para los teléfonos / no disminuirse

_____

4. temo / las tripulaciones / no poder llegar al aeropuerto

_____

5. espero / los técnicos / revisar bien los aviones

_____

6. el agente / lamenta / nosotros /no recibir más información sobre los vuelos

_____

MASTERY EXERCISES

EXERCISE I.   **Tell what a traveler should do before embarking on a trip.**

EXAMPLE: hacer un itinerario   **Es preciso** que el viajero **haga** un itinerario.

1. comprar el boleto de avión   _____

2. hacer reservación en un hotel   _____

3. tener su pasaporte al día   _____

4. ir al banco y sacar dinero   _____

5. hacer la maleta   _____

6. leer libros sobre los lugares que
   piensa visitar   _____

7. despedirse de la familia   _____

8. salir temprano de la casa   _____

9. estar en el aeropuerto dos horas
   antes del vuelo   _____

10. poner una batería nueva en la cámara   _____

EXERCISE J.   **Tell what these people should do to enjoy good health.**

EXAMPLE: Ernesto / comer bien   **Es importante** que Ernesto **coma** bien.

1. Andrea / hacer ejercicio todos los días   _____

2. Larry y Tomás / beber mucha agua   _____

3. tú / dormir bien   _____

4. yo / hacer todo en moderación   _____

5. Julie / no fumar   _____

6. Victoria / saber descansar   _____

7. Joaquín / no estar nervioso   _____

EXERCISE K.   **You are at a meeting of the school's literary club. Complete the questions and answers with the appropriate form of the present subjunctive.**

1. tener

   ¿Es importante que un autor _____ mucha imaginación?

   Sí, es muy importante que todos los autores _____ mucha imaginación.

2. ser

¿Es preciso que el cuento _____ verdadero?

No, no es preciso que los cuentos _____ verdaderos.

3. conocer

¿Es probable que el autor _____ bien al protagonista del cuento?

Es muy importante que los autores _____ bien a todos los personajes.

4. saber

¿Es necesario que el autor _____ desarrollar a los personajes?

Sí, es necesario que los autores _____ desarrollar a los personajes.

5. haber

¿Es probable que _____ relación entre la acción del cuento y la vida del autor?

Sí, es probable que _____ relación entre la acción del cuento y la vida del autor.

EXERCISE L.   **Joey isn't selling many tickets to a fund-raising event his team is planning. Using the expressions indicated, give the reasons people aren't buying tickets.**

1. Es posible que yo

_____

2. Es probable que mi familia

_____

3. Es dudoso que mis amigos

_____

4. Es importante que mi hermano y yo

_____

5. Es una lástima que mi novio

_____

6. Es necesario que nosotros

_____

EXERCISE M.   **You are giving an orientation session to new Spanish-speaking students at your school about the school teams. Using the expressions *es importante que …*, *es necesario que …*, *es posible que …*, *es dudoso que …*, and *es una lástima que …***

ACTIVIDADES

1. Conserving the environment is an important goal in today's society. Using the expressions *es necesario que…*, and *es importante que…*, prepare a list of eight things you feel people can do to accomplish this goal.

2. Indicate eight things that you feel that people should do as good citizens. Use the expressions *es necesario que…*, and *es importante que…* to introduce each one.

Uses of the Subjunctive Mood Tenses

◆ 1 ◆ DEPENDENT CLAUSES

The subjunctive in dependent clauses is introduced by the conjunction *que*.

a. The subjunctive tenses are used in a dependent clause when the verb in the main clause expresses advice, command, demand, desire, hope, permission, preference, prohibition, request, or suggestion. Here are some common verbs that require the subjunctive.

aconsejar *to advise*	**mandar** *to order*	**prohibir** *to forbid*
decir *to tell (someone to do something)*	**ordenar** *to order*	**querer** *to want*
desear *to wish*	**pedir** *to ask, to request*	**rogar** *to request, to beg*
esperar *to hope*	**permitir** *to permit, to allow*	**sugerir** *to suggest*
exigir *to demand*	**preferir** *to prefer*	**suplicar** *to implore, to beg*

El profesor **aconseja que** los alumnos **estudien.**	*The teacher advises the students to study (that the students study).*
Juan **quiere que** yo lo **llame** mañana.	*Juan wants me to call him tomorrow (that I call him tomorrow).*
La mamá **desea que** los niños se **acuesten** temprano.	*The mother wants the children to go to bed early (that the children go to bed early).*
Espero que compren la casa.	*I hope that they buy the house.*
Ella **ordena que hagan** la tarea.	*She orders them to do the assignment.*
Él me **pide que** le **pague.**	*He asks me to pay him.*
Mi padre **prohibe que** yo **vea** esa película.	*My father prohibits that I see that film.*
Quiero que Ud. **trabaje** mañana.	*I want you to work tomorrow.*
Ruego que me **prestes** atención.	*I beg you to pay attention to me (that you pay attention to me).*
Sugieren que vayamos en taxi.	*They suggest that we go by cab.*

NOTE: In each of the above sentences, the subject of the main verb is different from the subject of the dependent verb. If the subjects are the same, *que* is omitted and the infinitive form of the dependent verb is used.

Quiero trabajar mañana.	*I want to work tomorrow.*
Ella espera comprar la casa.	*She hopes to buy the house.*

EXERCISE A. **Express what parents ask of their children.**

EXAMPLE: los padres / exigir / los hijos / recibir buenas notas
Los padres **exigen** que los hijos **reciban** buenas notas.

1. mi mamá / querer / mis hermanos y yo / ayudar en casa

---

2. mi papá / prohibir / yo / mirar muchos programas de televisión

_____

3. los padres / esperar / los hijos / tener éxito en la vida

_____

4. mis padres / preferir / yo / trabajar en el verano

_____

5. mamá / permitir / tú / comer dulces

_____

6. papá / rogar / mi hermana / volver a casa temprano

_____

7. los padres / sugerir / Eduardo y Felipe / buscar trabajo

_____

8. mis padres / aconsejar / mi hermana / no salir por la noche

_____

EXERCISE B.   **Use the suggestions provided to express these people's ideas.**

asistir a una buena universidad	preparar la tarea a diario
tener su propio carro	quedarse en casa esta noche
no decir groserías	salir con los amigos
entrar en la sala	ser amable
ganar el campeonato	visitar con más frecuencia

EXAMPLE: Mi mamá prohibe que el perro **entre en la sala.**

1. Felipe quiere que su equipo favorito _____.

2. Mi abuela desea que mi hermano y yo _____.

3. Los padres de Sergio prohiben que él _____.

4. La consejera de Vicki espera que ella _____.

5. Los padres exigen que sus hijos _____.

6. Los profesores sugieren que los alumnos _____.

7. Yo ruego que mi hermana _____.

8. Los señores dicen que los invitados _____.

9. Los días de escuela mis padres prohiben que yo _____.

10. El pronosticador del tiempo aconseja que todo el mundo _____.

b. The subjunctive is used after verbs of feeling or emotion, such as fear, joy, sorrow, regret, surprise. Such verbs include:

alegrarse (de) *to be glad*	**sorprenderse (de)** *to be surprised*
lamentar (que) *to be sorry about, to regret*	**temer (que)** *to fear*
sentir (que) *to be sorry, to regret*	**tener miedo (de)** *to fear, to be afraid*

Temen que el gato **se caiga** del árbol.	*They fear that the cat will fall out of the tree.*
Nos alegramos de que tú **vengas.**	*We are happy that you are coming.*
Siento que ella **no esté** aquí.	*I regret that she isn't here.*
Los alumnos **se sorprenden de que** **no hay** clases hoy.	*The students are surprised that there are no classes today.*

EXERCISE C.   **Norma is on a cruise for the first time. Using the verb in parentheses, express her reactions to various things.**

EXAMPLE: Los miembros de la tripulación hablan muchos idiomas. (*sorprenderse*)
Norma **se sorprende de que** los miembros de la tripulación **hablen** muchos idiomas.

1. Los viajeros se visten con mucha elegancia. (*sorprenderse*)

_____

2. La comida es muy buena. (*alegrarse*)

_____

3. Hay una gran variedad de actividades todos los días. (*sorprenderse*)

_____

4. El mar está muy tranquilo. (*alegrarse*)

_____

5. Su hermana no la acompaña. (*lamentar*)

_____

6. El crucero dura solamente cinco días. (*sentir*)

_____

EXERCISE D.   **Using one of the following verbs, express what the people feel upon hearing various news items.**

alegrarse	temer	tener miedo de
sorprenderse	sentir	lamentar

EXAMPLE: El presidente visitará muchos países *(todos)*.
Todos **se alegran de que** el presidente **visite** muchos países.

1. La temporada de tormentas acabará mañana.

Los comerciantes _____.

2. El premio gordo de la lotería paga diez millones de dólares.

Mi padre _____.

3. Destruyen muchos edificios antiguos de la ciudad.

Los ciudadanos _____.

4. El equipo favorito no jugará ningún partido en su propio estadio.

Mis amigos _____.

5. Los alumnos no tendrán vacaciones de verano.

Yo _____.

6. No se abren las playas por causa de la contaminación.

Mis amigos y yo _____.

7. El dólar pierde su valor en el mercado mundial.

Los banqueros _____.

8. Hay muchos avances en la investigación de las enfermedades.

La gente _____.

9. El número de accidentes automovilísticos disminuye con gran velocidad.

La policía _____.

10. El uso de la computadora es uno de los pasatiempos más populares.

Yo _____.

c. **The subjunctive is used after verbs expressing doubt, disbelief, and denial, such as:**

dudar	*to doubt*	**negar**	*to deny*
no creer	*not to believe*	**pensar**	*to think*

Dudo que vengan temprano.	*I doubt that they will come early.*
Ella **niega que sea** la verdad.	*She denies that it is the truth.*
¿Piensa Ud. **que** él **sea** sincero?	*Do you think he is sincere?*
¿Crees que él **tenga** el dinero?	*Do you believe he has the money?*
No creo que él **tenga** el dinero.	*I don't believe he has the money.*

BUT

Creo que él **tiene** el dinero.	*I believe that he has the money.*

NOTES:

1. The verbs *creer* and *pensar,* when used interrogatively and negatively, indicate uncertainty and are usually followed by the subjunctive.

2. *Creer, pensar, no dudar,* and *no negar* indicate belief or certainty and are usually followed by the indicative.

Creo (Pienso, No dudo, No niego) que Julia **sabe** la respuesta.	*I believe (I think, I don't doubt, I don't deny) that Julia knows the answer.*

EXERCISE E.   Some friends accompany you on a shopping trip for a wristwatch. Use *dudar*, *no creer*, or *no pensar* to express their reaction to each wristwatch you look at.

EXAMPLE: Este reloj cuesta mucho. Rafael **no cree** que este reloj **cueste** mucho.

1. Este reloj vale mucho. Gabi _____.

2. Este reloj dura mucho tiempo. Elena y Nora _____.

3. Este reloj adelanta mucho. Sam _____.

4. Este reloj es de última moda. Tú _____.

5. Los números se distinguen fácilmente. Mirta y yo _____.

EXERCISE F.   Tell who denies the following statements.

EXAMPLE: La corte es injusta. (*el juez*)   El juez **niega que** la corte **sea** injusta.

1. Los precios aumentan otra vez. (*los comerciantes*)

_____

2. La princesa se casa con el chofer. (*el rey*)

_____

3. Los personajes de la novela son verdaderos. (*el autor*)

_____

4. La huelga es justificada. (*los trabajadores*)

_____

5. Los pronosticadores del tiempo saben pronosticar el tiempo. (*el público*)

_____

6. Yo no tengo la culpa. (*el criminal*)

_____

◆ 2 ◆ IMPERSONAL CONSTRUCTIONS

a. The subjunctive is used after certain impersonal expressions if the dependent verb has an expressed subject.

es dudoso *it is doubtful*	**es mejor** ⎫	**es posible** *it is possible*
es importante *it is important*	**más vale** ⎬ *it is better*	**es probable** *it is probable*
	es menester ⎭	
es imposible *it is impossible*	**es necesario** ⎫	
es una lástima *it is a pity*	**es preciso** ⎬ *it is necessary*	

Es dudoso que él lo **compre.**	*It is doubtful that he will buy it.*
Es importante que lo **hagamos.**	*It is important for us to do it (that we do it).*

Es necesario que Ud. coma.   *It is necessary for you to eat (that you eat).*

BUT

Es necesario comer.   *It is necessary to eat.*

b. The subjunctive is not used after impersonal expressions that express certainty.

es cierto   *it is certain*   es evidente   *it is evident*
es claro   *it is clear*   es verdad   *it is true*

Es verdad que mañana es su cumpleaños.   *It is true that tomorrow is her birthday.*

Es cierto que yo estudio mucho.   *It is true that I study a lot.*

BUT

No es cierto que yo estudie mucho.   *It is not true that I study a lot.*

EXERCISE G.   In your social studies class you have been compiling a list of what candidates for public office should do. Express your reaction to this using the expression indicated.

EXAMPLE: conocer a todos los electores (*imposible*)
    Es imposible que los candidatos **conozcan** a todos los electores.

1. no hacer promesas inalcanzables (*importante*)

_____

2. ser honrados (*necesario*)

_____

3. comprender bien los problemas (*dudoso*)

_____

4. escuchar las quejas de los electores (*preciso*)

_____

5. obedecer las leyes (*importante*)

_____

6. representar los deseos de los electores (*menester*)

_____

7. no ofender a ningún grupo de electores (*imposible*)

_____

8. responder a sus seguidores (*probable*)

_____

9. cumplir con su palabra (*dudoso*)

_____

10. no meterse en temas ajenos (*mejor*)

_____

EXERCISE H. You are working at the airport and have to prepare a message to passengers who have been delayed due to mechanical problems with the aircraft. Complete the message with the appropriate form of the verbs indicated.

Damas y caballeros, es evidente que nosotros _____ un problema grande. Es cierto
                                                    1. (tener)

que _____ una demora de los aviones porque es importante que los mecáni-
        2. (haber)

cos _____ tiempo suficiente para revisar bien los aviones. Es probable que la demora
        3. (tener)

_____ varias horas, pero más vale estar seguros de que todo _____
        4. (durar)   *5.* (estar)

en orden antes de despegar. Es menester que Uds. _____ con nosotros. Es
                                                          6. (cooperar)

dudoso que nosotros _____ atender las necesidades individuales de cada pasajero, pero
                            7. (poder)

más vale _____ de ayudar a unos que a nadie. Es una lástima que muchos de Uds. no
            8. (tratar)

_____ a sus destinos a la hora indicada en el horario. Es evidente que muchos de Uds.
        9. (llegar)

_____ mucha prisa por llegar, pero es imposible _____ las
        10. (tener)   *11.* (cambiar)

cosas. Es claro que nosotros _____ a hacer todo lo posible para ayudarlos. Si Uds. se
                                      12. (ir)

alejan de la puerta de salida, es preciso que Uds. _____ en los anuncios que se darán
                                                          13. (fijarse)

por altavoz. Es dudoso que el avión _____ antes de las nueve de la noche. Es probable
                                            14. (salir)

que yo _____ otro anuncio dentro de treinta minutos. Muchas gracias por su atención y
            15. (hacer)

cooperación.

EXERCISE I. Imagine that you are a freshman advisor. Tell a group of students about school life and what they should do to succeed.

EXAMPLE: es probable / Uds. / estar preocupados
            Es probable que Uds. **estén** preocupados.

1. es dudoso / Uds. / poder participar en todas las actividades de la escuela

_____

2. es necesario / cada estudiante / seguir las reglas de la escuela

_____

3. es importante / los alumnos / no llegar tarde a las clases

_____

4. es preciso / Uds. / estar bien preparados todos los días

_____

5. es mejor / los alumnos / hablar con los profesores

_____

6. es importante / nosotros / respetar los derechos de todos los alumnos

_____

7. es menester / los profesores / exigir mucho a los estudiantes

_____

◆ 3 ◆ SEQUENCE OF TENSES

a. The present tense of the subjunctive mood is generally used if the verb in the main clause is in the present indicative, the future, present perfect, or the imperative (command form).

Ella **ordena** que ellos **estudien** más.	*She orders them to study more (that they study more).*
Ella **ordenará** que ellos **estudien** más.	*She will order them to study more.*
Ella **ha ordenado** que ellos **estudien** más.	*She has ordered them to study more.*
Ordene Ud. **que** (ellos) **estudien** más.	*Order them to study more.*

b. The present-perfect subjunctive (*haya hablado* has spoken) is formed by the present subjunctive of *haber* and the past participle of the verb in the dependent clause. The perfect subjunctive is used if the verb in the main clause is in the present tense and the dependent verb represents an event that has taken place.

No **creo** que ellos **hayan** salido.	*I do not believe that they have left.*
Niego que ellos me **hayan visto**.	*I deny that they have seen me.*

EXERCISE J. **Mrs. Vega is very nervous about leaving her children with a babysitter. Express what she says to her husband.**

EXAMPLE: no creo / los niños / cenar bien   **No creo que** los niños **hayan cenado** bien.

1. espero / los niños / bañarse

_____

2. espero / ellos / no ver ese programa de televisión

_____

3. es importante / Jorge / prestar mucha atención

_____

4. dudo / Elvira / preparar la tarea aún

_____

5. es probable / Jorge y Víctor / seguir peleando

_____

6. ruego / no haber ninguna emergencia

_____

7. es evidente / Rosalinda / ser muy responsable

_____

8. lamento / nosotros / volver a dejar a los niños en casa

_____

9. es dudoso / tú / ayudarme

_____

10. es posible / Rosalinda / llamar por teléfono otra vez

_____

EXERCISE K. **You and a friend have been communicating over the Internet but you have reached a level of frustration. Complete this message that you send to your friend with the appropriate form of the verbs indicated.**

Querida Marta:

Yo temo que la tecnología moderna _____ terminar con nuestra amistad. En
                                                1. (poder)

mi mensaje anterior escribí: «Te suplico que _____ conmigo en seguida». Dudo
                                                       2. (comunicarse)

que tú _____ ese mensaje, ya que no me contestaste. Es importante que tú y yo
              3. (recibir)

_____ pronto. Prefiero que tú me _____ por teléfono. Es
         4. (hablar)   5. (llamar)

evidente que nosotros no _____ seguir comunicándonos por el Internet. Espero
                                    6. (poder)

que te _____ esta comunicación. Si me llamas por teléfono, no habrá duda de que la
              7. (llegar)

_____. Si no me llamas pronto, yo trataré de llamarte.
       8. (recibir)

                                                                    Hasta luego.

MASTERY EXERCISES

EXERCISE L. **Complete the following sentences with your opinions.**

1. Yo prefiero que mis padres _____.

2. Es necesario que mis hermanos y yo _____.

3. Tengo miedo de que los profesores _____.

4. Suplico que mis amigos _____.

5. No creo que ellos _____.

6. Es una lástima que mi mejor amigo(a) _____.

7. Es probable que yo _____.

8. Espero que toda mi familia _____.

9. Me alegro de que mi padre _____.

10. Mis padres sugieren que yo _____.

EXERCISE M. Complete this story with the appropriate form of the verbs indicated.

Mañana Pedro va a presentarse a un trabajo por primera vez. Es necesario que él _____

1. (despertarse)

temprano el primer día. Él quiere _____ una buena impresión. Su mamá teme que su hijo

2. (dar)

no _____ el reloj despertador. Ella le ruega a Pedro que _____

3. (oír) _4. (acostarse)_

temprano porque es importante que él _____ alerto en la oficina. Por eso ella prohibe que

5. (estar)

Pedro _____ con sus amigos por la noche. No permite que él _____ la

6. (salir) _7. (mirar)_

televisión hasta muy tarde. Ella quiere que su hijo _____ éxito en el trabajo y que

8. (tener)

_____ más responsable.

9. (ser)

Cuando Pedro asiste a la escuela es necesario que su mamá _____ en su cuarto para

10. (entrar)

despertarlo. Antes de acostarse ella le dice a Pedro que _____ el reloj despertador para

11. (poner)

las seis y media de la mañana. Ella le sugiere que _____ dos relojes para despertarse.

12. (usar)

Ella cree que _____ preciso que Pedro _____ bastante tiempo para

13. (ser) _14. (tener)_

desayunar también. Pero a la mañana siguiente, Pedro se despierta tarde. Su mamá teme que Pedro

_____ mal el reloj despertador. Es evidente que Pedro no _____ distinguir

15. (poner) _16. (saber)_

entre «AM» y «PM» en el reloj.

EXERCISE N. Several friends are planning a ski trip and will be staying at the home of another friend who lives near the ski area. Their host send them an e-mail in Spanish with some last-minute details. Express in Spanish what he says. You may wish to include the following:

- his doubt about the amount of snow tomorrow

- the need to get to the ski area early

- his hope for good weather for skiing

- other things he advises they bring with them (reading material, computer games, etc.)

- his hope that all goes and they enjoy themselves.

Frequently Used Verbal Expressions

Many Spanish verbs are used in idiomatic expressions. A list of common expressions follows

◆ 1 ◆ EXPRESSIONS WITH *HACER*

¿Qué tiempo hace?	*How's the weather?*
¿Qué tiempo hace en primavera?	*How's the weather in spring?*

hacer buen/mal tiempo   *to be good/bad weather*
Hace buen (mal) tiempo hoy.   *Today the weather is good (bad).*

hacer (mucho) calor/fresco/frío   *to be (very) warm/cool/cold (weather)*
Hizo mucho fresco anoche.   *It was very cool last night.*

hacer (mucho) sol   *to be (very) sunny*
Hace mucho sol a mediodía.   *It is very sunny at noon.*

hacer (mucho) viento   *to be (very) windy*
Hizo viento por la mañana.   *It was windy in the morning.*

hacer el favor de + infinitive   *please. . .*
Haga (Ud.) el favor de pasar la sal.   *Please pass the salt.*

hacer de + occupation   *to act as*
Miguel hace de presidente.   *Michael acts as president.*

hacer la maleta (el baúl)   *to pack one's suitcase (trunk)*
Hizo la maleta en seguida.   *He packed his suitcase at once.*

hace + time expression + preterit   *. . . ago*
Le hablé hace una semana.   *I spoke to her a week ago.*

hacer una pregunta   *to ask a question*
El alumno le hizo una pregunta al profesor.   *The student asked the teacher a question.*

hacer un viaje   *to take a trip*
Hacen un viaje a México.   *They take a trip to Mexico.*

hacer una visita   *to pay a visit*
Le hice una visita a mi tío.   *I paid a visit to my uncle.*

hacerse   *to become (through one's own efforts)*
El autor se hizo famoso.   *The author became famous.*

hacerse tarde   *to be getting late*
Se hace tarde.   *It's getting late.*

EXERCISE A.   **Complete each of the following statements with an expression with *hacer*.**

EXAMPLE: Yo no pude responder cuando el profesor _____ .
Yo no pude responder cuando el profesor **hizo la pregunta.**

1. Es un buen día para ir a la playa porque _____ .

2. En la primavera mis abuelos _____ a Francia.

3. ¿Juan? No sé. _____ que no lo veo.

4. ¿ _____ ? ¿Necesitaré usar guantes?

5. Cuando Elvira era pequeña, ella siempre _____ médica en las obras de la escuela.

6. _____ decirme dónde hay un teléfono público.

7. Regresamos a casa en seguida porque _____.

8. Cada domingo, Felipe _____ a sus abuelos.

9. Vicki _____ porque va a pasar una semana en las montañas.

10. _____ y todas las hojas se cayeron de los árboles.

EXERCISE B.   **Tell what you like to do in different weather conditions. Use the suggestions provided.**

EXAMPLE: Cuando hace mal tiempo, me gusta leer una novela.

SUGGESTIONS: quedarme en casa   jugar al tenis
                leer una novela   visitar a un amigo
                caminar por el parque   esquiar
                ir a la playa   ir al cine

1. Cuando _____
   _____ .

3. Cuando _____
   _____ .

2. Cuando _____
   _____ .

4. Cuando _____
   _____ .

5. Cuando _____

_____ .

7. Cuando _____

_____ .

6. Cuando _____

_____ .

EXERCISE C. **Neil just returned from a sightseeing trip with his grandparents. Use an expression with *hacer* to tell what he says about the trip.**

_____ una semana, mis abuelos y yo _____ al pueblo donde nació mi
_____1._____ _____2._____

abuelo. Pasamos tres días allí. Cada mañana, antes de vestirse, mi abuela _____ :
_____3._____

«¿ _____ hoy?» Nos tocó un clima muy variado. Un día _____ y la
____4.____ ____5.____

temperatura subió a los noventa grados. Otro día, especialmente por la noche, _____
_____6._____

cuando la temperatura bajó a los treinta grados. Pero por lo general, durante el día _____
_____7._____

porque _____ y también _____ . Cuando mis abuelos _____
____8.____ ____9.____ _____10._____

para el viaje, metieron ropa ligera y gruesa, pero yo no tenía ropa para el frío. Cada día seguimos la misma

rutina: nos despertamos temprano y al salir del hotel mi abuelo _____ guía. Conocimos
_____11._____

la escuela a la cual asistió, el parque donde pasaba su tiempo libre, y los lugares donde se reunía con sus

amigos. Me divertí pero le dije: «Abuelito, la próxima vez que yo _____ con ustedes,
_____12._____

_____ comenzar la excursión a mediodía. Me gusta dormir por la mañana».
_____13._____

◆ 2 ◆ EXPRESSIONS WITH *TENER*

tener . . . años *to be . . . years old*	
Ella **tiene veinte años**.	*She is twenty years old.*
¿Cuántos años **tiene** Ud.?	*How old are you?*
¿Qué edad **tiene** Ud.?	

tener (mucho) calor   *to be (very) warm*
Él tiene (mucho) calor.   *He is (very) warm.*

tener (mucho) frío   *to be (very) cold*

Nosotros tenemos (mucho) frío.   *We are (very) cold.*

NOTE: "To be warm" and "to be cold" translate as *hacer calor* and *hacer frío*, respectively, when referring to the weather, and as *estar caliente* and *estar frío, -a*, respectively, when referring to things.

tener (mucha) hambre   *to be (very) hungry*
¿Tiene Ud. (mucha) hambre?   *Are you (very) hungry?*

tener (mucha) sed   *to be (very) thirsty*
Tengo (mucha) sed.   *I am (very) thirsty.*

tener éxito   *to be successful*
Ud. siempre tiene éxito.   *You are always successful.*

tener ganas de   *to feel like*
Nosotros no tenemos ganas de comer.   *We don't feel like eating.*

tener razón   *to be right;*   **no tener razón**   *to be wrong*
Alfredo tiene razón.   *Alfred is right.*
Pablo no tiene razón.   *Paul is wrong.*

tener sueño   *to be sleepy*
¿Tiene Ud. sueño?   *Are you sleepy?*

tener cuidado   *to be careful*
Tenga cuidado con el experimento.   *Be careful with the experiment.*

tener prisa   *to be in a hurry*
El hombre tiene prisa.   *The man is in a hurry.*

tener (mucho) gusto en   *to be (very) glad to*
Tengo (mucho) gusto en conocerle.   *I am (very) glad to know you.*

tener miedo de + infinitive   *to be afraid to*
Ella tiene miedo de tocarlo.   *She is afraid to touch it.*
Ella le tiene miedo al perro.   *She is afraid of the dog.*

tener dolor de cabeza (estómago, muelas)   *to have a headache (stomachache, toothache)*
Tengo dolor de cabeza.   *I have a headache.*

tener que + infinitive   *to have to, must*
Tengo que estudiar.   *I have to (must) study.*

tener mucho (poco, algo) que hacer   *to have much (little, something) to do*
Tengo mucho que hacer   *I have much to do.*

tener la bondad de + infinitive   *please*
Tenga la bondad de esperar un
    momento.   *Please wait a minute.*

tener las manos frías (los ojos cansados)   *to have cold hands (tired eyes)*
Él tiene las manos frías (calientes).   *His hands are cold (warm).*
Tengo los ojos cansados.   *My eyes are tired.*
¿Qué tiene Ud.?   *What is the matter with you?*

tener que ver con   *to have to do with*
Esto no tiene nada que ver con aquello.   *This has nothing to do with that.*

EXERCISE D.   **Every evening Julia speaks to her best friend on the telephone and gives her the latest gossip about their friends. Complete her statements using an expression with *tener*.**

1. Luis _____ ir al cine porque quería ver la película que se acaba de estrenar.

2. Sarita no comió nada en la cafetería de la escuela porque ella _____ .

3. Víctor y Hugo no me vieron cuando corrían por la calle. Ellos _____ .

4. John _____. Bebió más de un litro de agua en diez minutos.

5. Había un perro en la calle y una señora atravesó la calle porque ella le _____ al perro.

6. Ali se acostó temprano anoche porque _____.

7. Grace llamó al dentista anoche porque ella _____.

8. Gustavo y Gloria, tus primos gemelos, celebraron su cumpleaños el domingo. ¿_____?

9. Le presté un suéter a Raquel porque ella _____.

10. Había mucho hielo en la calle. Cuando mi abuelo salió de la casa, yo le dije: «_____, abuelo».

11. Hoy Jim estaba muy preocupado pero no me contestó cuando le pregunté: «¿_____, Jim?»

12. Vi en el canal del tiempo que la temperatura en San Antonio pasó los cien grados. Los habitantes de San Antonio _____, ¿no crees?

13. Cuando mi hermana me pide ayuda, nunca me dice: «_____ ayudarme».

14. Otra vez no hablo con mi hermano porque él siempre cree que él _____.

15. Debemos terminar de hablar porque yo _____ estudiar para un examen.

EXERCISE E.   **Gladys is helping her younger brother study for a test. Express what he says in each situation, using an expression with *tener*.**

EXAMPLE: Ya han terminado las vacaciones y los jóvenes **tienen que volver a** la escuela.

1. Es medianoche y Felipe no se acuesta aunque él _____ .

2. Hace mucho calor y Paco está haciendo mucho ejercicio. Él debe _____ .

3. Los señores andaban lentamente porque no _____ .

4. Camarero, _____ de darme una servilleta.

5. Al conocer al padre de su amigo, Jorge le dijo: _____ en conocerle, señor.

6. Los alumnos estudian mucho porque ellos no _____ salir mal en el examen.

7. Mirta se desayuna muy temprano, a las seis de la mañana. Ahora es la una de la tarde.
   Ella debe _____ .

8. El autobús escolar llega a las siete y diez. Ya son las siete y ocho y Lourdes _____ porque
   no quiere perderlo.

9. Al ver el ratoncito, las personas _____ .

10. La temperatura bajó y los exploradores encendieron un fuego porque ellos _____ .

EXERCISE F.   **Answer the questions that a new neighbor asks you.**

1. ¿Cuántos años tienes?   _____

2. ¿Tomas aspirinas cuando tienes
   dolor de cabeza?   _____

3. ¿Tienes frío hoy?   _____

4. ¿Tienes que estudiar esta noche para
   un examen?   _____

5. ¿Tienen razón tus padres siempre?   _____

6. ¿Tienes hambre por la tarde?   _____

7. ¿Qué haces cuando tienes sed?   _____

8. ¿Qué haces cuando tienes sueño?   _____

9. ¿Tienes cuidado cuando andas en
   bicicleta en la calle?   _____

10. ¿Tienes algo que hacer esta tarde?   _____

◆ 3 ◆ EXPRESSIONS WITH *DAR*

dar a   *to face*
Mi ventana **da a** la avenida.   *My window faces the avenue.*

dar con alguien (algo)   *to meet, to come upon, to find someone (something)*
Yo **di con** mi amigo en la calle.   *I met my friend on the street.*

dar de comer a   *to feed*
Ellos **dan de comer a** los caballos.   *They feed the horses.*

dar la hora (las siete)   *to strike the hour (seven)*
El reloj **dio las siete**.   *The clock struck seven.*

dar(le) la mano a alguien   *to shake hands with someone*
Carlos **le dio la mano**.   *Charles shook hands with him.*

darse la mano   *to shake hands (with each other)*
Los amigos **se dan la mano**.   *The friends shake hands.*

dar las gracias a   *to thank*
Ella le **dio las gracias al** hombre por
    su bondad.   *She thanked the man for his kindness.*

dar los buenos días (las buenas noches) a alguien   *to say good morning (good night) to someone*
Le **doy los buenos días** a mi amigo.   *I say good morning to my friend.*

dar un paseo   *to take a walk or a ride*
Ellos **dan un paseo** por el parque.   *They take a walk (a ride) through the park.*

dar un paseo en automóvil (a caballo)   *to take an automobile ride (to go horseback riding)*
Doy un paseo en automóvil.   *I take an automobile ride.*

EXERCISE G.   **Vicky is studying in Salamanca, Spain and sends you this postcard. Complete her message with an expression with *dar*.**

Querida amiga:

Vivo con una familia simpática. Mi cuarto _____ 1. un patio grande. Hay un reloj grande en la

plaza mayor y el reloj _____ 2. cada hora. Aquí en España, los amigos _____ 3.

al saludarse. Me gusta _____ 4. por el centro de la ciudad porque es una ciudad muy antigua

y bonita. Ayer yo _____ 5. un chico que era mi compañero de asiento en el avión. Me invitó

a _____ 6. con él mañana después de las clases. Vamos a ir al parque. Hay muchos pájaros en el

parque y muchas personas les _____ 7. . También quiero _____ 8. por el

regalo de viaje que me diste. Es muy bonito y útil. Ya es tarde y voy a acostarme. Voy a _____ 9. .

Saludos,

Vicky

EXERCISE H.   **Answer the questions a new friend asks you about your customs.**

1. ¿Qué hora da el reloj cuando te despiertas todos los días?

_____

2. ¿Das un paseo por la mañana?

_____

3. ¿Prefieres dar un paseo en carro o a caballo?

_____

4. Si das con su amigo(-a) en la calle, ¿se dan Uds. la mano?

_____

5. Al despedirse de un amigo, ¿le das la mano?

_____

6. ¿Diste con el compañero de clase que buscabas?

_____

7. ¿Quién le da de comer a tu perro?

_____

8. ¿Les das las gracias a las personas que te ayudan?

_____

9. ¿Le das las buenas noches a tu familia antes de acostarte?

_____

10. ¿Tu cuarto da a la calle?

_____

◆ 4 ◆ EXPRESSIONS WITH _HABER_

hay (había, hubo, habrá, habría,	_there is, there are (there was, there were, there will be,_
ha habido)	_there would be, there has (have) been)_
Había muchos clientes en	
la tienda.	_There were many customers in the store._

haber lodo (luna, sol, neblina, polvo)	_to be muddy (moonlight, sunny, foggy, dusty)_
Hay (mucho) lodo hoy.	_It is (very) muddy today._
Había neblina anoche.	_It was foggy last night._

haber de + infinitive	_to be to, to be supposed to_
Han de venir mañana.	_They are to come tomorrow._

hay que + infinitive	_one must_
Hay que tener paciencia.	_One must have patience._

hay + noun + **que** + infinitive	_there is (there are) + noun + verb_
Hay trabajo que hacer.	_There is work to do._

EXERCISE I. **You are helping a friend study for a test. Complete each statement with one of the following expressions.**

había	han de	hay lodo	hay neblina	hay que
ha de	no hay de qué	hay luna	había polvo	hay . . . que

1. Jaime _____ venir al anochecer.

2. Cuando alguien me dice «muchas gracias», yo siempre contesto « _____ ».

3. _____ callarse para oír.

4. No me gusta dar un paseo después de la lluvia, cuando _____ en las calles.

5. _____ una caja de dulces en la mesa.

6. En una noche clara _____ .

7. _____ en el aire ayer.

8. Hoy _____; no se ve el sol.

9. En el campo _____ muchas cosas interesantes _____ ver.

10. Ellos _____ estar allí a las once.

◆ 5 ◆ OTHER VERBAL EXPRESSIONS

acabar de   *to have just*
Él **acaba** (**acababa**) **de** entrar.   *He has just (had just) entered.*

aprovecharse de   *to take advantage of (an opportunity)*
Él **se aprovecha de** cada oportunidad.   *He takes advantage of each opportunity.*

asistir a   *to attend*
Asistimos a la escuela.   *We attend school.*

bajar de   *to get off (the train, bus, etc.)*
El pasajero **baja del** tren.   *The passenger gets off the train.*

burlarse de   *to make fun of*
Tú **te burlas de** la muchacha.   *You make fun of the girl.*

cambiar de   *to change (seat, train, mind)*
Él **cambia de** asiento con su amigo.   *He changes seats with his friend.*
Ella **cambió de** opinión.   *She changed her mind.*

casarse con   *to marry*
Juan **se casó con** Isabel.   *Juan married Isabel.*

contar con   *to rely on, to count on*
Cuento con mis amigos.   *I rely on my friends.*

creer que sí (no)   *to think so (not)*
Creo que sí.   *I think so.*

cumplir . . . años   *to be . . . years old*
Hoy ella **cumple quince años.**   *Today she is fifteen years old.*

cumplir con (su promesa, su palabra)   *to fulfill, to keep (one's promise, one's word)*
Jane siempre **cumple con** su palabra.   *Jane always keeps her word.*

dedicarse a   *to devote oneself to*
Tomás **se dedica al** trabajo.   *Tomás devotes himself to the work.*

dejar caer   *to drop*
Ella **dejó caer** los platos.   *She dropped the plates.*

dejar de + *infinitive*   *to stop, to fail to*
Él **dejó de** comer.   *He stopped eating.*
No **deje de** hacerlo.   *Don't fail to do it.*

despedirse de   *to take leave of, to say goodbye to*
En la estación **me despedí de**
     mis amigos.   *In the station I said goodbye to my friends.*

echarse a + *infinitive*   *to begin, to start to*
El niño **se echa a llorar.**   *The boy begins to cry.*

echar de menos *to miss*
Echo de menos a mis amigos.   *I miss my friends.*

echar una carta al correo *to mail a letter*
Eché una carta al correo ayer.   *I mailed the letter yesterday.*

enamorarse de *to fall in love with*
David *se* **enamoró** *de* Dolores.   *David fell in love with Dolores.*

entrar en *to enter*
Yo **entré en** el cuarto.   *I entered the room.*

estar a punto de
estar para ⎫   *to be about to*
Ellos **estaban a punto de** salir.   *They were about to leave.*

estar de pie *to be standing*
Todos **estaban de** pie.   *All were standing.*

estar por *to be in favor of, to be about to*
Yo **estoy por** ir al cine.   *I am in favor of going to the movies.*
                                                       I am about to go to the movies.

gozar de *to enjoy*
Él **goza de** buena salud.   *He enjoys good health.*

jugar a *to play (a game)*
Nosotros **jugamos al** tenis.   *We play tennis.*

llegar a ser + noun *to become*
Llegó a ser presidente.   *He became president.*

llevar a cabo *to carry out*
La secretaria **llevó a cabo** las órdenes de su jefe. *The secretary carried out the orders of her boss.*

negarse a + infinitive *to refuse to*
Ella **se niega a firmar** el cheque.   *She refuses to sign the check.*

ocuparse de *to busy oneself with, to be concerned with, to attend to*
La secretaria **se ocupa del** correo.   *The secretary attends to the mail.*

pensar de *to think of (have an opinion about)*
¿Qué **piensas de** mi nueva bicicleta?   *What do you think of my new bicycle?*

pensar en *to think of, to think about (direct one's thoughts to)*
Juan nunca **piensa en** sus amigos.   *John never thinks about his friends.*

poner la mesa *to set the table.*
María **pone la mesa.**   *Mary sets the table.*

ponerse + article of clothing *to put on*
Yo me **pongo el abrigo.**   *I put on my coat.*

ponerse + adjective *to become (involuntarily)*
Ella **se puso pálida.**   *She became pale.*

ponerse a + infinitive *to begin to*
Los niños **se pusieron a correr.**   *The children began to run.*

ponerse el sol *to set (referring to the sun)*
¿A qué hora **se pone el sol?**   *At what time does the sun set?*

ponerse en camino (en marcha) *to start out, to set out*
Ellos **se pusieron en camino**
    (en marcha) tarde.   *They started out late.*

prestar atención   *to pay attention*
Tomás no **presta atención** en
    la clase.   *Thomas doesn't pay attention in class.*

querer a   *to love (someone)*
Quiero a mis padres.   *I love my parents.*

querer decir   *to mean*
¿Qué **quiere decir** Ud.?   *What do you mean?*

quitarse + article of clothing   *to take off*
El señor **se quita el sombrero.**   *The man takes off his hat.*

reírse de   *to laugh at*
Ella **se ríe del** muchacho.   *She laughs at the boy.*

salir bien (mal)   *to come out well (poorly), to pass (fail)*
Salí bien en el examen.   *I passed the examination.*

salir   *to rise (referring to the sun)*
El sol **sale** en el este.   *The sun rises in the east.*

salir de   *to leave, to go out of*
Salgo de la escuela a las tres.   *I leave school at three o'clock.*

servirse de   *to use, to make use of*
Él **se sirve de** la madera para
    hacer una mesa.   *He uses the wood to make a table.*

soñar con   *to dream of*
Yo **sueño con** las vacaciones.   *I dream of the vacation.*

subir a   *to get on (the train, bus, etc.)*
Subo al autobús.   *I get on the bus.*

subir (bajar) la escalera   *to go upstairs (downstairs)*
Ella **sube** la escalera.   *She goes upstairs.*
Ella **baja** la escalera.   *She goes downstairs.*

tardar en + infinitive   *to delay in*
El tren **tardó en** llegar.   *The train delayed in arriving.*

tratar de + infinitive   *to try to*
Trato de estudiar.   *I try to study.*

volver a + infinitive   *to + verb + again*
Ella **vuelve a** cantar.   *She sings again.*

EXERCISE J.   **Several friends are discussing different topics. Complete what they say with the appropriate form of the following verbal expressions.**

soñar con	volver a	tardar en	salir mal
negarse a	enamorarse de	pensar de	querer decir
estar para	estar de pie	ponerse	prestar atención
llegar a ser	estar por	reírse de	

1. Freddy _____ rojo cuando Gloria le besó.

2. Mi padre _____ prestarme dinero.

3. Yo _____ porque no hay asientos.

4. Enrique _____ ganar la carrera.

5. Los videos _____ llegar a las tiendas. Todavía no los tienen.

6. El hermano de Felipe _____ mi hermana. Van a casarse.

7. ¿Qué _____ (Uds.) la película que vimos anoche?

8. Cuando el chico se cayó, nosotros empezamos a _____ él.

9. Víctor no comprende nada. Siempre me pregunta: «¿Qué _____ eso?»

10. Elena está muy contenta porque decidió que quiere _____ enfermera.

11. ¿Quiénes _____ ir a ver el partido de fútbol mañana?

12. Felipe _____ llamarme anoche pero yo no estaba en casa.

13. Joey siempre se pierde cuando conduce el carro porque él no _____ a las instrucciones que le dan.

14. Miguel no puede salir por quince días porque él _____ en los exámenes.

15. Yo _____ salir de la casa cuando sonó el teléfono.

EXERCISE K.   **Ricky's younger brother likes to ask him a lot of questions. Answer his questions.**

1. ¿Qué quiere decir «amistad»?

_____

2. Para llegar al quinto piso, ¿hay que subir o bajar la escalera?

_____

3. ¿A qué hora salió el sol ayer?

_____

4. ¿Tratas de cocinar algunas veces?

_____

5. ¿Te quitas el abrigo al entrar en la casa o al salir de la casa?

_____

6. ¿De qué te sirves tú para cortar la carne?

_____

7. ¿Quieres a nuestros parientes?

_____

8. ¿En dónde entras tú para ver un objeto de arte?

_____

9. ¿Te pones enfermo cuando comes frutas verdes?

_____

10. ¿Te ocupas tú de los problemas de tus amigos?

_____

11. ¿Qué piensas tú de tus maestros?

_____

12. ¿Llevas a cabo los quehaceres que te da papá?

_____

13. ¿Echas de menos a tus compañeros de clase durante el verano?

_____

14. ¿Cumples siempre con tu palabra?

_____

15. ¿Echas una carta al correo antes o después de escribirla?

_____

MASTERY EXERCISES

EXERCISE L. **Vicente and Elena went shopping together. Complete his description of their shopping trip with the appropriate verbal expression from the choices given.**

(1–14)

vuelvo a pensar en	bajamos	entramos en
cambié de opinión	había	pienso
quiero	nos ponemos a	se ha puesto
cumplir con mi promesa	cumple	me doy cuenta de
se ha puesto	dimos con	

_____ muchas personas cuando Elena y yo _____ la tienda. Yo _____
        1.   2.   3.

comprar un lector de MP3 para mi hermano. El domingo él _____ quince años y yo quería
                                                                                          4.

_____ de comprarle un regalo bonito. Nosotros _____ al sótano, donde
        5.   6.

venden aparatos electrónicos. Cuando vi los precios de los lectores de MP3 yo _____ . Elena y
                                                                                                          7.

yo _____ buscar otro regalo pero nosotros no _____ nada porque todo estaba
        8.   9.

carísimo. Yo _____ mucho a mi hermano pero yo no _____ gastar todo mi dinero
                    10.   11.

en un regalo para él. Yo _____ qué le gustaría a él. Mientras tanto, yo _____
                                12.   13.

que Elena _____ contenta.
                14.

(15-27)

tener paciencia	aprovecharse de	salir de
había	hay que	tenía prisa
estaba para	di con	subió
tengo ganas de	nos pusimos de acuerdo	tenía que
di las gracias		

Elena decidió _____ 15. estar en la tienda para buscar algo para sí misma. Ella revisó el directorio

de la tienda y _____ 16. al segundo piso, donde _____ 17. ropa para mujeres. Ella y

yo _____ 18. de reunirnos en media hora. Yo _____ 19. _____ 20. ese

departmento cuando vi algo que yo _____ 21. comprar para mí mismo. Era una computadora que

estaba bien barata. Yo siempre _____ 22. tener mi propia computadora en mi cuarto. Yo cogí una de

las computadoras y por fin yo _____ 23. un dependiente. Yo le dije que yo _____ 24.

pero él me dijo que _____ 25. _____ 26. porque en ese momento todos los dependientes

estaban ocupados. Yo le _____ 27. por su ayuda y pagué la cuenta en la caja. A mi hermano le compré

un videojuego. Dejaré que lo pruebe en mi nueva computadora. Eso es un buen regalo, ¿verdad?

EXERCISE M. You are trying to encourage a Spanish-speaking friend to go with you to a special exhibit at the museum that has just opened. Write an e-mail invitation in Spanish. You may wish to include the following:

- when the tickets to the exhibit are for

- what weather is predicted for that day

- the artist whose work is being exhibited

- when you saw a previous exhibit by this artist

- how famous he has become since then

- the importance of paying attention to the guide

- what you can do after the exhibit

- some words of encouragement

CHAPTER

20

Negation

◆ 1 ◆ NEGATIVES

a. *No* is the most common negative. It always precedes the conjugated verb.

Ella **no** mira la televisión.   *She doesn't watch television.*

¿**No** leíste esta novela?   *Didn't you read this novel?*

b. Other negatives are:

nada	*nothing, (not) anything*	**nunca**	*never, (not) ever*
nadie	*no one, nobody, (not) anyone*	**jamás**	*never, not … ever, ever*
ni . . . ni	*neither . . . nor; not . . . either . . . or . . .*	**tampoco**	*neither, not either*
ninguno, –a	*no, none, (not) any*		

c. In Spanish, double negatives are acceptable and occur frequently. If one of the negatives is *no*, it precedes the verb. If *no* is omitted, the other negative must precede the verb.

No oigo **nada.**   } *I don't hear anything.*
Nada oigo.

Ella **no** canta **nunca.**   } *She never sings.*
Ella **nunca** canta.

d. *Nadie* can be used as the subject or the object of the verb. When *nadie* is the object of the verb, it is preceded by the preposition *a.*

Nadie habla.   } *No one speaks.*
No habla **nadie.**

BUT

No llamo a **nadie.**   *I don't call anyone (anybody).*

A **nadie** llamo.   *I call no one (nobody).*

e. *Ninguno* drops the final *-o* and takes a written accent mark over the *u* if it comes immediately before a masculine singular noun. If a preposition comes between *ninguno* and the noun, the full form is used.

Ningún equipo ganó.   *No team won.*

Ninguno de los equipos ganó.   *None of the teams won.*

Ninguna persona es perfecta.   *No person is perfect.*

f. *Jamás* in an affirmative question means *ever.*

¿Has estado **jamás** en El Paso?   *Have you ever been in El Paso?*

g. Negatives are used after such expressions as *más que* (more than), *mejor que* (better than), *peor que* (worse than), and *sin* (without), to express an affirmative idea.

más que nunca   *more than ever*   **sin decir nada**   *without saying anything*

mejor que nadie   *better than anyone*

EXERCISE A.   You and a friend just returned from an unsuccessful shopping trip and your mother wants to know about it. Answer her questions.

EXAMPLE: ¿Compraste el regalo para tu hermano?   **No, no compré** el regalo para mi hermano.

1. ¿Encontraste los guantes negros?   _____

2. ¿Buscaste el suéter para tu abuela?   _____

3. ¿Llevaste el cinturón para devolverlo?   _____

4. ¿Había muchas personas en las tiendas?   _____

5. ¿Compraste videojuegos?   _____

6. ¿Comieron Uds. en el centro?   _____

7. ¿Gastaste mucho dinero?   _____

EXERCISE B.   You are not in the best mood and your sister persists in asking you questions. Answer her questions.

EXAMPLE: ¿Qué tienes?   **No** tengo **nada.**

1. ¿Qué dejaste en el carro?   _____

2. ¿Qué perdiste en la calle?   _____

3. ¿Qué comieron tú y Alfonso?   _____

4. ¿Qué buscas ahora?   _____

5. ¿Qué sacaste de mi cuarto?   _____

EXERCISE C.   Jack is telling his brother the things he and his friends have never done. Tell what he says.

EXAMPLE: volar en avión (*Jamie*)   **Jamie nunca (jamás) ha volado** en avión.

1. montar a caballo (*Susana y Valerie*)   _____

2. ir a un partido de fútbol (Gregory)   _____

3. conducir un carro (yo)   _____

4. esquiar en las montañas (Harry y yo)   _____

5. remar en un lago (David y Larry)   _____

6. correr en un maratón (tú)   _____

EXERCISE D. The substitute teacher is describing what happened in one of her classes today. Tell what she says.

EXAMPLE: tener el libro   **Nadie** tuvo el libro.

1. hacer la tarea _____

2. contestar las preguntas _____

3. estar listo para el examen _____

4. saber la materia _____

5. compartir las respuestas correctas _____

6. querer trabajar _____

EXERCISE E. Mariluz is not paying attention in class. Give her responses to the teacher's questions.

EXAMPLE: ¿A quién le hablas?   **No** le hablo a **nadie**.

1. ¿A quién ayudas? _____

2. ¿A quién saludas? _____

3. ¿A quién le silbas? _____

4. ¿A quién le contestas? _____

5. ¿A quién miras? _____

6. ¿A quién le cuchicheas? _____

EXERCISE F. It's the beginning of the school year and your mother wants to know what school supplies you have. Answer her questions.

EXAMPLE: ¿Qué útiles tienes?   **No** tengo **ningunos** útiles.

1. bolígrafo _____

2. regla _____

3. compás _____

4. cuadernos _____

5. marcadores _____

6. calculadora _____

7. carpetas _____

EXERCISE G. Gigi is telling her mother what her friends do not do.

EXAMPLE: pasar la aspiradora / lavar los platos / Celia
Celia **no pasa** la aspiradora **ni lava** los platos.

1. sacar al perro / dar de comer al perro / Carmen

   _____

2. hacer la cama / arreglar su cuarto / Felipe y Rogelio

   _____

3. preparar la comida / ir de compras / Kim

   _____

4. secar los platos / planchar la ropa / Miriam y Victoria

   _____

5. poner la mesa / quitar la mesa / Eugenia

   _____

EXERCISE H. Sheila is telling Marcos the things she doesn't do or doesn't like to do. Marcos doesn't do these things either. Express what Marcos responds.

EXAMPLE: SHEILA: Yo no sé conducir un carro.
          MARCOS: Yo **no** sé conducir tampoco.

1. SHEILA: Yo no monto a caballo.

   MARCOS: _____

2. SHEILA: No me gusta visitar los museos.

   MARCOS: _____

3. SHEILA: Nunca veo las películas de ciencia-ficción.

   MARCOS: _____

4. SHEILA: Yo no juego a muchos deportes.

   MARCOS: _____

5. SHEILA: No me gustan las fiestas formales.

   MARCOS: _____

EXERCISE I. Janice describes what happened when she accompanied her father downtown. Complete her description with the appropriate negative expressions.

Hoy _____ pude hacer lo que quería porque tuve que acompañar a mi papá a su oficina. La oficina
               1.

_____ está lejos de la casa, está en el centro. _____ había ido al centro porque era
         2.   3.

domingo. _____ vimos _____ en el centro: _____ tienda estaba
                  4.   5.   6.

abierta, no había _____ trabajadores en el edificio, _____ se paseaba en las calles
                         7.   8.

del centro. Mi papá _____ tenía la llave del edificio y tocó a la puerta. _____

9.
10.

contestó. _____ el guardia del edificio apareció. Nosotros _____ pasamos

11.
12.

mucho tiempo allí. Mi papá buscó un teléfono pero _____ teléfono de la calle funcionó.

13.

Yo tenía mucha sed pero _____ pudimos comprar _____ refresco.

14.
15.

_____ los cafés _____ los restaurantes estaban abiertos. Decidimos volver a

16.
17.

casa. _____ tardamos en llegar porque _____ había _____

18.
19.
20.

tráfico en la carretera. Cuando llegamos a casa, mi papá recibió un recado de un compañero de trabajo. Él había

ido a la oficina pero _____ pudo entrar _____ .

21.
22.

◆ 2 ◆ NEGATIVE EXPRESSIONS

Some useful negative expressions are:

Ni yo tampoco. *Me neither.*

Ya no vive aquí. *He / She / You (sing. formal) no longer lives here.*

No me cobró más que un dólar. *He / She / You charged me only a dollar.*

de ninguna manera } *by no means*		**ni siquiera**	*not even*
de ningún modo		**Creo que no.**	*I don't think so.*
No lo creo.	*I don't believe it.*	**¡No me digas!**	*Don't tell me! (You don't say!)*
De nada.	*You're welcome.*	**No me gusta nada.**	*I don't like it at all.*
No es así.	*It is not so.*	**No puede ser.**	*It can't be.*
No es para tanto.	*It's not such a big deal.*	**No puedo más.**	*I can't take it anymore.*
No hay más remedio.	*It can't be helped.*	**¿No te parece?**	*Don't you think so?*
		¿Por qué no?	*Why not?*
No importa.	*It doesn't matter.*		

EXERCISE J.   **Use the following expressions to tell how you would respond to the various statements.**

No puede ser.	No hay más remedio.	De ningún modo.
De nada.	Ni yo tampoco.	No puedo más.
No me importa.	No me cobró más que	¡No me digas!
No me gusta nada.	un dólar.	ya no

EXAMPLE: ¿Vive la familia Leal en esta casa?
La familia Leal **ya no** vive aquí.

1. Muchas gracias por el regalo.

_____

2. Ya llevamos tres horas estudiando para el examen.

_____

3. Mañana es el partido y el pronóstico dice lluvia.

4. ¿Qué te parece mi corbata nueva?

_____

5. Tú vas a acompañarme al centro, ¿verdad?

_____

6. ¿Sabías que el hermano de Javier salió con Mirta?

_____

7. Yo no quiero ir al concierto el sábado.

_____

8. Pagué seis dólares por la pelota.

_____

9. Estoy sentado en tu asiento.

_____

10. ¡Mira el reloj! ¡Ya son las siete!

_____

(**EXERCISE K.**)   **Alison left the following message on her friend's answering machine. Complete it using the expressions provided below.**

por qué no	ni siquiera	no lo creo
no es para tanto	ni tú tampoco	no te parece
de ninguna manera	no importa	

_____ pero anoche me llamó Luis por teléfono. _____ nos habíamos saludado
 1.   2.

cuando me invitó a salir con él. _____ pero siempre he dicho que _____ saldría
                                   3.   4.

con él. Tú siempre has dicho que _____ saldrías con él. _____ pero le dije que sí
                                   5.   6.

iría al baile con él. ¿ _____ ? Hice bien. ¿ _____ ? ¡Llámame!
                        7.   8.

⟨ MASTERY EXERCISES ⟩

(**EXERCISE L.**)   **Answer the questions an exchange student asks you. Respond negatively to each question, using an appropriate negative expression.**

1. ¿Cuándo estuviste en España?   _____

2. ¿Aprendes el latín o el francés?   _____

3. ¿Qué hacen tú y tus amigos hoy?   _____

4. ¿Has viajado jamás a Costa Rica?   _____

5. ¿Vas al museo o a la biblioteca? _____

6. ¿Tiene tu amigo algunos libros
interesantes? _____

7. ¿Qué tienes en la mano? _____

8. ¿Cuándo van tus amigos a Sudamérica?
¿Vas tú también? _____

9. ¿Tienes algún problema? _____

10. ¿A quién visitaste ayer? _____

EXERCISE M. **You are talking to a friend on the telephone. Your younger brother comments on everything you say making it negative. Tell what he says.**

EXAMPLE: Yo tengo muchos amigos   Él **no** tiene **ningunos** amigos.

1. Mis amigos vienen a mi casa o yo
voy a su casa. _____

2. Alguien me invitó a una fiesta. _____

3. Yo siempre trabajo. _____

4. Yo me atrevo a hacer todo. _____

5. Yo tengo un monopatín nuevo. _____

6. Yo veo a mis amigos todos los días. _____

7. Juana y su prima lo saben. _____

8. Yo le expliqué todo. _____

9. Yo voy al concierto también. _____

10. Sí, todos han vuelto. _____

EXERCISE N. **Hector is writing a blog post in Spanish about a concert he attended last night. Express in Spanish what he says. Be sure to use as many negative words and expressions as you can. You may wish to include the following:**

• a statement about poor attendance at the concert

• reasons for the low attendance (for example, the lack of advertising and promotion of the concert)

• some people's positive reaction to the groups' performance

• the applause, or lack thereof

• something about the group's popularity

• Hector's reaction to this concert

• his friends reaction to this concert

⬥ A C T I V I D A D E S ⬥

1. You are helping the team coach prepare the players for a special game. Make a list of 10 activities the players should not do before the game. Use as many of the negative words and expressions you have learned as you can.

2. Imagine that you just returned from a weekend camp reunion and that you did not enjoy it at all. Write an entry in your journal in which you describe the disappointing time you had. Use as many of the negative words and expressions you have learned as you can.

Nouns, Pronouns, and Prepositions

CHAPTER

Nouns and Articles

◆ 1 ◆ NOUNS

a. Gender of Nouns

1. Most nouns in Spanish are either masculine or feminine. Nouns ending in *-o* and nouns referring to male beings are generally masculine. Nouns ending in *-a, -d, -ión* or *-z* and nouns referring to female beings are generally feminine.

MASCULINE		FEMININE			
libro	*book*	pluma	*pen*	verdad	*truth*
muchacho	*boy*	muchacha	*girl*	nación	*nation*
padre	*father*	madre	*mother*	voz	*voice*

2. Some nouns are either masculine or feminine.

estudiante	*student*
adolescente	*adolescent*

3. Some nouns are gender ambiguous.

mar	*sea*	dote	*dowry, natural gift, talent*
azúcar	*sugar*		

NOTE: Notice the following exceptions.

Feminine nouns ending in *-o*		Masculine nouns ending in *-a*			
mano	*hand*	tranvía	*streetcar*	problema	*problem*
radio	*radio*	clima	*climate*	programa	*programa*
		drama	*drama*	mapa	*map*
		idioma	*language*	poeta	*poet*

4. The gender of nouns ending in a consonant must be learned individually.

MASCULINE		FEMININE	
lápiz	*pencil*	flor	*flower*
papel	*paper*	sal	*salt*

NOTES:

1. The articles used before masculine singular nouns are *el* (the) and *un* (a, an).
   The articles used before feminine singular nouns are *la* (the) and *una* (a, an).

MASCULINE		FEMININE	
el hombre	*the man*	*la* mujer	*the woman*
un cuaderno	*a notebook*	*una* mesa	*a table*

2. The article is generally repeated before each noun in a series.

Necesito *un* lápiz y *una* pluma.	*I need a pencil and a pen.*
Compro *el* suéter y *la* camisa.	*I buy the sweater and the shirt.*

191

EXERCISE A. You are visiting a toy store with a young child. Tell the things that you see there.

EXAMPLE: la lancha

1. _____

5. _____

2. _____

6. _____

3. _____

7. _____

4. _____

8. _____

9. _____

10. _____

EXERCISE B.   **Tell what each person saw when they first entered a hotel lobby.**

EXAMPLE: Gloria / sofá elegante   Gloria **vio un** sofá elegante.

1. Arturo / restaurante francés   _____

2. Esteban y Miriam / lámpara grande   _____

3. yo / ascensor abierto   _____

4. Lola / espejo antiguo   _____

5. Víctor / pintura moderna   _____

6. Sofía y Linda / alfombra persa   _____

7. Greg / escultura modernista   _____

8. Nadia / retrato del dueño   _____

EXERCISE C.   **You are preparing for a vocabulary quiz. Read the definitions and give the appropriate word, and article.**

EXAMPLES: sesenta minutos   **una hora**
                    el hombre que repara zapatos   **el zapatero**

1. doce meses   _____

2. un lugar como Cleveland o Dallas   _____

3. el hombre que escribe novelas   _____

4. la parte temprana del día   _____

5. el español, el árabe o el japonés   _____

6. España, Colombia o los Estados Unidos   _____

7. un instrumento que da la hora   _____

8. el lugar donde curan a los enfermos   _____

9. la persona que da clases   _____

10. la persona que toma clases _____

11. lo que se usa para escribir y no se borra _____

12. el instrumento para medir _____

13. el libro que explica las palabras _____

14. la máquina que resuelve problemas
complicados _____

15. la lista de las clases de una persona _____

16. el vehículo que se usa para viajar
rápidamente _____

17. el lugar donde llegan los trenes _____

18. lo que se necesita para ver bien de noche _____

19. lo que las personas usan para ver mejor _____

20. la parte del cuerpo que usamos para escribir _____

b. Plural of Nouns

1. Nouns ending in a vowel form the plural by adding *-s*.

libro	libro*s*	hombre	hombre*s*
tarjeta	tarjeta*s*	clase	clase*s*

2. Nouns ending in a consonant form the plural by adding *-es*.

profesor	profesor*es*
flor	flor*es*

3. Nouns ending in *-z* change *z* to *c* before adding *-es*.

lápiz	lápi*ces*
vez	ve*ces*

4. Nouns ending in *-n* or *-s* add *-es* and an accent mark is added or dropped to keep the
original stress.

joven	jóven*es*	francés	france*ses*
examen	exámen*es*	nación	nacion*es*

NOTES:

1. *Países* requires the accent mark to preserve the original stress of *país*.
2. The plural of *plan, planes*, requires no accent mark.

5. Nouns ending in *-s* where the final syllable is unstressed remain the same in the plural.

paragua*s*	*umbrella*	paragua*s*	*umbrellas*

BUT

mes	*month*	meses	*months*

6. The masculine plural form of these nouns may refer to both the male and female members of a group.

los padres	*the fathers, the father and mother, the parents*
los hijos	*the sons, the son and daughter, the children*
los niños	*the little boys, the little boy and girl, the children*
los reyes	*the kings, the king and queen, the rulers*
los señores Luna	*the Luna brothers (for example), Mr. and Mrs. Luna*

EXERCISE D. **Kristy is telling her friends at school about what happened to her during the weekend. Complete what she says with the plural form of the nouns indicated.**

El viernes por la noche unos _____ y yo fuimos a cenar a un restaurante de _____.
　　　　　　　　　　　　　　　　1. (amigo)　　　　　　　　　　　　　　　　　　　　　　　　　*2.* (marisco)

Aunque es un restaurante muy grande y hay dos _____ amplios, había muchas
　　　　　　　　　　　　　　　　　　　　　　　　　　　　3. (comedor)

_____ allí y tuvimos que esperar más de cuarenta _____ para sentarnos a la
　4. (persona)　　　　　　　　　　　　　　　　　　　　　　　　　*5.* (minuto)

mesa. Los _____ estaban muy ocupados y por fin nos dieron un menú. Tuvimos que pedir tres
　　　　6. (mesero)

_____ más. Preparan unos _____ deliciosos con muchas _____ de
　7. (menú)　　　　　　　　　　　*8.* (plato)　　　　　　　　　　　　　　　*9.* (variedad)

pescado. Yo pedí un coctel de _____ para comenzar. Pedimos dos _____, que
　　　　　　　　　　　　　10. (camarón)　　　　　　　　　　　　　*11.* (ensalada)

compartimos entre los cuatro. Como plato principal yo pedí _____ en salsa picante. Pedimos
　　　　　　　　　　　　　　　　　　　　　　　　　　12. (mejillón)

tres _____ y los compartimos también. Tuvimos que pedir la cuenta dos _____
　　13. (postre)　　　　　　　　　　　　　　　　　　　　　　　　　　　　　　　　　*14.* (vez)

porque el mesero estaba muy ocupado.

　　El resto de la noche no me sentí bien. Me desperté a eso de las tres, sudando y con mucho dolor de

estómago. Me temblaban las _____ y tenía _____ en todo el cuerpo. Desperté
　　　　　　　　　　　　15. (mano)　　　　　　*16.* (mancha)

a mis _____ y ellos decidieron llevarme a la sala de _____ del hospital.
　　17. (padre)　　　　　　　　　　　　　　　　　　　　　　　*18.* (emergencia)

Allí dos _____ me atendieron. Ellos me hicieron muchas _____ sobre mis
　　　19. (doctor)　　　　　　　　　　　　　　　　　　　　　　　*20.* (pregunta)

_____ recientes. Querían saber qué _____ había comido y bebido, si tomo
　21. (actividad)　　　　　　　　　　　　　*22.* (cosa)

_____ y si tengo _____. Después de los _____ médicos,
　23. (medicamento)　　　　　　*24.* (alergia)　　　　　　　　　　　*25.* (examen)

me dieron dos _____ y me recetaron unas _____ Volvimos a casa y me acosté
　　　　　　26. (inyección)　　　　　　　　　　　　*27.* (píldora)

otra vez. Dormí profundamente por ocho _____ y me desperté perfectamente y con muchas
　　　　　　　　　　　　　　　　　　　28. (hora)

_____ de comer.
　29. (gana)

c. Nouns Describing Materials or Contents

Nouns describing the materials or ingredients of which something is made are preceded by *de.*

un anillo de oro	*a gold ring (a ring of gold)*
una corbata de seda	*a silk tie (a tie of silk)*
un pastel de manzana	*an apple pie (a pie of apple)*
un sándwich de pollo	*a chicken sandwich (a sandwich of chicken)*

EXERCISE E. Janice and Ralph are going to a formal party. Describe what each wears using the suggestions provided.

SUGGESTIONS:
un vestido de seda
un traje de lana
una camisa de algodón
un saco de terciopelo
un cinturón de piel

zapatos de piel
una corbata de seda
un reloj de oro
un anillo de plata

1. Janice lleva _____

_____.

2. Ralph lleva _____

_____.

EXERCISE F. You are planning a dinner party and find the following ingredients in the refrigerator. Plan the menu using these ingredients.

cebollas	pepinos	manzanas
tomates	papas	camarones
carne de res	naranjas	aguacate
lechuga		

UN COCTEL_____

UNA SOPA _____

UN GUISADO_____

UNA ENSALADA_____

UN PASTEL_____

◆ 2 ◆ ARTICLES

a. Definite Articles

There are four definite articles in Spanish that correspond to English *the*.

	SINGULAR	PLURAL
MASCULINE	**el**	**los**
FEMININE	**la**	**las**

Articles agree in number and gender with the nouns they modify.

MASCULINE		FEMININE	
el muchacho	*the boy*	**la** muchacha	*the girl*
los muchachos	*the boys*	**las** muchachas	*the girls*
un muchacho	*a boy*	**una** muchacha	*a girl*
unos muchachos	*some boys*	**unas** muchachas	*some girls*

NOTES:

1. **Feminine nouns that begin with the stressed sound of *a* (or *ha*) take the articles *el* and *un* in the singular. In the plural, the articles are *las* and *unas*.**

   el agua *the water*   **las** aguas *the waters*

   un agua *one water*   **unas** aguas *some waters*

   el ala *the wing*   **las** alas *the wings*

   un ala *a wing*   **unas** alas *some wings*

   el hacha *the ax*   **las** hachas *the axes*

   un hacha *one ax*   **unas** hachas *some axes*

   BUT

   la amistad *friendship* } (Initial *a* is not stressed.)
   la alumna *the (female) student*

2. **The masculine article *el* contracts with the prepositions *de* and *a*, as follows:**

   a + el = al
   de + el = del

   Va **al** cine.   *He goes to the movies.*
   Habla **del** niño.   *He speaks of the child.*

   BUT

   Va a **la** playa.   *He goes to the beach.*
   Habla **de los** niños.   *He speaks of the children.*

3. **The neuter article *lo*, used with adjectives, does not vary in form.**

   lo bueno y **lo** malo   *the good and the bad (that which is good and that which is bad)*

b. Indefinite Articles

There are four indefinite articles in Spanish that correspond to English *a (an), some, several,* and *a few.*

	SINGULAR	PLURAL
MASCULINE	**un**	**unos**
FEMININE	**una**	**unas**

un primo	*a cousin*	**unos** primos	*some cousins*
una camisa	*a shirt*	**unas** camisas	*a few shirts*

EXERCISE G. As you accompany a Spanish-speaking student around your school, he identifies what he sees. Express what he says.

EXAMPLE: gimnasio: **un** gimnasio

1. aula de clase _____

2. laboratorios _____

3. auditorio _____

4. carteles _____

5. biblioteca _____

6. cafetería _____

7. salones de arte _____

8. oficinas _____

9. computadoras _____

10. ascensor _____

EXERCISE H. Felipe decided to empty his bookbag. Tell what he took out of it and left on the table.

1. _____

2. _____

3. _____

4. _____

5. _____

6. _____

7. _____

8. _____

9. _____

10. _____

c. Uses of the Articles

The definite article is used:

1. before the names of languages and other subjects of study, unless the subjects of study follow *hablar, en,* or *de.*

El japonés es una lengua.	*Japanese is a language.*
Estudio *el* español.	*I study Spanish.*
La fisica es dificil.	*Physics is difficult.*

   BUT

Él habla español.	*He speaks Spanish.*
Escriben en francés.	*They write in French.*
Mi libro de historia está en casa.	*My history book is at home.*

2. before titles (except when speaking directly to a person).

El señor Pardo es alto.	*Mr. Pardo is tall.*
La doctora Pérez está aquí.	*Dr. Pérez is here.*

   BUT

Buenas tardes, señor Pardo.	*Good afternoon, Mr. Pardo.*

3. before the following geographic names.

la América Central *Central America*	el Canadá *Canada*
la América del Norte *North America*	los Estados Unidos *the United States*
la América del Sur *South America*	el Perú *Peru*
la Argentina *Argentina*	el Japón *Japan*
la Florida *Florida*	la China *China*

   BUT

Alemania *Germany*	Inglaterra *England*
España *Spain*	Italia *Italy*
Europa *Europe*	México *Mexico*
Francia *France*	Rusia *Russia*

   NOTE: Current usage tends to omit the definite article before the names of countries.

   Vivo en Estados Unidos.   *I live in the United States.*

4. before the days of the week, to express the English word *on*.

No voy a *la* escuela los domingos.   *I don't go to school on Sundays.*

5. before the words *escuela, clase,* and *iglesia* when they follow a preposition.

Voy a *la* escuela.   *I'm going to school.*

Están en *la* iglesia.   *They are in church.*

6. before parts of the body and articles of clothing.

Ella se lava *las* manos.   *She washes her hands.*

Ella se pone *la* blusa.   *She puts on her blouse.*

7. before the names of seasons.

Hace calor en *el* verano.   *It's hot in summer.*

8. before nouns in a general or abstract sense.

Los libros son útiles.   *Books are useful.*

La altura me espanta.   *Height frightens me.*

9. before nouns of weight or measure.

Cuesta diez centavos *la* libra.   *It costs ten cents a pound.*

10. before certain time expressions and when expressing the time of day.

el mes próximo *next month*

la semana pasada *last week*

Es *la* una.   *It's one o'clock.*

Te llamaré a *las* cinco y media   *I'll call you at five thirty.*

11. The indefinite article is used to express the English word *a (an)*.

Tengo *un* hermano.   *I have a brother.*

12. The indefinite article is omitted before a noun expressing nationality, profession, or occupation when it follows the verb *ser.*

Tomás es alemán.   *Tomás is German.*

Ese hombre es panadero.   *That man is a baker.*

Ella va a ser médico.   *She's going to be a doctor.*

BUT

If the noun is modified, the indefinite article is used.

Deseo ser *un* ingeniero bueno.   *I want to be a good engineer.*

EXERCISE I.   **Explain each of the following.**

EXAMPLE: chino / lengua   El chino **es una** lengua.

1. flan / postre   _____

2. leche / bebida   _____

3. química / ciencia   _____

4. Florida / estado   _____

5. América del Sur / continente   _____

6. Canadá / nación _____

7. primavera / estación _____

8. melocotón / fruta _____

9. miércoles / día _____

10. consomé / sopa _____

11. maíz / legumbre _____

12. voleibol / deporte _____

EXERCISE J. **Jane is studying new vocabulary words. Express the Spanish word for the following items.**

EXAMPLE: Es un carro.

1. _____

3. _____

2. _____

4. _____

5. _____

8. _____

6. _____

9. _____

7. _____

10. _____

EXERCISE K.   Answer the questions a friend asks.

1. ¿Cuándo celebras tu cumpleaños?   _____

2. ¿Qué estación prefieres?   _____

3. ¿Qué deporte te gusta más?   _____

4. ¿Qué lengua hablan tú y tu familia
   en casa?   _____

5. ¿Cuál es tu clase más difícil?   _____

6. ¿Quién enseña esa clase?   _____

7. ¿Qué haces los sábados por la tarde?   _____

8. ¿Qué hora es?   _____

9. ¿Qué hace tu padre?   _____

10. ¿Qué países de América del Sur
    piensas visitar?   _____

d. Omission of the Articles

1. **The definite article is omitted:**

   a. before a noun in apposition.

   Lima, capital del Perú, es
   una ciudad interesante.   *Lima, the capital of Peru, is an interesting city.*

   b. with names of rulers.

   Carlos Quinto fue un rey español.   *Charles the Fifth was a Spanish king.*

2. **The indefinite article is omitted:**

   a. before an unmodified noun expressing nationality, religion, rank, or occupation following the verb *ser.*

Soy norteamericano.	*I am an American.*
¿Es Ud. protestante?	*Are you a Protestant?*
Carolina es princesa.	*Carolina is a princess.*
Reymundo es dentista.	*Reymundo is a dentist.*

   BUT

   Es un abogado famoso.   *He is a famous lawyer.*

   b. with the following words:

cien:	cien dólares *a hundred dollars*
cierto/a:	cierta persona *a certain person*
mil:	mil habitantes *a thousand inhabitants*
otro/a:	otro alumno *another student*
qué:	¡Qué lástima! *What a pity!*
tal:	tal hijo *such a son*

EXERCISE L.   **Tell how each of these people earns a living.**

EXAMPLE: Victoria Alba es **actriz.**

1. Luis Posada es _____

_____ .

2. La señora Chávez es _____

_____ .

3. El señor Laredo es _____
_____ .

5. El señor Ferrer es _____
_____ .

4. Virginia Ramos es _____
_____ .

6. Gloria Goya es _____
_____ .

EXERCISE M. Selma visited her father's office and took several messages while she waited for him. Complete the messages she took.

EXAMPLE: Miriam / secretaria / Sra. Vela / llamó
Miriam, secretaria **de la** Sra. Vela, llamó.

1. Vicente Gala / hijo / Sr. Arturo Gala / cambió su cita

_____

2. Sr. Pidal / representante / compañía de telecomunicaciones / llamará más tarde.

_____

3. Sra. Solana / directora / agencia federal / llamó dos veces

_____

4. Ángel López / dueño / periódico «La palabra» / llegará a las cuatro

_____

5. Laura Sotomayor / ayudante / Alicia Báez / dejó otro número de teléfono

_____

EXERCISE N. Using the cues provided, answer the questions the registrar asks you as you register for a summer program in Salamanca, Spain.

1. ¿Cuál es su nacionalidad? *(norteamericano)*

_____

2. ¿Cuál es su profesión? *(estudiante)*

_____

3. ¿Qué clase de estudiante es Ud.? *(diligente)*

_____

4. ¿Qué piensa ser Ud.? *(programador de computadoras)*

_____

5. ¿En qué hotel se queda Ud.? *(Carlos I)*

_____

6. ¿Por qué escogió Ud. ese hotel? *(limpio y céntrico)*

_____

7. ¿Cuánto pagó Ud. por el programa de estudios? *($1.000)*

_____

MASTERY EXERCISES

EXERCISE O. **Your Spanish teacher has asked the students to complete the biographical statement he wants to use with his classes next year. Complete his statement with the appropriate articles, if needed.**

Yo soy _____ señor Valencia. Mi padre es de _____ Puerto Rico y mi
              1.   2.

madre es de _____ Canadá, pero yo nací en _____ Estados Unidos. Asistí a
                    3.   4.

_____ Universidad de Maryland, donde estudié _____ lenguas extranjeras:
        5.   6.

_____ español y _____ portugués. Soy bilingüe porque desde chico hablo
        7.   8.

_____ inglés y _____ español. Mis intereses principales son _____
        9.   10.   11.

deportes y _____ viajes. Soy _____ buen jugador de _____
                  12.   13.   14.

tenis y me gusta _____ fútbol también. He visitado muchos países extranjeros. De chico
                          15.

pasaba las vacaciones de _____ invierno en _____ Puerto Rico y _____
                                  16.   17.   18.

veranos en _____ Canadá. También he viajado a _____ España y a _____
                  19.   20.   21.

América del Sur. Visité _____ Colombia, _____ Venezuela, _____
                                22.   23.   24.

Argentina, _____ Perú y _____ Ecuador. Soy _____ profesor de
                  25.   26.   27.

idiomas extranjeros y creo ser _____ profesor interesante y divertido. Yo comencé mi carrera
                                      28.

de _____ profesor en _____ colegio privado, _____ Colegio Felipe
          29.   30.   31.

_____ Segundo. Tengo _____ sola meta para mis alumnos: poder comunicarse en
        32.   33.

_____ otra lengua. Si trabajamos juntos, Uds. podrán lograrla.
        34.

EXERCISE P.   You are writing to a new Spanish-speaking email buddy, in which you introduce yourself and tell about yourself in Spanish. You may wish to express the following:

- your place of birth and your nationality

- where your siblings were born

- the school you attend

- your favorite subjects

- whether you are a good student or not

- what you want to be

- the area I which you may wish to specialize

- a competition in which you excelled

- the name of the activity advisor and his/her reaction to your participation in the competition

- the result of the competition

ACTIVIDADES

1. Make a list of the school supplies you will need for the new school year. Explain why you will need each item.

2. You are going off to college and are planning what you need for your room in the dormitory. Make a list of the items you will need to furnish your dorm room and explain why each item is necessary.

3. A friend is planning to visit you soon. Write your friend a letter in which you describe the places you can visit together and give a reason for each one.

22

Pronouns

◆ 1 ◆ SUBJECT PRONOUNS

SINGULAR	PLURAL
yo *I*	nosotros, -as *we*
tú *you* (familiar)	vosotros, -as *you* (familiar)
usted (Ud.) *you*	ustedes (Uds.) *you*
él *he*	ellos *they* (masculine)
ella *she*	ellas *they* (feminine)

In Spanish subject pronouns are not used as often as in English. Since the verb ending indicates the subject, subject pronouns are used in Spanish for clarity, emphasis, and politeness.

Ella canta mientras **él** toca el piano.	*She sings while he plays the piano.*
Juan, **yo** debo tomar la decisión.	*Juan, I should make the decision.*
Pase y tome asiento, por favor.	*Please come in and have a seat.*

NOTES:

1. Even though subject pronouns are usually omitted, *usted* (*Ud.*), and *ustedes* (*Uds.*) are often used for politeness.

2. The *vosotros* (familiar plural) form is used in Spain but rarely in Spanish America, where the *ustedes* form is preferred.

3. The English pronoun *it* is not expressed as a subject in Spanish.

¿Dónde está? Está allí.	*Where is it? It's over there.*
¿Qué es? Es un disco.	*What is it? It's a record.*

EXERCISE A. Sarita wants to know the sports and games your friends practice. Use the correct subject pronouns in your responses.

EXAMPLE: Lucinda / baloncesto   **Ella** practica el baloncesto.

1. Alicia y tú / boliche _____

2. Enrique / béisbol _____

3. Mirella / tenis _____

4. Alberto y Rafael / fútbol americano _____

5. tú / ajedrez _____

6. Estela y Alba / natación _____

7. Gianni / fútbol _____

8. Verónica / juego de damas _____

25

(**EXERCISE B.**)   **A friend at school is asking you about the weekend. Answer his questions using the correct subject pronoun and the cues provided.**

1. ¿Fuiste al cine este fin de semana? (*sí*)

_____

2. ¿Fueron Carlos y Eddy también? (*sí*))

_____

3. ¿Vieron Uds. una película romántica? (*sí*)

_____

4. ¿Prepararon tú y Jaime el proyecto para la clase de historia? (*sí*)

_____

5. ¿Saliste tú con tu familia el domingo por la tarde? (*sí*)

_____

6. ¿A qué hora regresaron Uds. a casa? (*8:00*)

_____

7. ¿Qué vas a hacer el fin de semana que viene? (*trabajar*)

_____

8. ¿Cómo son tus compañeros de trabajo? (*simpáticos*)

_____

9. ¿Podemos tú y yo salir después del trabajo el sábado? (*sí*)

_____

10. ¿Puede ir Silvia también? (*sí*)

_____

◆ 2 ◆ PREPOSITIONAL PRONOUNS

a. Prepositions are words that define a relationship to a person, place, or thing.

Frequently Used Prepositions

a	*to, at*	**entre**	*between, among*
cerca de	*near*	**hacia**	*toward*
con	*with*	**para**	*for*
contra	*against*	**por**	*for*
de	*of, from*	**sin**	*without*
en	*in, on*	**sobre**	*on top of, over*

b. Prepositional pronouns are used as the objects of a preposition, and always follow the preposition.

No es para Uds.; es para nosotros.   *It's not for you; it's for us.*

When a personal pronoun follows a preposition, it takes the following forms:

SINGULAR		PLURAL	
mí	*me*	**nosotros, -as**	*us*
ti	*you* (familiar)	**vosotros, -as**	*you* (familiar)
usted (Ud.)	*you*	**ustedes (Uds.)**	*you*
él	*him, it*	**ellos**	*them* (masculine)
ella	*her, it*	**ellas**	*them* (feminine)

c. The pronouns *mí* and *ti* combine with the preposition *con* as follows:

conmigo *with me*   **contigo** *with you*

NOTES:

1. The forms of the prepositional pronouns are the same as those of the subject pronouns, except for *mí* and *ti*.

2. The pronouns *mí* and *ti* combine with the preposition *con* as follows:
   conmigo *with me*   contigo *with you*

3. The forms *conmigo* and *contigo* do not change in gender and number.

4. The familiar plural form *vosotros, -as* is used in Spain but rarely in Spanish America, where the form *ustedes* (*Uds.*) is preferred.

EXERCISE C. Everyone forgets things sometimes. Tell what these people forgot, using the correct prepositional pronoun.

EXAMPLE: Mi papá puso las llaves en la mesa del comedor y luego salió de la casa sin **ellas**.

1. Mi mamá me dio dinero para las compras pero yo salí de la casa sin _____ .

2. El niño no pudo encontrar su osito de peluche pero se durmió sin _____ .

3. Mirta dejó la raqueta de tenis en el carro y fue a la cancha de tenis sin _____ .

4. El profesor no metió los exámenes en su mochila y llegó a la clase sin _____ .

5. Yo dejé los anteojos en casa y tuve que ver la película sin _____ .

6. Ayer por la mañana yo perdí el autobús escolar y el autobús escolar salió sin. _____ .

7. Claudio no esperó a sus amigos en el estadio y entró en _____ sin _____ .

8. Bob y yo siempre llegamos tarde. Por eso Ken entró en el restaurante sin _____ .

EXERCISE D.   Answer the questions a friend asks you. Use a prepositional pronoun in your responses.

EXAMPLE: ¿Saliste con Mirta? (*sí*)   Sí, yo salí con **ella.**

1. ¿Vas a la fiesta en casa de Lisa y Mirta? (*sí*) _____

2. ¿Va Gladys con Frank? (*sí*) _____

3. ¿Viven Lisa y Mirta cerca de tu abuela? (*no*) _____

4. ¿Puedes ir a la fiesta sin tu hermano? (*no*) _____

5. ¿Compraste un regalo para Mirta? (*sí*) _____

6. ¿Tomas un taxi conmigo? (*sí*) _____

7. ¿Dividimos la cuota entre tú y yo? (*sí*) _____

8. ¿Va tu papá por ti por la noche? (*sí*) _____

9. ¿Puedo regresar con Uds.? (*sí*) _____

10. ¿Todavía piensas en Tommy? (*no*) _____

◆ 3 ◆ DIRECT-OBJECT PRONOUNS

a. Direct objects tell who or what received the action of the verb and answer the questions *whom?* or *what?* Direct-object pronouns replace direct objects and agree with them in gender and number.

SINGULAR		PLURAL	
me	*me*	nos	*us*
te	*you*	os	*you ((familiar)*
lo	*him, you* (m. formal) *it* (m.)	los	*them, you* (masculine)
la	*her, you* (f. formal); *it* (f.)	las	*them, you* (f.)

NOTES:

1. *Le* is sometimes used instead of *lo.*

2. The plural form of both *le* and *lo* is *los.*

b. The direct-object pronoun is usually placed directly before the verb.

¿Quién lee el libro?   *Who reads the book?*
El alumno **lo** lee.   *The student reads it.*

¿Compró Lola las manzanas?   *Did Lola buy the apples?*
Lola no **las** compró.   *Lola didn't buy them.*

c. The direct object pronoun precedes the main verb or is attached to an infinitive.

Vas a escribir una carta.   *You are going to write a letter.*

La vas a escribir.
Vas a escribirla. $\Big\}$ *You are going to write it.*

Ellos no **te** quieren ver.
Ellos no quieren ver**te**. $\Big\}$ *They don't want to see you.*

d. Direct-object pronouns follow the affirmative command, but they come immediately before the verb in the negative command.

Cómpre**lo**.   *Buy it.*

BUT

No **lo** compre.   *Don't buy it.*

NOTE: When the direct-object pronoun follows the affirmative command, an accent mark is normally required on the stressed vowel of the verb to keep the original stress. If the affirmative command has only one syllable (*ten*), no accent mark is required (*tenlo*).

EXERCISE E.   **You are trying out for a school team and went to the doctor for a full physical examination. Answer the questions that a friend asks about the physical. Use direct-object pronouns in your responses.**

EXAMPLE: ¿Quién sacó la sangre? (*la enfermera*)   La enfermera **la** sacó.

1. ¿Quién hizo la cita? (*mi mamá*)   _____

2. ¿Quién revisó tu vista? (*el médico*)   _____

3. ¿Quién dio el examen físico? (*el médico*)   _____

4. ¿Quién sacó las radiografías? (*un técnico*)   _____

5. ¿Quién llenó el formulario para la escuela? (*una secretaria*)   _____

6. ¿Quién firmó el formulario? (*el médico*)   _____

7. ¿Quién escribió la receta para tus anteojos? (*el médico*)   _____

EXERCISE F.   **Before you leave for school, your mother asks you a series of questions. Follow the example and restate her question and express your responses.**

EXAMPLE: apagar el radio

          MAMÁ: **¿Lo apagaste?**

          TÚ: **Sí, *lo* apagué.**   *OR*   **No, no *lo* apagué.**

1. guardar la ropa sucia

     MAMÁ: _____

     TÚ: _____

2. hacer la cama

MAMÁ: _____

TÚ: _____

3. cerrar las ventanas

MAMÁ: _____

TÚ: _____

4. escuchar el pronóstico del tiempo

MAMÁ: _____

TÚ: _____

5. llevar un suéter

MAMÁ: _____

TÚ: _____

6. tomar el desayuno

MAMÁ: _____

TÚ: _____

7. tener todos los libros

MAMÁ: _____

TÚ: _____

EXERCISE G. You are helping a friend plan a surprise party for her sister. She wants to know what you are going to do.

EXAMPLE: colgar los adornos (*sí, no*)
¿**Vas a colgar*los*? (¿*Los* vas a colgar?)**
Sí, voy a colgar*los*. (Sí, *los* voy a colgar.)

OR No, **no voy a colgarlos. (No, no *los* voy a colgar.)**

1. comprar los refrescos (*sí*)

ELLA: _____

TÚ: _____

2. poner la mesa (*no*)

ELLA: _____

TÚ: _____

3. escribir las invitaciones (*sí*)

ELLA: _____

TÚ: _____

4. escoger los MP3 (*sí*)

ELLA: _____

TÚ: _____

5. invitar a los padres (*no*)

ELLA: _____

TÚ: _____

6. preparar un pastel (*no*)

ELLA: _____

TÚ: _____

(EXERCISE H.)   **Your Spanish teacher is telling the class what to do before the first examination. Express what she says.**

EXAMPLE: estudiar las lecciones   **Estúdienlas.**

1. no dejar los libros en la escuela

_____

2. aprender el vocabulario de memoria

_____

3. traer una pluma

_____

4. practicar los diálogos con un compañero

_____

5. buscar las palabras desconocidas en un diccionario

_____

6. revisar el examen bien

_____

7. no hacer muchas preguntas durante el examen

_____

(EXERCISE I.)   **Answer the questions that a friend asks you. Use a direct object pronoun in your responses.**

EXAMPLE: ¿Mandas muchas tarjetas?
             Sí, **las** mando.

       OR   No, no **las** mando.

1. ¿Escuchas a tus profesores?   _____

2. ¿Ayudas a tu hermana menor?   _____

3. ¿Compras muchas revistas de deportes?   _____

4. ¿Bebes muchos refrescos?   _____

5. ¿Lees el periódico todos los días?   _____

6. ¿Invitas a tus amigos a ir al cine contigo? _____

7. ¿Quieres buscar nuevos pasatiempos? _____

8. ¿Visitas a tus abuelos con frecuencia? _____

9. ¿Juegas al tenis? _____

10. ¿Piensas vender tu bicicleta? _____

◆ 4 ◆ INDIRECT-OBJECT PRONOUNS

a. Indirect objects tell to whom or for whom the action of the verb is performed and answer the question *to whom*? Indirect-object pronouns replace indirect objects and agree with them in gender and number.

SINGULAR		PLURAL	
me	*to me*	nos	*to us*
te	*to you* ((familiar)	os	*to you* ((familiar)
le	*to you* (formal), *to him, to her*	les	*to you* ((formal), *to them* (m. & f.)

NOTES:

1. The forms *le* and *les* are used as both masculine and feminine indirect-object pronouns.

2. If the meaning is not clear or if we wish to add emphasis, a phrase with *a* + prepositional pronoun may be used in addition to the indirect-object pronouns.

   (Clarity)   Yo les escribo a ellas.   *I write to them.*
   (Emphasis) A mí me encanta bailar; a Uds. no.   *I love to dance; you don't.*

   Sentences with both indirect object and indirect-object pronouns are very common in Spanish.

3. The forms *me, te, nos,* and *os* are also used for direct-object pronouns and for reflexive pronouns.

4. The indirect-object pronoun may be identified in English by the preposition *to* + *a person*. The *to* may be expressed or implied.

   Les lee el cuento.   *She reads the story to them. (She reads them the story.)*

b. The indirect-object pronoun is usually placed before the verb.

   Yo *te* doy el regalo.   *I give the gift to you.*
   Él *me* manda un paquete.   *He sends a package to me. (He sends me a package.)*

c. When a verb is followed by an infinitive, indirect-object pronouns precede the verb or are attached to the infinitive.

   ¿*Me* quieres decir algo importante?
   ¿Quieres decir*me* algo importante?   } *Do you want to tell me something important?*

d. The indirect-object pronoun is attached to the end of an affirmative command, but it is placed before a negative command.

Díga*me* la verdad.   *Tell the truth to me. (Tell me the truth.)*

BUT

No *me* diga la verdad.   *Don't tell the truth to me. (Don't tell me the truth.)*

NOTE: When the indirect-object pronoun follows and is attached to the affirmative command, an accent mark is normally required on the stressed vowel of the verb in order to keep the original stress.

EXERCISE J.   You and your brother are talking about the dinner you had with your family in a restaurant last night. The waiter confused everyone's order. Using the cue in parentheses, tell what each person was served.

EXAMPLE: Mi papá pidió pescado. (*pavo*)   El camarero **le** sirvió pavo.

1. Yo pedí papas fritas. (*arroz*) _____

2. Elvira pidió una hamburguesa. (*ensalada*) _____

3. Mi abuelo pidió te caliente. (*refresco*) _____

4. Mi mamá y yo pedimos flan. (*pastel*) _____

5. Jennifer y Pablo pidieron pollo. (*carne asada*) _____

6. Tú pediste un coctel de camarones. (*ceviche*) _____

7. Jamie pidió sopa de verduras. (*consomé*) _____

EXERCISE K.   John is very upset because although he is always very caring and generous when his friends celebrate their birthdays, they do not reciprocate. Express what he says.

EXAMPLE: a Verónica / mandar una tarjeta   Yo **le** mandé una tarjeta.

1. a Beto / dar un disco compacto

_____

2. a Rosa y a Phyllis / llevar flores

_____

3. a Lorenzo / comprar boletos para un concierto

_____

4. a ti / regalar un monopatín

_____

5. a mis primos / mandar una suscripción de revista

_____

6. a mí / nadie / dar nada

_____

EXERCISE L. Mandy is not talking to her friends and Janine is trying to "patch things up" between them. Express the suggestions Janine makes and Mandy's responses.

EXAMPLE: pedir una disculpa a Sara y a Amy
      JANINE: Tú puedes **pedirles** una disculpa.
      MANDY: Yo no **les voy a pedir** una disculpa.

1. escribir una carta a Valerie

    JANINE: _____

    MANDY: _____

2. ofrecer una explicación a Janice y a Emma

    JANINE: _____

    MANDY: _____

3. hablar por teléfono a Gary

    JANINE: _____

    MANDY: _____

4. dar un regalito a Bárbara y a Alicia

    JANINE: _____

    MANDY: _____

5. mandar una tarjeta a Héctor

    JANINE: _____

    MANDY: _____

6. explicar por qué estás enojada conmigo

    JANINE: _____

    MANDY: _____

EXERCISE M. Robert found a trunk in the attic of his house. As he goes through its contents with his mother, she tells him what to do with them. Express what his mother says.

EXAMPLE: dar las fotos / a tu abuela   **Dale** las fotos.

1. regalar estas pulseras / a tus tías _____

2. mostrar este anillo / al joyero _____

3. mandar este disco / a tu tío _____

4. ofrecer esta ropa / a una caridad _____

5. dar esta cadena / a mí _____

6. regalar estos libros / a tus amigos _____

EXERCISE N. Mrs. Núñez is telling her children how to behave at a family reunion. Express what she says.

EXAMPLE: a tus primos / dar la mano / no gritar   **Denles** la mano; no les griten.

1. a su tío / cantar «Las mañanitas» / no cantar otra canción

_____

2. a sus primos / contar un chiste / no hacer una broma

_____

3. a su tía / ayudar / no dar más trabajo

_____

4. a su tío / dar el regalo / no esconder el regalo

_____

5. a sus tíos / hablar con cortesía / no contestar groseramente

_____

◆ 5 ◆ DOUBLE-OBJECT PRONOUNS

a. When a verb has two object pronouns, the indirect-object pronoun (usually referring to a person) precedes the direct-object pronoun (usually a thing).

Pedro me lo da.	*Peter gives it to me.*
Pedro te la da.	*Peter gives it to you.* (fam.)
Pedro se los da.	*Peter gives them to you (him, her, them).*
Pedro nos las da.	*Peter gives them to us.*

NOTES:

1. *Le* and *les* change to *se* before *lo, la, los, las.*

Pedro **le** da el libro.	*Peter gives the book to you (him, her).*
Pedro **se** lo da.	*Peter gives it to you (him, her).*

2. The various meanings of *se* may be clarified by adding *a Ud.* (*Uds.*), *a él* (*ella*), *a ellos* (*ellas*).

Su padre **se** lo da a ella (a ellas).	*Her father gives it to her (them).*

b. The position of double-object pronouns is the same as for single object pronouns.

Me lo da.	*He gives it to me.*
Desea dár**melo**. **Me lo** desea dar.	*He wants to give it to me.*
Está dándo**melo**. **Me lo** está dando.	*He is giving it to me.*
¡Dé**melo** (Ud.)!	*Give it to me.*
BUT	
¡No **me lo** dé (Ud.)!	*Don't give it to me.*

NOTE: When both object pronouns are attached to the verb, an accent mark is placed on the stressed syllable.

EXERCISE O.   Ricky is reviewing a unit on careers and wants to be sure that he understands them. His sister confirms his statements using double-object pronouns. Express what she says.

EXAMPLE: La enfermera les da medicina a los enfermos.   Sí, la enfermera **se la** da.

1. El peluquero les corta el pelo a las personas.

_____

2. La profesora les enseña la lección a los alumnos.

_____

3. El banquero le presta dinero al público.

_____

4. El dependiente les vende cosas a los compradores.

_____

5. El cocinero nos prepara la comida.

_____

6. El arquitecto nos muestra algunos diseños.

_____

7. El camarero les sirve la comida a los clientes.

_____

8. El fotógrafo les saca fotos a las personas.

_____

9. El abogado les da consejos legales a los clientes.

_____

10. El científico nos mejora la vida.

_____

EXERCISE P.   You help a friend empty her locker at the end of the school year. She finds that many of the things in it belong to other friends. Express what you suggest she do.

EXAMPLE: Este suéter es de Marisol.
           Se lo debes devolver.

   OR   Debes **devolvérselo**.

1. Este diccionario es de la señorita Almeda. _____

2. Esta raqueta de tenis es tuya.   _____

3. Estos aretes son de mi prima Adela.   _____

4. Estos bolígrafos son de Enrique y Tomás. _____

5. Estas camisetas son de Nanette.   _____

6. Este cartel es del amigo de Francisco. _____

7. Esta calculadora es tuya también. _____

8. Estas cartas son de Isabel. _____

EXERCISE Q. **You don't mind lending some of your things to friends but your brother disapproves of this practice. Express what your friends ask and what your brother says.**

EXAMPLE: Rogelio va a participar en una competencia de tenis y te pide prestada tu raqueta de tenis.

ROGELIO: **Préstamela**.
TU HERMANO: No **se la** prestes.

1. Jerry va a la playa y quiere usar tus anteojos de sol.

JERRY: _____

TU HERMANO: _____

2. Alfredo y Gustavo van a una fiesta en casa de sus primos y buscan ciertos discos compactos.

ELLOS: _____

TU HERMANO: _____

3. Laura tiene que llevar a su abuela al aeropuerto, pero su carro está en la estación de servicio.

LAURA: _____

TU HERMANO: _____

4. El hermano de Felipe se inscribió en una carrera de bicicleta, pero no le ha llegado su bicicleta nueva.

FELIPE: _____

TU HERMANO: _____

5. Gregorio sabe que tú no puedes ir a esquiar con ellos este fin de semana y quiere usar tus esquís.

GREGORIO: _____

TU HERMANO: _____

◆ 6 ◆ *GUSTAR* AND OTHER VERBS WITH INDIRECT-OBJECT PRONOUNS

a. Gustar (to please) is used to express "to like."

Me gusta la película.	*I like the film.*
La película me gusta.	(Literally: *The film pleases me.*)
Te gustan los dibujos animados.	*You like the cartoons.*
Los dibujos animados te gustan.	(Literally: *The cartoons please you.*)
Nos gusta nadar.	*We like to swim (swimming).*
Nadar nos gusta.	(Literally: *To swim [swimming] pleases us.*)

NOTE: While it is more common to place the thing that is liked (noun or verb) after the verb *gustar*, it may also precede the verb.

b. *Gustar* is preceded by an indirect-object pronoun. The form of *gustar* agrees with the subject, which generally follows it.

Te gusta la fiesta.	*You like the party.*
Te gust**an** las fiestas.	*You like the parties.*
Nos gust**a** la canción.	*We like the song.*
Nos gust**an** las canciones.	*We like the songs.*
Me gusta bailar.	*I like to dance.*

> NOTE: If the thing liked is not a noun but an action (expressed by a verb in the infinitive), *gustar* is used in the third-person singular.
>
> Me gusta bailar y cantar.   *I like to dance and sing.*

c. To clarify the indirect-object pronouns *le* and *les*, or to give emphasis, the indirect object normally precedes the indirect-object pronoun.

A Tina no **le** gusta volar.	*Tina doesn't like to fly.*
A los alumnos no **les** gustan los exámenes.	*The students don't like examinations.*
A Cándida **le** gusta el pastel.	*Candida likes the cake.*
A mí **me** gusta dormir.	*I like to sleep.*

d. Other Verbs Like *Gustar*

encantar
fascinar } *to delight* (Used for things that someone likes a lot or loves.)

Me encantan los conciertos.	*I love concerts.*

parecer *to seem*

La película nos pareció corta.	*The film seemed short to us.*
Los cuentos nos parecieron aburridos.	*The stories seemed boring to us.*

> NOTE: Since *parecer* is usually followed by an adjective, the adjective must agree in number and gender with the item described.
>
> **doler**   *to be painful, to cause sorrow*
>
> Me duele la cabeza.   *I have a headache.*
>
> **faltar**   *to be lacking, to need*
>
> Me faltan cinco dólares.   *I lack five dollars.*
>
> **quedar (a uno)**   *to remain (to someone), to have left*
>
> Le queda un día de vacaciones.   *He has one day of vacation left.*
>
> **tocar (a uno)**   *to be one's turn*
>
> A ti te toca sacar la basura.   *It's your turn to take out the garbage.*

(EXERCISE R.)   **Express what some friends say about their likes and dislikes.**

EXAMPLE: a ti / gustar / las tortillas   A ti **te gustan** las tortillas.

1.   a Luis / no gustar / las legumbres

2. a mí / gustar / el café

_____

3. a ellos / no gustar / los tes naturales

_____

4. a nosotros / gustar / conocer restaurantes nuevos

_____

5. a Silvia / encantar / los dulces

_____

6. a ti / fascinar / los postres de chocolate

_____

7. a Rafael y a Clara / gusta / compartir la comida

_____

8. a mí / no gustar / el servicio malo en un restaurante

_____

9. a nosotros / no gustar / pedir solamente un plato

_____

10. a Jackie / gustar / hablar y comer al mismo tiempo

_____

EXERCISE S. **Hugo just returned from a trip to Peru and Macchu Picchu. Express what he describes about the trip he made with two friends.**

EXAMPLE: a mí / tocar / hablar de mi viaje   A mí **me toca** hablar de mi viaje.

1. a nosotros / encantar / la familia con que vivimos

_____

2. a Daniel / faltar / muchas conveniencias norteamericanas

_____

3. a mí / parecer / una experiencia formidable

_____

4. a Manolo y a mí / doler la cabeza / por la altura

_____

5. a nosotros / fascinar / visitar las ruinas arqueológicas

_____

6. a mí / encantar / las vistas desde los picos de las montañas

_____

7. a Manolo / no quedar / ningún rollo de película

_____

8. a ellos / faltar / dinero para comprar curiosidades peruanas

_____

9. a mí / gustar / hablar español y conocer a nuevos amigos

_____

10. a Uds. / faltar / visitar este país

_____

MASTERY EXERCISES

EXERCISE T. **Ruth was absent from school today and Alicia is bringing her up-to-date about what happened there. Ruth can't believe what she hears. Express Ruth's reaction using as many pronouns as possible.**

EXAMPLE: Elena le prestó diez dólares a Carolina.   ¿**Se los** prestó ella?

1. Gloria comió el almuerzo con Alfredo.

_____

2. Jackie quería pedirle prestado el trabajo a Gustavo.

_____

3. Yo invité a Felipe a ir al baile conmigo.

_____

4. Mike y Luke le hicieron muchas preguntas al profesor.

_____

5. Fred vino a la escuela sin el proyecto de arte.

_____

6. Janice le devolvió los aretes a Nancy.

_____

7. Tú y yo tenemos que planear la celebración del Día de los Muertos.

_____

8. Los alumnos escogieron a Roberto para representarnos en el concurso.

_____

9. El director del grupo teatral le dio el papel principal a Elvira.

_____

10. Todos los muchachos te echaron de menos a ti hoy.

_____

EXERCISE U. You and your family had a garage sale. You are writing an electronic message in Spanish to a friend in Lima, in which you describe some of the objects that were for sale. Select four items and prepare a description of each one. Tell if it was sold, to whom in the family the object belonged, some reactions to the objects by family members and/or the buyers, and the success of the tale. Use as many pronouns as possible.

SUGGESTIONS: a lamp   a football pennant   a bicycle
a chess set   a tennis racquet   other toys
a doll

EXAMPLE: La lámpara era de mi abuela. A mi madre le encantaba mucho esa lámpara. Ella no quería venderla. La escondió debajo de una mesa y ahora no sabe donde ponerla en la casa.

CHAPTER

23

Prepositions

Prepositions relate two elements of a sentence: noun to noun, verb to noun or pronoun, or verb to infinitive.

una cadena **de** plata	*a silver chain*	Ellos trabajan **con**migo.	*They work with me.*
Entro **en** la tienda.	*I enter the store.*	La niña comenzó **a** llorar.	*The girl began to cry.*

◆ 1 ◆ PREPOSITIONAL MODIFIERS

a. A preposition + noun modifying another noun is equivalent to an adjective.

una taza **de** café	*a cup of coffee*	una copa **para** vino	*a wine glass*
un anillo **de** oro	*a gold ring*		

b. A preposition + noun modifying a verb is equivalent to an adverb.

El anciano camina **con** cuidado.   *The old man walks carefully (with care).*

EXERCISE A.   You are in a gift shop. Tell what the objects you see are made of, or explain their purpose.

EXAMPLE: un marco / plástico   un jarro / limonada
Un marco **de** plástico.   Un jarro **para** limonada.

1. figura / porcelana _____

2. un baúl / madera _____

3. platos / ensalada _____

4. aretes / plata _____

5. espejo / lata _____

6. flores / seda _____

7. copas / champaña _____

8. anillo / oro _____

9. camiseta / algodón _____

10. servilletas / papel _____

EXERCISE B.   **Tell how these people do the actions described.**

EXAMPLE: Estela habla. (*rapidez*)   Estela habla **con** rapidez.

1. Mi mamá recibe a los invitados. (*gusto*)

_____

2. Mi hermana conduce el carro. (*cuidado*)

_____

3. Yo bailo. (*entusiasmo*)

_____

4. Victoria cuida a su hermanita. (*cariño*)

_____

5. Gustavo abre la carta de la universidad.
(*miedo*)

_____

6. El cajero cuenta el dinero. (*exactitud*)

_____

7. Pilar canta. (*dulzura*)

_____

8. Mi papá arma el juguete. (*precisión*)

_____

◆ 2 ◆ USES OF THE PREPOSITION A

a. The preposition *a* is used to indicate direction or destination.

Ella dobla **a** la izquierda.	*She turns to the left.*
Vamos **al** estadio.	*We are going to the stadium.*
Ella llegó **a** la estación.	*She arrived at the station.*

NOTES:

1. The preposition *a* (to) combines with *el* (the) to form the contraction *al* (to the).

Ellos van **al** concierto.	*They are going to the concert.*
La mamá riñe **al** niño.	*The mother scolds the child.*

2. The preposition *a* never forms a contraction with the other articles (*la, los, las*).

Marta va **a** la escuela.	*Marta goes to the school.*
El dependiente les habla **a** los clientes.	*The salesperson speaks to the customers.*

3. In some expressions, *a* plus the definite article is used where there is no equivalent in English.

Nosotros jugamos **al** golf.	*We play golf.*

EXERCISE C.   **Based on the drawings below, tell where Joe is going.**

EXAMPLE: Joe va al aeropuerto.

1. _____

2. _____

3. _____

6. _____

4. _____

7. _____

5. _____

8. _____

b. The preposition *a* is required before the direct object of a verb if the direct object is a person, a personalized group, a pet, or something personified.

Juan visita **a** María.	*John visits Mary.*
Ella ve **al** cliente.	*She looks at the customer.*
Yo invito **a** mis primos.	*I invite my friends.*
Douglas saca **al** gato.	*Douglas takes the cat out.*
BUT	
Ellos visitan la feria.	*They visit the fair.*
Joyce saca el papel.	*Joyce takes out the paper.*

c. The preposition *a* is required before the pronouns *¿quién?*, *¿quiénes?*, *nadie*, and *alguien*, when they refer to a person.

No veo **a** nadie.	*I don't see anyone.*
Conocí **a** alguien en la fiesta.	*I met someone at the party.*
¿**A** quién buscamos?	*Whom do we look for?*

NOTES:

1. When used before a direct object, the preposition *a* (personal *a*) has no equivalent in English. When used before an indirect object, it translates as "to."

Vemos **a** nuestra tía.	*We see our aunt.*
Le hablamos **a** nuestra tía.	*We speak to our aunt.*

2. The personal *a* is not used after the verb *tener* (to have).

Tiene un hermano menor.	*He/she has a younger brother.*
Tengo muchos parientes.	*I have many relatives.*

EXERCISE D. Tell who saw or met whom at a company picnic.

EXAMPLE: yo / conocer / el dueño de la compañía   Yo conocí **al** dueño **de** la compañía.

1. Gladys / ver / su antiguo jefe _____

2. Felipe / conocer / la familia de su socio _____

3. nosotros / conocer / el esposo de la presidenta _____

4. la secretaria / conocer / los hijos de su jefe _____

5. el contador / conocer / todos los empleados _____

6. mi madre / ver / la telefonista _____

7. mi hermano y yo / conocer / muchos niños _____

8. yo / ver / los colegas de mi papá _____

EXERCISE E. Adam and his friends are discussing their plans for the evening. Tell what each one intends to do.

EXAMPLE: Adam / hablar / un amigo   Adam piensa hablar **a** un amigo.

1. Rogelio / jugar / los naipes _____

2. Jessie y yo / ver / una película _____

3. Gordon / escuchar / discos _____

4. Elvira / acompañar / sus hermanas _____

5. yo / llamar / Michael   _____

6. Sharon / esperar / su novio   _____

EXERCISE F.   A new Internet friend has sent you a series of questions to answer. Use complete sentences and the cues in parentheses to answer the questions.

1. ¿A quiénes ves todos los días? (*los amigos*)

   _____

2. ¿Conoces a muchos jóvenes de tu edad? (*sí*)

   _____

3. ¿Tienes muchos amigos? (*sí*)

   _____

4. ¿A quién ayudas tú? (*mi abuelo*)

   _____

5. ¿A quién llamas tú al llegar a casa? (*nadie*)

   _____

6. ¿A quién admiras tú? (*un vecino*)

   _____

7. ¿Con qué frecuencia visitas al peluquero? (cada mes)

   _____

8. ¿A quién buscas para resolver un problema? (*mi padre*)

   _____

9. ¿Amas a tus hermanos? (*sí*)

   _____

10. ¿Escuchas a tus amigos atentamente? (*a veces*)

    _____

◆ 3 ◆ USES OF THE PREPOSITION DE

a. The preposition *de* corresponds to *of, from,* or *about*.

¿**De** quién hablas?	*About whom are you speaking?*
Hablo **del** presidente.	*I'm speaking about the president.*
Recibí saludos **de** Elsa.	*I received regards from Elsa.*

NOTES:

1. The preposition *de* (of, from) combines with *el* (the) to form *del* (of the, from the, about).

Guy es el presidente **del** «Círculo Español».	*Guy is the president of the Spanish Club.*
Yo saqué dinero **del** banco.	*I took out money from the bank.*

2. The preposition *de* never combines with the other articles (*la, los, las*) to form a single word.

Recibí un paquete **de** las muchachas.   *I received a package from the girls.*

EXERCISE G.   Tell what these people are talking about.

EXAMPLE: los padres / las vacaciones   Los padres hablan **de** las vacaciones.

1. yo / los deportes   _____

2. el alcalde / la huelga de los taxistas   _____

3. nosotros / el tiempo   _____

4. tú / el examen de la clase de ciencia   _____

5. los amigos / la fiesta   _____

6. el profesor / las notas de los alumnos   _____

b. In Spanish, possession is expressed as follows: noun (thing possessed) followed by *de* plus noun (possessor). This is equivalent to the English possessive expressed with *of*. In Spanish there is no apostrophe to indicate possession.

la camisa **de** Raúl   *the book of Raúl (Raúl's book)*
la muñeca **de** la niña   *the doll of the girl (the girl's doll)*
los juguetes **de** los niños   *the toys of the children (the children's toys)*

c. ¿*De quién, -es?* (Whose?) is used to ask to whom something belongs.

¿**De quién** son las revistas?   *Whose (sing.) magazines are they?*
¿**De quiénes** son los tenis?   *To whom (pl.) do the sneakers belong?*

EXERCISE H.   Tell to whom these objects belong.

EXAMPLE: la calculadora / el maestro   Es la calculadora **del** maestro.

1. el cuadro / pintor   _____

2. la bandeja / mesera   _____

3. el martillo / carpintero   _____

4. los instrumentos musicales / músicos   _____

5. la mochila / alumno   _____

6. la estufa / cocinera   _____

7. el edificio / dueño   _____

8. las muñecas / niñas   _____

◆ *4* ◆ PREPOSITIONS WITH INFINITIVES

In Spanish, the infinitive is the only verb form that may immediately follow a preposition.

Ella salió **sin** cerrar la puerta.   *She went out without closing the door.*

Vamos **a** nadar en la piscina.   *We are going to swim in the pool.*

Ellos acaban **de** llegar.   *They have just arrived.*

a. Verbs Requiring *a* Before an Infinitive

Verbs expressing beginning, motion, teaching or learning, helping, and several others require the preposition *a* before an infinitive.

(1) **Beginning**

comenzar a + infinitive	
empezar a + infinitive	*to begin to* + infinitive
ponerse a + infinitive	

El bebé se pone a llorar.   *The baby begins to cry.*

Empezamos a comer.   *We began to eat.*

(2) **Motion**

ir a + infinitive *to go to* + verb

Va a abrir la carta.   *He's going to open the letter.*

correr a + infinitive   *to run to* + infinitive

Corren a saludar a su papá.   *They run to greet their father.*

venir a + infinitive *to come to* + infinitive

Viene a disculparse.   *He / She is coming to ask for forgiveness.*

acercarse a + infinitive *to approach*

Se acerca a leer el anuncio.   *He/she approaches to read the announcement.*

apresurarse a + infinitive *to hurry to*

Me apresuro a hacer una llamada telefónica.   *I hurry to make a telephone call.*

(3) **Teaching or Learning**

enseñar a + infinitive *to teach to* + infinitive

Mi mamá me enseña a conducir.   *My mother teaches me to drive.*

aprender a + infinitive *to learn to* + infinitive

Aprendemos a bailar.   *We are learning to dance.*

(4) **Helping**

ayudar a + infinitive *to help (to)* + infinitive

Yo te ayudo a cocinar.   *I help you cook.*

(5) **Other Verbs**

acostumbrarse a + infinitive *to become accustomed to*

atreverse a + infinitive *to dare to*

convidar a + infinitive *to invite to*

decidirse a + infinitive *to decide to*

dedicarse a + infinitive *to devote oneself to*

invitar a + infinitive *to invite to*
llegar a + infinitive *to succeed in*
negarse a + infinitive *to refuse to*
obligar a + infinitive *to force, to compel to*

Se dedica **a** tocar el piano.	*He devotes himself to playing the piano.*
Te invité **a** cenar conmigo.	*I invited you to have dinner with me.*
Ella llegó **a** ser doctora.	*She succeeded in becoming a doctor.*
Se negaron **a** pagar la cuenta.	*They refused to pay the bill.*

b. Verbs Requiring *de* Before an Infinitive

The following verbs require *de* before an infinitive:

acabar de *to have just*	**dejar de** *to fail to, to stop*
acordarse de *to remember to*	**encargarse de** *to take charge of*
alegrarse de *to be glad*	**olvidarse de** *to forget to*
cesar de *to stop*	**tratar de** *to try to*

Cesó **de** nevar.	*It stopped snowing.*
La niña dejó **de** llorar.	*The girl stopped crying.*
Me olvidé **de** echar la carta.	*I forgot to mail the letter.*
Tratará **de** ir a la fiesta.	*He / She will try to go to the party.*

c. Verbs Requiring *en* Before an Infinitive

The following verbs require the preposition *en* before an infinitive:

consentir (ie) en *to consent to*	**meterse en** *to become involved in*
consistir en *to consist of*	**quedar en** *to agree to*
convenir en *to agree to*	**tardar en** *to be long in, to delay in*
insistir en *to insist on*	

Consiente **en** venir.	*He / She consents to come.*
Tarda **en** llegar.	*He / She delays in arriving.*

d. Other Common Prepositions

al (from **a** + **el**) + infinitive *on, upon*	**en vez de** *instead of*
antes de *before*	**sin** *without*
después de *after*	

Al entrar en la casa, saludó a los invitados.	*Upon entering the house, he/she greeted the guests.*
Antes de salir de la casa, cerré las ventanas.	*Before going out, I closed the windows.*

e. Verbs Requiring No Preposition Before an Infinitive

deber *ought to, must*	**pensar (ie)** *to intend*
dejar *to let, to allow*	**poder (ue)** *to be able, can*
desear *to desire*	**querer (ie)** *to want*
esperar *to hope, to expect*	**saber** *to know (how)*
hacer *to make, to have (something done)*	**soler (ue)** *to be in the habit of*
lograr *to succeed in*	**ver** *to see*
oír *to hear*	

Debe hacer el trabajo.	*He/She ought to do the work.*
No me dejó entrar.	*He/She did not let me enter.*
Me hace reír.	*He/She makes me laugh.*
Hizo construir una casa.	*He/She had a house built.*
Logró convencerlo.	*He/She succeeded in convincing him.*
No lo oímos salir.	*We didn't hear him leave.*
Quiero comprar un traje.	*I want to buy a suit.*
¿Sabe Ud. tocar el piano?	*Do you know how to play the piano?*
Suele comer temprano.	*He/She is in the habit of eating early.*
Lo vi jugar.	*I saw him playing.*

EXERCISE I.   **Tell what the following people are doing.**

EXAMPLE: mi hermana / enseñarme / bailar.   Mi hermana **me enseña a** bailar.

1. el médico / apresurarse / cuidar al enfermo

_____

2. la joven / aprender / conducir un carro

_____

3. el niño / negarse / comer el cereal

_____

4. mi amiga / convidar / cenar con ella

_____

5. los padres / dedicarse / educar a los hijos

_____

6. los alumnos / venir / estudiar juntos para el examen

_____

7. la nieta / correr / saludar a los abuelos

_____

8. el equipo / empezar / jugar el partido a las diez

_____

9. todos los amigos / ayudar / colgar los adornos

_____

10. el alumno tímido / no atreverse / hablar en la clase

_____

EXERCISE J. Complete the message that Albert left on his friend's answering machine with the appropriate preposition.

Ya cesó _____ nevar. Acabo _____ entrar en la casa y me acordé _____ llamarte.
　　　　　　　　1.　　　　　　　　　　　　　　2.　　　　　　　　　　　　　　　　　　　3.

Me alegro _____ recibir tu respuesta afirmative a mi invitación. No dejes _____ traer tus nue-
　　　　　　　4.　　　　　　　　　　　　　　　　　　　　　　　　　　　　　　　5.

vos discos compactos. Yo me encargaré _____ comprar unos refrescos. No te olvides _____
　　　　　　　　　　　　　　　　　　　　6.　　　　　　　　　　　　　　　　　　　　　　　　7.

tomar el autobús número 20 para llegar a mi casa. Trata _____ llegar antes _____ las cinco.
　　　　　　　　　　　　　　　　　　　　　　　　　　8.　　　　　　　　　　9.

EXERCISE K. Tell what these people are planning to do. Use an expression from each column.

A	B
deber	nadar en una piscina
desear	comer en un restaurante
esperar	pasar las vacaciones en una isla tropical
hacer	asistir a un baile formal
pensar	visitar a los abuelos
poder	alquilar varios videos
preferir	encontrar un trabajo para el verano
querer	ir al centro comercial
soler	lavar la alfombra

EXAMPLE:　Mi mamá **hace lavar la alfombra.**

1. Hugo _____.

2. Luisa y Kyoko _____.

3. Larry y yo _____.

4. Jeffrey _____.

5. Tú _____.

6. Gloria _____.

7. Yo _____.

8. Nosotros _____.

EXERCISE L. Complete each sentence with your own ideas using an infinitive.

EXAMPLE:　Yo debo **empezar a** ahorrar dinero para **ir a** la universidad.

1. Yo puedo _____.

2. Yo espero _____.

3. Yo suelo _____.

4. Yo pienso _____.

5. Yo quiero _____.

6. Yo debo _____.

EXERCISE M.   Complete the story Jack is telling a friend about his plans with some other friends with the appropriate preposition, if one is needed.

Cada año, unos amigos del campamento de verano y yo solemos _____1_____ reunirnos _____2_____ pasar un fin de semana juntos. Este año, en vez, vamos _____3_____ ir a casa de uno de ellos, pensamos _____4_____ ir a las montañas porque ellos desean _____5_____ esquiar. Yo no sé _____6_____ esquiar muy bien, pero yo consentí _____7_____ acompañarlos porque tengo muchas ganas _____8_____ verlos. Mis amigos me dijeron que yo podría _____9_____ alquilar los esquís allí. Debo _____10_____ salir muy temprano el viernes por la mañana. El autobús tarda tres horas _____11_____ llegar a las montañas. Antes _____12_____ ir, debo _____13_____ comprar ropa gruesa porque ellos insisten _____14_____ pasar mucho tiempo al aire libre y va _____15_____ hacer mucho frío allí. Ellos van _____16_____ ayudarme a aprender _____17_____ esquiar. Trataré _____18_____ aprender aunque no me gusta mucho practicar _____19_____ los deportes de invierno. Eddie se encarga _____20_____ hacer las reservaciones porque él suele _____21_____ pasar cada otro fin de semana allí. El precio del fin de semana consiste _____22_____ viajar en autobús y alojarse en una pensión con comidas cerca de la montaña donde vamos _____23_____ esquiar. Ya comencé _____24_____ hacer la maleta. No debo _____25_____ olvidarme _____26_____ llevar una gorra y guantes. Trataré _____27_____ divertirme y acostumbrarme _____28_____ pasar tiempo en el frío y la nieve. No dejaré _____29_____ contarte los acontecimientos del fin de semana después _____30_____ volver a casa. Espero _____31_____ lograr _____32_____ aprender _____33_____ esquiar mejor.

EXERCISE N.   Using the cues provided, answer the questions that an exchange student at school asks you.

1. ¿Vas a llamar a tu amigo(-a) hoy? *(sí)*

_____

2. ¿Qué deseas hacer esta tarde? *(ir a la librería)*

_____

3. ¿Piensas hacer un viaje el año que viene? *(sí)*

_____

4. ¿Te olvidaste de traer los anteojos de sol hoy? *(no)*

_____

5. ¿Qué lengua aprendes a hablar? *(japonés)*

_____

6. ¿Sabes conducir un carro? *(sí)*

7. ¿Sueles practicar la costumbre de pensar antes de hablar? *(a veces)*

_____

8. ¿Tratas de conversar en japonés? *(sí)*

_____

9. ¿Te alegras de vivir en esta ciudad? *(sí)*

_____

10. ¿Te gusta divertirte en vez de trabajar? *(sí)*

_____

◆ 5 ◆ FREQUENTLY USED EXPRESSIONS WITH PREPOSITIONS

a causa de *because of*

No jugaron el partido **a causa del** mal tiempo.	*They didn't play the game because of the bad weather.*

a eso de *about* + time

Llegaré **a eso de** las siete.	*I'll arrive about seven o'clock.*

a fines de *at the end of*

Pago las cuentas **a fines del** mes.	*I pay the bills at the end of the month.*

a mediados de *in the middle of*

Las cuentas llegan **a mediados del** mes.	*The bills arrive in the middle of the month.*

a pesar de *in spite of*

A pesar de la herida, el atleta compitió en la carrera.	*In spite of the injury, the athlete competed in the race.*

a pie *on foot*

Voy al centro comercial **a pie**.	*I go to the mall on foot.*

a principios de *at the beginning of, early in*

Tenemos vacaciones a **principios de** junio.	*We have vacation at the beginning of June.*

a tiempo *on time*

Me gusta llegar **a tiempo**.	*I like to arrive on time.*

a través de *through, across*

Puedo ver el parque **a través** de la ventana.	*I can see the park through the window.*

al aire libre *outdoors, in the open air*

Prefieren comer **al aire libre**.	*They prefer eating outdoors.*

de hoy en adelante *from now on, henceforth*

De hoy en adelante, no voy a comer dulces.	*From now on I'm not going to eat candy.*

de otro modo *otherwise*

Termino la tarea ahora; **de otro modo** no podré ir al cine.	*I finish the assignment now; otherwise, I won't be able to go to the movies.*

de pie *standing*

En la clase debo estar **de pie** cuando contesto una pregunta.	*In class I have to be standing when I answer a question.*

de vez en cuando *from time to time*

De vez en cuando me gusta no hacer nada.	*From time to time I like to do nothing.*

desde luego *of course*

Desde luego, vimos el desfile.	*Of course we saw the parade.*

en cuanto a *as for, in regard to*

En cuanto a la deuda, te la pago pronto.	*As for the debt, I'll pay it to you soon.*

en efecto *in fact, really; yes, indeed* (as a response)

En efecto, te llamo más tarde.	*Yes, indeed, I'll call you later.*

en siete días *(in) seven days (a week)*

Tengo que entregar el trabajo **en siete días.**	*I have to hand in the work in seven days.*

en quince días *(in) fifteen days (two weeks)*

Regreso **en quince días.**	*I return in fifteen days (two weeks).*

en vez de *instead of*

Compré la blusa roja **en vez de** la negra.	*I bought the red blouse instead of the black one.*

EXERCISE O.   **Complete the response Lydia is writing to an e-mail message from a friend.**

Anoche fuimos al cine _____ pronóstico del tiempo. Dijeron que iba a empezar a nevar
                          1.(in spite of)

_____ las ocho de la noche y _____ tuvieron razón por primera vez. Llegamos al
    2. (about)   *3.* (in fact)

cine _____ y _____ la película oí a un señor decir que se había asomado
        4. (on time)   *5.* (in the middle of)

_____ de la puerta del cine y caía mucha nieve. Cuando salimos del cine había muchas personas
    6. (through)

_____ en la parada del autobús, pero ningún autobús llegó y tuvimos que regresar a casa
    7. (standing)

_____. No me gusta estar _____ cuando nieva. _____ la
    8. (on foot)   *9.* (out of doors)   *10.* (Because of)

nevada cancelaron las clases hasta _____ la semana que viene. _____,
                                        11. (the beginning of)   *12.* (Of course)

esta noticia me dio alegría pero si perdemos más días de clases, vamos a tener clases hasta _____
                                                                                                13. (the end of)

junio, _____ _____ junio. _____, voy a prestar
        14. (instead of)   *15.* (the middle of)   *16.* (From now on)

más atención al pronóstico del tiempo. _____ la película, no me gustó nada.
                                            17. (In regard to)

♦ 6 ♦ PARA AND POR

Both *para* and *por* have similar basic meanings in English. However, the use of *para* or *por* depends on the Spanish context. Their meanings in English may vary with the context.

a. *Para*

(1) *Para* expresses purpose or goal.

Estudia para abogado.	*He studies to be a lawyer.*

Ahorré dinero para comprarlo.   *I saved money in order to buy it.*

Trabaja para ganar dinero.   *He works to earn money.*

(2) *Para* **expresses the special use of an object.**

Compré un cepillo para los dientes.   *I bought a toothbrush.*

Es una taza para café.   *It is a coffee cup.*

BUT

Es una taza de café.   *It is a cup of coffee.*

(3) *Para* **expresses destination or direction.**

Salieron para el centro.   *They left for downtown.*

Este regalo es para ellos.   *This gift is for them.*

(4) *Para* **indicates a time or date in the future.**

Necesito la camisa para mañana.   *I need the shirt for (by) tomorrow.*

Estarán aquí para las cinco.   *They will be here by five o'clock.*

(5) *Para* **means** *for* **or** *considering that,* **when comparing a person, object, or situation with others of its kind.**

Para niño, se porta bien.   *For a child, he behaves himself.*

Ella es alta para su edad.   *She is tall considering her age.*

(6) *Estar para* **+ infinitive means** *to be about to.*

Estoy para salir.   *I am about to leave.*

EXERCISE P.   Tell what you need these things for.

EXAMPLE: impermeable   Necesito un impermeable **para** protegerme de la lluvia.

1. diccionario   _____

2. traje de baño   _____

3. peine   _____

4. champú   _____

5. toalla   _____

6. dinero   _____

7. cámara   _____

EXERCISE Q.   Tell why these people are going to these destinations.

EXAMPLE: yo / tienda / suéter   Yo voy a la tienda para comprar un suéter.

1. José / parque / fútbol   _____

2. Luis y Joan / cine / película   _____

3. Clara y yo / centro comercial / regalos   _____

4. mis amigos / montañas / esquiar   _____

5. Dennis / restaurante / sandwich   _____

6. mi papá / río / pescar   _____

7. tú / casa de una amiga / televisión   _____

EXERCISE R.   **Complete the statements you hear around the dinner table at a friend's house.**

1. Deben estudiar mucho _____ asistir a la universidad.

2. _____ gozar de la buena salud, deben comer muchas frutas frescas.

3. Beber mucha agua es bueno _____ limpiar el cuerpo.

4. Dame un plato _____ ensalada, _____ favor.

5. _____ joven, eres muy listo.

6. Saldremos _____ el campo pasadomañana.

7. _____ alegrar a todo el mundo, debes sonreír mucho.

8. _____ ser un buen atleta, hay que practicar mucho.

9. Tendré el dinero _____ el sábado.

10. Estoy _____ ir al centro. Ven conmigo.

b. *Por*

(1) *Por* **introduces the agent (doer) in a passive construction.**

Esta novela fue escrita **por** Carlos Fuentes.	*This novel was written by Carlos Fuentes.*

(2) *Por* **expresses in exchange for.**

Pagamos diez dólares **por** la pluma.	*We paid ten dollars for the pen.*
Quiero cambiar estos dólares **por** pesetas.	*I want to exchange these dollars for pesetas.*

(3) *Por* **means along, through, by, and around after a verb of motion.**

Salieron **por** la puerta de atrás.	*They left through the back door.*
Caminé **por** el río.	*I walked along the river.*
Pasamos **por** allí ayer.	*We came by there yesterday.*

(4) *Por* **expresses the duration of an action.**

Fue a la escuela de verano **por** seis semanas.	*He went to summer school for six weeks.*
Estudió **por** dos horas.	*She studied for two hours.*

(5) *Por* **means for the sake of and on behalf of.**

Lo hago **por** ti.	*I am doing it for you.*
Habló **por** todo el mundo.	*He spoke on behalf of everyone.*

(6) *Estar por* + infinitive means to be in favor of.

Están **por** salir.   *They are in favor of leaving.*

(7) *Por* (meaning *for*) is used after *enviar* (to send), *ir* (to go), *luchar* (to fight), *mandar* (to send), *preguntar* (to ask).

Envía (Manda) **por** el médico.   *He sends for the doctor.*

Voy **por** leche.   *I am going for milk.*

Luchan **por** su patria.   *They fight for their country.*

Preguntó **por** mi mamá.   *He asked for (about) my mother.*

NOTES:

1. *Por* and *para* are not used with the verbs *buscar* (to look for, to seek), *esperar* (to wait for, to await), and *pedir* (to ask for, to request).

Buscan un hotel.   *They are looking for a hotel.*

Esperé el tren.   *I waited for the train.*

Pidió un vaso de leche.   *She asked for a glass of milk.*

2. *En* is used instead of *por* to mean by means of transportation.

Mandé la carta por avión.   *I sent the letter by air.*

BUT

Viajé por México en autobús.   *I traveled through Mexico by bus.*

EXERCISE S.   **Answer the questions a younger cousin asks you while you are visiting relatives.**

1. ¿Te gusta dar un paseo por el centro comercial?

_____

2. ¿A quién visitas para curar un dolor de muelas?

_____

3. ¿Estás por ir conmigo al parque ahora mismo?

_____

4. ¿Has estudiado la lección para el lunes?

_____

5. ¿Tienes que correr a la escuela para llegar a tiempo?

_____

6. ¿Has viajado alguna vez por el Canadá?

_____

7. ¿Para qué es el jabón?

_____

8. ¿Lucharías por la justicia?

_____

9. ¿Envía tu mamá por el médico cuando tú tienes fiebre?

_____

10. ¿Hay un estante para libros en tu cuarto?

_____

(EXERCISE T.)   **Complete the story that Rosa tells about a friend with _por_ or _para_, if needed.**

Ayer _____ la tarde fui de compras con mi hermana. Yo quería comprar un regalo _____
       1.   *2.*

un amigo que va a estudiar en México _____ seis meses. Él sale _____ México el primero
                                     3.   *4.*

del próximo mes. Caminamos _____ el centro comercial buscando _____ un regalo
                                        5.   *6.*

apropiado _____ él. Es difícil comprar un regalo _____ él. La última vez que le di un regalo
               7.   *8.*

le compré un suéter pero, él lo cambió _____ otro. Era un suéter bonito, hecho _____ un
                                        9.   *10.*

diseñador famoso y pagué mucho _____ él. Me dijo que no era su talla. _____ un joven,
                                   11.   *12.*

su gusto en ropa es muy conservador. Otra amiga nos dijo que ella quería encontrarnos en el centro comercial

_____ tomar un café. Esperamos _____ más de media hora pero nunca llegó. Quizás había
       13.   *14.*

problema en el metro porque ella viaja _____ transporte público. La buscamos _____ todas
                                      15.   *16.*

partes en el centro comercial pero no dimos con ella. Buscamos _____ el regalo _____
                                         17.   *18.*

casi dos horas y mi hermana se puso furiosa. _____ fin caminamos _____ una librería y
                                        19.   *20.*

tomé la decisión de comprar un diccionario inglés-español _____ él. Si no le gusta lo puede cambiar
                                             21.

_____ otro libro. Compré papel de envoltura _____ regalo en otra tienda. Era tarde
    22.   *23.*

cuando fuimos al estacionamiento _____ recoger el carro y nos dimos cuenta de que no teníamos
                                          24.

bastante dinero en efectivo _____ pagar _____ la cuota.
                                 25.   *26.*

⟨ MASTERY EXERCISES ⟩

(EXERCISE U.)   **Express your feelings by completing each sentence with an infinitive and the necessary prepositions.**

EXAMPLE: Yo aprendí a conducir un carro y logré hacerlo en un mes.
                  Yo espero **llegar a** ser médico y **curar a** los enfermos.

1. Yo pienso _____

2. Yo no me atrevo _____

3. Yo dejo _____

4. Yo insisto _____

5. Yo me niego _____

6. Yo consiento _____

7. Yo me acuerdo _____

8. Yo me apresuro _____

(**EXERCISE V.**)   **Complete this story with the appropriate prepositions.**

El viaje _____ la carretera era larga y solitaria. Yo suelo _____ dormirme en los viajes
1.   2.

_____ automóvil pero esta vez no podía _____ hacerlo. Nosotros íbamos _____
3.   4.   5.

visitar varias universidades _____ mi hermana. _____ distraerme, traté _____
6.   7.   8.

meterme _____ jugar _____ un juego. Contaría las placas de los carros que pasamos. Conté
9.   10.

las placas _____ media hora y me decidí _____ dejar _____ hacerlo porque
11.   12.   13.

solamente conté diez. No me atrevía _____ decirles _____ mis papás que yo estaba
14.   15.

aburrido. Me obligarían _____ empezar _____ leer una novela _____ la clase
16.   17.   18.

_____ inglés. _____ decirles algo, cerré los ojos y comencé _____ soñar. En el
19.   20.   21.

sueño, yo buscaba _____ un lugar donde había mucha gente y mucho ruido. Tardamos tres horas
22.

_____ llegar a la primera universidad. Yo insistí _____ ir a la cafetería _____
23.   24.   25.

tomar un refresco. Quería caminar y estirarme las piernas _____ un rato. Mi hermana se negó
26.

_____ acompañarnos a la cafetería porque quería _____ caminar _____ los
27.   28.   29.

terrenos universitarios _____ conocer los diferentes edificios. Mis padres se decidieron _____
30.   31.

acompañarla. Yo me dediqué _____ buscar _____ el estadio y el gimnasio porque me
32.   33.

interesan mucho los deportes. _____ media hora yo caminaba en círculos hasta_____ fin
34.   35.

los encontré. Nos citamos_____ encontrarnos en la cafetería_____ las cinco. Cuando
36.   37.

pasamos_____ el pueblo donde está la universidad, mi mamá dijo que quería _____
38.   39.

pasar la noche allí. Ella logró_____ convencer a mi papá y_____ visitar la universidad
40.   41.

buscamos _____ hotel _____ pasar la noche. _____ la mañana, damos un
42.   43.   44.

paseo por el pueblo. _____ hacer esto, mi hermana insistió_____ volver_____
45.   46.   47.

visitar la biblioteca de la universidad. _____ el mes que viene ella piensa_____ volver
48.   49.

_____ visitar esta universidad.
50.

EXERCISE W. You are preparing for the college/scholarship application process. Write an email message to a Spanish-speaking friend in another state or country in which you describe the process. You may wish to include the following:

- how you're spending your time now

- your plan to apply for a scholarship

- the reason for seeking a scholarship

- what you need to present to a scholarship committee (outstanding grades, an essay, etc.)

- how this task affects your current activities

- your career goals

- faculty members who can help you

- when you will meet them

- what type of summer job you will seek

- your parents' reaction if you win the scholarship

- how this experience has changed how you use your free time

ACTIVIDADES

1. Prepare a short story in Spanish in which you describe a day or afternoon you spent with a friend. Be sure to use as many verbs requiring prepositions in the story as you can.

2. Write your friend a letter in which you talk about your plans for the future and your reasons for deciding on those plans. Be sure to use as many verbs requiring prepositions in the letter as you can.

3. In celebration of good health and nutrition months, prepare a list of things people should do to improve their lives. Use *por* or *para* in as many of them as you can.

Adjectives / Adverbs and Related Structures

Adjectives

◆ 1 ◆ GENDER OF ADJECTIVES

Adjectives agree in gender (masculine or feminine) with the nouns they describe.

Adjectives ending in *-o* form the feminine by changing *-o* to *-a*. Most adjectives ending in a consonant form the feminine by adding *-a*.

ri**c**o, ri**c**a *rich*	alemán, aleman**a** *German*
delgad**o**, delgad**a** *thin*	hablador, hablador**a** *talkative*
cómi**c**o, cómi**c**a *funny*	trabajador, trabajador**a** *hard-working*
español, español**a** *Spanish*	

Some adjectives, many of them ending in *-e*, have the same form for both the masculine and the feminine.

difícil, difícil *difficult*	grande, grande *large*
fuerte *strong*	estable *stable*
amable, amable *nice*	agrícola, agrícola *agricultural*
inteligente *intelligent*	

◆ 2 ◆ PLURAL OF ADJECTIVES

The plural of adjectives is formed by:

a. adding *-s* when the singular form ends in a vowel.

cómico**s**, alemana**s**, amable**s**

b. adding *-es* when the singular form ends in a consonant.

español**es**, hablador**es**, difícil**es**

NOTES:

1. Adjectives with singular forms ending in *-z* change *z* to *c* in the plural.

   feli**z**, feli**ces**   *happy*

2. Some adjectives add or drop an accent mark in order to keep the original stress.

   joven, j**ó**venes   *young*

   portugu**é**s, portuguesa, portugueses, portuguesas   *Portuguese*

   ingl**é**s, inglesa, ingleses, inglesas   *English*

   cort**é**s, corteses   *polite*

EXERCISE A. Manny is describing some of his friends. Express what he says.

EXAMPLE: Jeanette / cómico   Jeanette **es** cómic**a.**

1. Andrés / fuerte _____

2. Ruth / cortés _____

3. Silvia y Estela / simpático _____

4. Carlos / diligente _____

5. Catherine / francés _____

6. Douglas y Fernando / perezoso _____

7. Jaime / tacaño _____

8. Gina y Rosa / guapo _____

9. Vicente y Pilar / antipático _____

10. Laura / encantador _____

11. Donald / responsable _____

12. Harriet y Diana / hablador _____

EXERCISE B. How would you describe your teachers? Express how each one is by completing the statement with the appropriate form of one of the following adjectives.

aburrido	divertido	inteligente	justo
bondadoso	estricto	interesante	olvidadizo
creativo	hablador	joven	severo

EXAMPLE: La profesora de historia es **interesante.**

1. El profesor / La profesora de música es _____.

2. El profesor / La profesora de español es _____.

3. El profesor / La profesora de historia es _____.

4. El profesor / La profesora de educación física es _____.

5. El profesor / La profesora de inglés es _____.

6. El profesor / La profesora de ciencia es _____.

7. El profesor / La profesora de matemáticas es _____.

8. El profesor / La profesora de arte es _____.

EXERCISE C. Using the adjectives below, tell how you and the people indicated differ.

alegre	cómico	hablador	tímido
amable	diligente	quieto	trabajador
antipático	generoso	serio	responsable

EXAMPLE: tu hermano   Mi hermano es **responsable,** yo soy **cómico.**

1. tu mejor amigo(-a)   _____

2. tus padres   _____

3. tus hermanos(-as)   _____

4. tu primo(-a)   _____

EXERCISE D.   **Adam and David rarely agree with each other. Express what David responds to Adam's statements.**

EXAMPLE: La película es **interesante.**   La película es **aburrida.**

1. Es una pieza de música clásica.   _____

2. Los actores son conocidos.   _____

3. Es un cine antiguo.   _____

4. El argumento de la película se basa en
     un acontecimiento imaginario.   _____

5. La fotografía está borrosa.   _____

6. El director recibió una reseña buena. _____

7. Es un cine cómodo.   _____

8. El protagonista es viejo.   _____

9. Las palomitas son sabrosas.   _____

10. Las entradas son caras.   _____

◆ *3* ◆ POSITION OF ADJECTIVES

a. Descriptive adjectives normally follow the nouns they describe.
una **película cómica**   *a funny film*   el **carro rojo**   *the red car*

b. Descriptive adjectives may stand before the noun to emphasize the quality of the adjective or its inherent characteristic.

Vi los pájaros, con sus **coloridas plumas.**   *I saw the birds, with their colorful feathers.*

El verano me trae **bonitos recuerdos.**   *Summer brings me beautiful memories.*

NOTES:

1. Some adjectives have different meanings, depending on their position.

Lincoln fue un *gran* hombre.   *Lincoln was a great man.*

BUT

Mi padre es un **hombre** *grande*.   *My father is a big man.*

2. The following adjectives may change their meaning according to their position:

	AFTER THE NOUN	BEFORE THE NOUN
antiguo, -a	*old (ancient)*	*old (former, old-time)*
cierto, -a	*sure; true*	*a certain*
grande	*large, big*	*great*
mismo, -a	*him (her, it)-self*	*same*
nuevo, -a	*new*	*another, different*
pobre	*poor*	*unfortunate*
simple	*silly, simpleminded*	*simple, mere*

3. Limiting adjectives (numbers, possessive and demonstrative adjectives, adjectives of quantity) usually precede the noun.

tres lápices	*three pens*	**esa** mujer	*that woman*
ningún hombre	*no man*	**tal** cosa	*such a thing*
sus hermanos	*his brothers*	**más** pan	*more bread*

COMMONLY USED LIMITING ADJECTIVES	
algunos, -as *some*	**poco, -a, -os, -as** *little, few*
cada *each, every*	**tal** *such (a)*
cuanto, -a, -os, -as *as much*	**tanto, -a, -os, -as** *so much, so many*
más *more*	**todo, -a, -os, -as** *all, every*
menos *less*	**unos, -as** *some*
ningunos, -as *no, not any*	**unos, -as cuantos, -as** *a few*
numerosos, -as *numerous*	**varios, -as** *several*

◆ 4 ◆ AGREEMENT OF ADJECTIVES

a. Adjectives agree in gender and number with the nouns they describe.

Elena es tímida.   *Elena is shy (timid).*
Los dueños son ricos.   *The owners are rich.*

b. An adjective modifying two or more nouns of different gender is masculine plural.

La rosa y el clavel son bonitos.   *The rose and the carnation are pretty.*

EXERCISE E.   **Make a list of the things you saw on a recent trip to Costa Rica.**

EXAMPLE: iglesia / mucho, antiguo   **muchas** iglesias **antiguas**

1. selva / varios, tropical   _____

2. mar / uno, tranquilo   _____

3. montaña / uno, impresionante   _____

4. flor / numeroso, exótico   _____

5. hotel / alguno, elegante   _____

6. vista / mucho, panorámico   _____

7. insecto / varios, feo   _____

8. persona / tanto, simpático   _____

9. animal / numeroso, salvaje   _____

10. planta / mucho, verde   _____

EXERCISE F.   **Mr. Salinas is being relocated to another city. Complete the e-mail message he sends to his family with the appropriate forms of the adjectives given.**

Querida familia:

Yo ya encontré _____ casa _____ . Es _____ casa _____
                1. (un)   2. (perfecto)   3. (un)   4. (grande)

y _____ . _____ casa es de dos pisos. Hay _____ cuartos
    5. (cómodo)   6. (Este)   7. (ocho)

_____ y _____ de sol. En la sala hay _____ chimenea _____ .
  8. (amplio)   9. (lleno)   10. (un)   11. (antiguo)

Hay _____ jardín _____ con _____ árboles _____
    12. (un)   13. (extenso)   14. (mucho)   15. (viejo)

y flores _____ . También hay _____ piscina _____ pero tiene
    17. (bonito)   18. (un)   19. (amplio)

_____ forma _____ . Parece _____ oreja _____ . Los
  20. (un)   21. (extraño)   22. (un)   23. (humano)

dueños de la casa son _____ pareja _____ . También conocí a _____
        24. (un)   25. (simpático)   26. (un)

vecinos _____ . Creo que _____ _____ casa les va a gustar a
    27. (amable)   28. (este)   29. (nuevo)

todos Uds. Nos veremos _____ semana _____ cuando Uds. vengan a conocer
        30. (el)   31. (próximo)

_____ ciudad _____ y _____ que pronto será su casa
  32. (este)   33. (interesante)   34. (divertido)

_____ .
  35. (nuevo)

Hasta pronto,

Papá

◆ 5 ◆ SHORTENED FORMS OF ADJECTIVES

a. The following adjectives drop the final *-o* when used before a masculine singular noun:

uno	*one, a, an*	→	**un** pastel	*one (a) cake*
bueno	*good*	→	un **buen** jugador	*a good player*
malo	*bad*	→	un **mal** rato	*a bad time*
primero	*first*	→	el **primer** mes	*the first month*
tercero	*third*	→	el **tercer** día	*the third day*
alguno	*some*	→	**algún** año	*some year*
ninguno	*no, not any*	→	**ningún** pensamiento	*no thought*

NOTES:

1. The adjectives *alguno* and *ninguno* require an accent mark when the *-o* is dropped: *algún, ningún.*

2. If a preposition comes between the adjective and the noun, the full form of the adjective is used.

el primero del mes	*the first of the month*
ninguno de los amigos	*none of the friends*

b. *Santo* becomes *San* before the masculine name of a saint, except with names beginning with *To-* or *Do-*.

San Felipe	*Saint Philip*	San Antonio	*Saint Anthony*

BUT

Santo Tomás	*Saint Thomas*	Santo Domingo	*Saint Dominic*

c. *Grande* becomes *gran* when used before a singular noun of either gender.

un gran pintor
una gran pintora } *a great painter*

BUT

un río grande	*a large river*
una montaña grande	*a large mountain*

d. *Ciento* becomes *cien* before a noun of either gender and before the numbers *mil* and *millones*. This short form is not used with multiples of *ciento* (like *doscientos* and *trescientos*) or in combination with any other number.

cien hombres (mujeres)	*one (a) hundred men (women)*
cien mil dólares	*one (a) hundred thousand dollars*
cien millones de habitantes	*one (a) hundred million inhabitants*

BUT

seiscientos ganadores	*six hundred winners*
doscientas habitaciones	*two hundred rooms*
ciento treinta y dos comidas	*one (a) hundred thirty-two meals*

EXERCISE G.   Jeremy wants to see how well you answer the trivia questions he asks you. Use a form of *bueno, malo, santo, primero, tercero, ninguno* or *alguno* in your responses.

EXAMPLE: ¿Qué dices al ver a tus padres por la mañana?   **Buenos días.**

1. ¿Qué dices al describir el tiempo cuando llueve?

_____

2. ¿Qué dices al describir el tiempo cuando hace un sol brillante?

_____

3. ¿Qué dices cuando te preguntan el precio de estos zapatos? (*$100*)

_____

4. ¿Qué dices al identificar la capital de la República Dominicana?

_____

5. ¿Qué dices cuando te preguntan «¿Cuándo conocerás Madrid?»?

_____

6. ¿Qué dices al identificar el nombre español de «Saint Andrew»?

_____

7. ¿Qué dices al contestar la pregunta «¿Cuántos cuartos hay en ese hotel?»? (*191*)

_____

8. ¿Qué dices al identificar la fecha de Año Nuevo?

_____

9. ¿Qué dices al despedirte de tus padres por la noche?

_____

10. ¿Qué dices cuando le deseas éxito a alguien?

_____

11. ¿Qué le dices a alguien cuando él (ella) se sienta a comer?

_____

12. ¿Qué dices para completar el siguiente trío de islas: San Juan, Santa Cruz y . . . ?

_____

13. ¿Qué dices cuando identificas las tres carabelas de Cristóbal Colón: la Niña, la Pinta y . . . ?

_____

14. ¿Qué dices al identificar el equivalente del cuarto piso en un edificio en México?

_____

15. ¿Qué dices al explicarle a un hombre que no tiene problemas?

_____

MASTERY EXERCISES

EXERCISE H. **Describe some of the things you see as you walk through a flea market. Use the following adjectives.**

antiguo	feo	largo	pequeño	viejo
ciento	grande	nuevo	raro	

EXAMPLE: una espada larga

1. _____

5. _____

2. _____

6. _____

3. _____

7. _____

4. _____

8. _____

EXERCISE I. Express your opinion about the following topics using two adjectives in each sentence.

EXAMPLE: la natación (*un deporte*)   La natación es un deporte **divertido** y **saludable.**

1. el invierno (*una estación*)

_____

2. los juegos electrónicos y el ajedrez (*pasatiempos*)

_____

3. la leche (*una bebida*)

_____

4. la contaminación y las enfermedades (*problemas*)

_____

5. el avión (*un modo de transporte*)

_____

6. Puerto Rico (*una isla*)

_____

7. los chícharos y las espinacas (*legumbres*)

_____

8. el Día de la Raza y el Día de la Independencia de los Estados Unidos (*días festivos*)

_____

EXERCISE J.   **You are preparing a blog in Spanish for your class' Web site about a Spanish-speaking country you have visited. Include the following information:**

- the place
- how many times you have visited there
- your impressions of the place and the local inhabitants
- some historical background about the places you have previously visited there
- something about these places (cities)
- what you like most/least about the place
- a special wish you have for this trip
- a current event about this place

ACTIVIDADES

1. Prepare a list of questions you would ask a new pen pal to find out about his/her physical and personality traits.

2. Write a description of yourself that will help an Internet pen pal identify you in a group of people. Then, describe your personality traits.

3. Write a short paragraph of six to ten sentences in which you describe two of the following:

your friends   your school and classes
your teachers   your favorite musical personality or group, entertainer, athlete, or team.

4. Write a short paragraph of six to ten sentences in which you describe your vision of the world and society twenty years from now.

Demonstrative Adjectives and Pronouns

◆ 1 ◆ DEMONSTRATIVE ADJECTIVES

Demonstrative adjectives precede the nouns they modify and agree with them in gender (masculine or feminine) and number (singular or plural).

MASCULINE	FEMININE	MEANING
este	esta	this
estos	estas	these
ese	esa	that
esos	esas	those
aquel	aquella	that
aquellos	aquellas	those

este papel	this paper
esas ventanas	those windows

NOTES:

1. *Este* (this), *estos* (these), etc. refer to what is near or directly concerns the speaker. *Ese* (that), *esos* (these), etc. refer to what is not so near or does not directly concern the person addressed. *Aquel* (that), *aquellos* (those), etc. refer to what is remote from both the speaker and the person addressed, or does not directly concern either.

Esta novela es interesante.	*This novel is interesting.*
Raúl, quiero **ese** libro que tienes en la mano.	*Raúl, I want that book that you have in your hand.*
Raúl, prefiero **aquel** libro.	*Raúl, I prefer that book over there.*

2. The adverbs *aquí* (here), *ahí* (there), and *allí* ([over] there) correspond to the demonstratives *este*, *ese*, and *aquel*, respectively.

Pon
{
esta silla **aquí**
esa mesa **ahí**
aquella lámpara **allí**
}

Put
{
this chair (here)
that table (there)
that lamp (over there)
}

EXERCISE A. Paco received money for his birthday and wants to buy some sports equipment with it. Express what he asks the salesperson in the sports shop.

EXAMPLE: raqueta de tenis   ¿Cuánto vale **esta raqueta de tenis?**

1. bicicleta _____

2. guante de béisbol _____

3. pelota de fútbol _____

4. patines _____

5. monopatín _____

6. pelotas de golf _____

7. zapatos de tenis _____

8. traje de baño _____

9. tienda de campaña _____

10. compás _____

EXERCISE B. **Lisa and a friend are visiting a museum. Express what they say about the things they see, using the proper form of *ese*.**

EXAMPLE: pintura / oscura **Esa** pintura es muy oscura.

1. estatuas / modernas _____

2. tapices / antiguos _____

3. templo / griego _____

4. muebles / incómodos _____

5. retrato / interesante _____

6. escalera / alta _____

7. paisaje / sereno _____

8. cuadros / feos _____

EXERCISE C. **Alfonso and a friend are walking around the perimeter of "El Parque del Buen Retiro" in Madrid. Express what they see as they look into the park. Use the proper form of *aquel*.**

EXAMPLE: árboles / viejos **Aquellos** árboles son muy viejos.

1. lago / grande _____

2. monumentos / interesantes _____

3. flores / bonitas _____

4. estatua / famosa _____

5. paseo / largo _____

6. barcos / divertidos _____

7. palmera / alta _____

EXERCISE D.   Hilda is in a souvenir shop in Mexico. Express what she would like to see. Use the proper demonstrative adjective.

EXAMPLE: camiseta / ahí   Quisiera ver **esa** camiseta.

1. llavero / allí   _____

2. figura de barro / aquí   _____

3. sarape / ahí   _____

4. juego de ajedrez / aquí   _____

5. huaraches / allí   _____

6. muñeca / allí   _____

7. canasta / ahí   _____

8. acuarela / aquí   _____

9. sombrero de charro / allí _____

10. aretes de plata / ahí   _____

EXERCISE E.   Elsa just moved into a new neighborhood. Answer the questions she asks a neighbor about the area, using the appropriate demonstrative adjective.

EXAMPLE: ¿Venden buen pan en la panadería de allí?
             Sí, venden buen pan en **aquella** panadería.

1. ¿Venden periódicos en la librería de ahí?

   _____

2. ¿Hay un buen surtido de frutas en el supermercado de aquí?

   _____

3. ¿Juegan al tenis en el parque de allí?

   _____

4. ¿Es seguro caminar por las calles de ahí por la noche?

   _____

5. ¿Limpian bien la ropa en la tintorería de allí?

   _____

6. ¿Son buenos los cafés de ahí?

   _____

7. ¿Trabajan muchas personas en las fábricas de allí?

   _____

8. ¿Sirven buena comida en el restaurante de aquí?

   _____

9. ¿Pasan muchos taxis por la avenida de allí?

_____

10. ¿Tienen buenas películas en el cine de aquí?

_____

◆ 2 ◆ DEMONSTRATIVE PRONOUNS

MASCULINE	FEMININE	NEUTER	MEANING
este	**esta**	**esto**	_this (one)_
estos	**estas**		_these_
ese	**esa**	**eso**	_that (one)_
esos	**esas**		_those_
aquel	**aquella**	**aquello**	_that (one)_
aquellos	**aquellas**		_those_

a. Demonstrative pronouns agree in number and gender with the nouns they replace.

este cuadro y aquel (cuadro)   _this painting and that (one)_

b. The neuter forms _esto, eso, aquello_ refer to general statements, ideas, or an object of indeterminate gender. These forms do not vary in gender and number.

Es un hotel tranquilo, y eso   _It is a quiet hotel, and the_
 les gusta a los huéspedes.   _guests like that._

The question _¿Qué es esto (eso, aquello)?_ uses the neuter form because the noun's gender is unknown. After the noun has been mentioned, the form of the demonstrative adjective or pronoun must correspond to the noun.

¿Qué es esto? —Es una piedra.   _What is this? —It is a stone._

¿Es grande esta piedra? —Sí.   _Is this stone large? —Yes._

> **EXERCISE F.** Roberto and Emilio are buying school supplies for the new school year. They rarely agree on what to buy. Express what they say in the following dialogue using an appropriate demonstrative pronoun.

EXAMPLE: ROBERTO: Me gustan **estas** plumas.
     EMILIO: Yo prefiero **aquellas** de allí.

1. ROBERTO: Debes comprar este libro.

  EMILIO: Voy a comprar _____ de ahí.

2. ROBERTO: Esas gomas son muy buenas.

  EMILIO: Yo siempre uso _____ de aquí.

3. ROBERTO: ¿Te sirven estos cuadernos?

  EMILIO: No, _____ de allí son más útiles.

4. ROBERTO: Aquellas mochilas son muy baratas.

   EMILIO: Sí, pero _____ de aquí son de mejor calidad.

5. ROBERTO: Esta revista es buena para la tarea de la clase de inglés.

   EMILIO: Prefiero _____ de allí porque trata sobre los deportes.

6. ROBERTO: Estos bolígrafos son bonitos.

   EMILIO: Voy a comprar dos de _____ de ahí.

⬭ **EXERCISE G.**   Gladys is packing for a trip and is explaining why she chose the clothing she will take. Complete her statements with the appropriate demonstrative pronoun.

EXAMPLE: Llevo esta blusa porque **esa** de ahí no va bien con aquella falda.

1. No llevo ese chaleco porque _____ de aquí es más bonito.

2. Estos zapatos son más cómodos que _____ de allí.

3. Voy a llevar aquel traje de baño porque es más nuevo que _____ de aquí.

4. Esos pantalones cortos son más prácticos que _____ de allí.

5. Aquellas sandalias están más de moda que _____ de ahí.

6. Estos suéteres son más ligeros que _____ de allí.

7. Esa falda negra es más útil que _____ de aquí de flores.

8. La única bolsa que voy a llevar es _____ de ahí.

⬭ **EXERCISE H.**   Lucy is tired of listening to the questions her younger sister asks when they go out together. Complete her questions with the appropriate demonstrative pronoun based on the cue given.

EXAMPLE: (*aquí*) ¿Qué quiere decir **esto**?

1. (*ahí*) ¿Qué es _____ ?

2. (*aquí / allí*) Yo quiero ver _____ y _____ .

3. (*ahí*) ¿Comprendes _____ ?

4. (*aquí*) ¿Viste _____ ?

5. (*aquí / ahí*) ¡Lee _____ , no leas _____ !

6. (*ahí*) Yo no recuerdo _____ .

7. (*aquí*) Yo sé _____ .

8. (*allí*) ¿Quién dijo _____ ?

9. (*ahí*) ¿Oíste _____ ?

10. (*allí*) ¿De quién es _____ ?

c. The pronoun *este* (*esta, estos, estas*) also means *the latter* (*the latest, the most recently mentioned*); *aquel* (*aquella, aquellos, aquellas*) also means *the former* (*the most remotely mentioned*).

Ana y Susana: **esta es** rubia,   *Ann and Susan: the former is brunette,*
   aquella es morena.   *the latter is blonde.*

NOTE: In English, we usually say "the former and the latter." In Spanish, the order is reversed: *esta* (the latter) comes first.

EXERCISE I.   **Monty likes to comment on a variety of topics. Express what he says using the appropriate demonstrative pronouns.**

EXAMPLE: Tengo dos cartas de Juan. En **esta** escribe en español y en **aquella** escribe en inglés.

1. Vicente es de la Argentina y Harry es de Inglaterra. _____ es inglés y

_____ es argentino.

2. Carmen escribe poemas originales. A Daniel le gusta contar chistes. _____ es muy cómico y

_____ es muy creativa.

3. Mis hermanos practican muchos deportes. Los hermanos de Berta leen muchas novelas.

_____ son serios y _____ son activos.

4. El hermano menor de Julia siempre dice «por favor» y «gracias». Mi hermano menor nunca dice nada.

_____ es descortés y _____ es cortés.

5. José mide seis pies. Arturo mide cuatro pies y siete pulgadas. _____ es bajo y

_____ es alto.

EXERCISE J.   **Julio is usually at a loss for words and just repeats comments his friends make. Express what he says using the appropriate forms of este and aquel.**

EXAMPLE: La bicicleta roja es más ligera que la bicicleta negra.
            Si, **esta** pesa más que **aquella.**

1. Nancy estudia más que Felipe.

   Sí, _____ es menos diligente que _____ .

2. La tortilla española es más sabrosa que los huevos fritos.

   Sí, _____ son menos sabrosos que _____ .

3. Los videojuegos son más divertidos que los juegos de mesa.

   Sí, _____ son menos divertidos que _____ .

4. Las películas de ciencia-ficción son emocionantes pero las películas policíacas son más emocionantes.

   Sí, _____ son más emocionantes que _____ .

5. El fútbol americano es divertido pero el fútbol es más divertido.

   Sí, _____ es más divertido que _____ .

d. The definite article (*el, la, los, las*) followed by *de* (that of, the one of) or *que* (the one that) functions like a demonstrative pronoun.

el (la) de Luis	*that of (the one of) Luis; Luis's*
los (las) de Luis	*those of (the ones of) Luis; Luis's*
el (la) que está aquí	*the one that is here*
los (las) que están aquí	*the ones that are here*
El profesor de Raúl es más estricto que el de Pedro.	*Raul's teacher is stricter than Pedro's.*
El suéter de Nadia es muy parecido al que lleva Marta.	*Nadia's sweater is very similar to the one that Martha's is wearing.*

EXERCISE K. Mrs. Perales sent this e-mail message to one of her twin sons who are away at camp. Complete her message with the demonstrative pronoun, using the appropriate form of the article (*el, la, los, las*).

Querido Hugo:

Hoy fui al centro para buscar las cosas que tú y tu hermano me pidieron. Pude encontrar _____ que tú me pediste pero _____ de tu hermano fueron más difíciles. En la tienda de deportes encontré la máscara de béisbol que me pediste pero no pude encontrar _____ de bucear de tu hermano. Les mandaré las cosas en dos paquetes pero tengan cuidado al abrirlos porque tu paquete será muy parecido a _____ de tu hermano. Todavía no encuentro la ropa que te falta ni _____ de tu hermano. El sábado voy a otra tienda. Es una tienda nueva y el surtido es mejor que _____ de la tienda donde siempre hago las compras. Será más fácil encontrar los pantalones que tú quieres, pero _____ que quiere tu hermano ya no se ven en las tiendas. Si tengo suerte, podré terminar mis quehaceres y _____ que Uds. me encargaron. Hasta luego.

Tu mamá

MASTERY EXERCISES

EXERCISE L. You are on a sightseeing bus traveling through the countryside in Spain. You and the other passengers on the bus comment about what you see. Describe five things you see, using a demonstrative adjective in each.

SUGGESTIONS: aldea iglesia castillo calle
toros montañas paisaje flores

EXAMPLE: **Esas** casas son de piedra.
Aquella torre es muy alta.

1. _____
2. _____

3. _____

4. _____

5. _____

EXERCISE M. **Armando usually agrees with what his friends say. Express what he says, using the appropriate form of *este* and *aquel*.**

EXAMPLE: El italiano es un idioma bonito pero el español es más bonito.
Este es un idioma más bonito que **aquel**.

1. El helado es un postre rico pero el flan es más rico.

_____

2. Las novelas son buenos regalos pero los MP3 son mejores regalos.

_____

3. Un concurso de deletrear es emocionante pero una carrera es más emocionante.

_____

4. La riqueza es una meta difícil de alcanzar, pero la fama es una meta más difícil de alcanzar.

_____

5. Los videojuegos son entretenimientos más divertidos que los juegos de mesa.

_____

EXERCISE N. **Andrés and Beatriz are preparing for a picnic in the park to which they have invited their friends. Express what they say in Spanish.**

1. Those decorations are very nice.

_____

2. Put this table under that tree over there.

_____

3. You can put these things on those blankets over there.

_____

4. Put these plates on this table and those on that one over there.

_____

5. Which compact disks do you prefer, these or those?

_____

6. Chairs? I didn't think about that.

_____

7. What is that?

_____

8. I brought this dish and and those of my mother.

_____

9. Where can we hide these games?

_____

10. That's a good idea.

_____

◄ A C T I V I D A D E S ►

A friend is helping you set up your room in the college dormitory. Prepare a list indicating where you will place each of your belongings illustrated in the picture. Use as many demonstrative adjectives and pronouns as you can.

CHAPTER

26

Possession

◆ 1 ◆ EXPRESSING POSSESSION

a. Possession is normally expressed in Spanish by *de + the possessor.*

la camisa **de José**	*Jose's shirt*
los hijos **de los señores Ruiz**	*the Ruiz's children*
las muñecas **de la niña**	*the girl's dolls*
la bicicleta **de mi amigo**	*my friend's bicycle*

b. When the preposition *de* is followed by the definite article *el,* the contraction *del* is formed.

el babero **del** bebé	*the baby's bib*

c. When followed by a form of *ser, ¿De quién,-es . . . ?* is equivalent to the English interrogative "Whose . . . ?".

¿De quién es el carro?	*Whose car is it?*
¿De quién son los lápices?	*Whose pencils are these?*
¿De quiénes es la casa?	*Whose house is it?*
¿De quiénes son los patines?	*Whose skates are these?*

EXERCISE A. As you and your family go through customs in Mexico, the customs inspector wants to know to whom different items belong. Express the questions he asks.

EXAMPLE: muñeca   **¿De quién es** la muñeca?

1. calculadora _____

2. teléfono celular _____

3. cuaderno electrónico _____

4. revistas _____

5. patines _____

6. anteojos _____

EXERCISE B. Using the questions you prepared in Exercise A, express how your father answers them according to the cues provided.

EXAMPLE: la muñeca / mi hija   La muñeca es **de mi hija.**

1. la calculadora / Carlos _____

2. el teléfono celular / mi esposa _____

3. el cuaderno electrónico / el joven _____

4. las revistas / mis hijos   _____

5. los patines / mi sobrina   _____

6. los lentes de sol / los jóvenes   _____

EXERCISE C.   **A friend is helping you clean the car after a family motor trip. Express the question your friend asks to find out to whom different items belong and then answer his questions.**

EXAMPLE: zapatos / Frank
               ¿De quién son estos zapatos?   Estos zapatos **son de Frank.**

1. novelas / Grace y Emma

_____

2. juego electrónico / mi hermano

_____

3. dulces / mi mamá

_____

4. refresco / mi abuelo

_____

5. cartera / mi papá

_____

6. sombrero / el señor Velasco

_____

◆ 2 ◆ POSSESSIVE ADJECTIVES

In Spanish there are two sets of possessive adjectives: a short form and a long form.

SHORT FORM	LONG FORM	MEANING
mi, mis	**mío, -a, -os, -as**	*my*
tu, tus	**tuyo, -a, -os, -as**	*your* (fam. sing.)
su, sus	**suyo, -a, -os, -as**	*his, her, its, their; your* (formal)
nuestro, -a, -os, -as	**nuestro,-a,-os,-as**	*our*
vuestro, -a, -os, -as	**vuestro,-a,-os,-as**	*your* (fam. pl.)

a. The short forms of possessive adjectives precede the noun.

mi casa	*my house*	**tus** pañuelos	*your handkerchiefs*
su fotografía	*his (her, its, your, their) photograph*	**nuestros** juguetes	*our toys*
nuestra escuela	*our school*		

b. The long forms of possessive adjectives follow the noun.

un libro **mío**	*a book of mine*	unos primos **nuestros**	*some cousins of ours*
una amiga **tuya**	*a friend of yours*		

NOTES:

1. Possessive adjectives agree in gender (masculine or feminine) and number (singular or plural) with the person or thing possessed, not with the possessor.

nuestra abuela	*our grandmother*
nuestras abuelas	*our grandmothers*
una cinta **tuya**	*a tape of yours (your tape)*
unas cintas **suyas**	*his / her/ its/ their/ your (formal)/ your (pl.) tapes*

2. *Nuestro* and *vuestro* have four forms. The other possessive adjectives have two forms.

3. To avoid ambiguity, *su* and *sus* may be replaced by the article plus de *Ud., de Uds., de él, de ella, de ellos,* or *de ellas.*

Yo vi a **su** mamá.	*I saw his (her, your, their) mother.*
Yo vi a la mamá **de ella**.	*I saw her mother.*

4. The definite article is used instead of the possessive adjective with parts of the body or wearing apparel when the possessor is clear.

El niño abrió **los** ojos.	*The boy opened his eyes.*
Yo me lavé **las** manos.	*I washed my hands.*
María se puso **los** lentes de sol.	*María put on her sunglasses.*

BUT

María se puso **mis** lentes de sol.	*María put on my sunglasses.*

EXERCISE D.   **Vivian is showing Frank a carton she found in the attic. He wants to know to whom these items belonged. Express what Vivian says.**

EXAMPLE: FRANK: ¿Eran **mis** botas?
　　　　　 VIVIAN   Sí, eran **tus** botas.

1. FRANK: ¿Eran estos trenes eléctricos de Sergio y Luis?

VIVIAN: _____

2. FRANK: ¿Era este reloj de Gloria?

VIVIAN: _____

3. FRANK: ¿Eran estos sombreros de mi abuela?

VIVIAN: _____

4. FRANK: ¿Eran estas camisetas de nuestros padres?

VIVIAN: _____

5. FRANK: ¿Era mi camión?

VIVIAN: _____

6. FRANK: ¿Era tu cadena de plata?

VIVIAN: _____

7. FRANK: ¿Era la máscara de Luis?

VIVIAN: _____

EXERCISE E.   **Jean and Alice are trying to have a conversation while the stereo blasts in the background. Complete their conversation.**

EXAMPLE: JEAN: El gato de Vicki está enfermo y debe llevarlo al veterinario.
              ALICE: ¿Qué debe llevar al veterinario?
              JEAN: Su gato.

1. JEAN: Tengo unos discos compactos nuevos. Vamos a escucharlos.
        ALICE: ¿Qué vamos a escuchar?
        JEAN: _____

2. JEAN: Yo tengo una bicicleta nueva. Mi hermana siempre quiere usarla.
        ALICE: ¿Qué quiere usar?
        JEAN: _____

3. JEAN: Debemos empezar a trabajar en el proyecto que vamos a hacer juntas para la clase de ciencia.
        ALICE: ¿Qué debemos hacer?
        JEAN: _____

4. JEAN: Elvira pidió prestadas las botas de Nora. Debe devolvérselas.
        ALICE: ¿Qué debe devolver?
        JEAN: _____

5. JEAN: Tú nunca sigues las instrucciones que te da la maestra.
        ALICE: ¿Qué nunca sigo?
        JEAN: _____

6. JEAN: Felipe tiene unos amigos muy simpáticos.
        ALICE: ¿Quiénes son simpáticos?
        JEAN: _____

7. JEAN: Paula siempre tiene buenas sugerencias para divertirse.
        ALICE: ¿Qué son buenas?
        JEAN: _____

8. JEAN: Yo le presté una llave a Berta pero ella la perdió.
        ALICE: ¿Qué perdió?
        JEAN: _____

EXERCISE F.   **Martin is telling his mother what happened in kindergarten today. Express what he says.**

EXAMPLE: Morgan se quitó los zapatos en la clase.

1. Kevin se cayó en el patio y se lastimó _____ rodilla.

2. Jorge levantó _____ mano para hacer una pregunta.

3. Yo me lavé _____ manos antes de comer.

4. Grace se cortó _____ el dedo con las tijeras.

5. Ralph no quiso leer porque olvidó _____ anteojos.

6. Mimi no quiso quitarse _____ suéter en la clase.

7. La maestra le dijo a otra maestra que le dolía _____ cabeza.

EXERCISE G. **Mrs. Pacheco borrowed several items to make everything look nice for an anniversary dinner for her parents. Answer the questions her sister-in-law asks about different items.**

EXAMPLE: ¿Son tus platos?   Sí, son **los platos míos.**

1. ¿Es el mantel de tu mamá? _____

2. ¿Son mis servilletas? _____

3. ¿Son los candeleros de Sofía? _____

4. ¿Son las copas de Hilda? _____

5. ¿Es el florero de la señora Álvarez? _____

6. ¿Son los cubiertos de Uds.? _____

7. ¿Es el videojuego de Pablo? _____

8. ¿Son los adornos de la tía Anita? _____

EXERCISE H. **Renee and Celia are college roommates. Celia likes to compare her things with those of their friends. Answer the questions she asks.**

EXAMPLE: Mi anillo es de plata. ¿Y tu anillo?
El anillo mío es de plata también.

1. Todas mis faldas son largas. ¿Y las faldas de Vivian?

   _____

2. Mis guantes son de piel. ¿Y tus guantes?

   _____

3. Todos mis zapatos son nuevos. ¿Y los zapatos de Carol y Elena?

   _____

4. Mi suéter es de casimir. ¿Y el suéter de Berta?

   _____

5. Mi computadora tiene muchísima memoria. ¿Y la computadora de Pedro?

_____

6. Mi televisor mide veintisiete pulgadas. ¿Y el televisor de Uds.?

_____

7. Mi calendario es electrónico. ¿Y tu calendario?

_____

8. Todas las notas que recibo son sobresalientes. ¿Y tus notas?

_____

(**EXERCISE I.**) **There is a lot of commotion in the student dormitory on the last day of school. They realize that many of the things they have do not belong to them. React to the statements that your roommate Sandy makes.**

EXAMPLE: SANDY: Enrique tiene los discos compactos de Beto.
            USTED: Tienes razón, no son los discos compactos suyos; son los de Beto.

1. SANDY: Javier tiene el traje de baño de Chuck.

   USTED: _____

2. SANDY: Lee tiene los libros de Marisa y Linda.

   USTED: _____

3. SANDY: Fred y yo tenemos las llaves de Adam.

   USTED: _____

4. SANDY: Tú tienes mi gorra.

   USTED: _____

5. SANDY: Esteban tiene el diccionario de Rocío.

   USTED: _____

6. SANDY: Nilda tiene los zapatos de Raquel.

   USTED: _____

7. SANDY: Blanca y Sarita tienen los exámenes de Teresa.

   USTED: _____

◆ 3 ◆ POSSESSIVE PRONOUNS

el mío, la mía, los míos, las mías   *mine*
el tuyo, la tuya, los tuyos, las tuyas   *yours* (fam. sing.)
el suyo, la suya, los suyos, las suyas   *his, hers, its, theirs; yours*
el nuestro, la nuestra, los nuestros, las nuestras   *ours*
el vuestro, la vuestra, los vuestros, las vuestras   *yours* (fam. pl.)

a. Possessive pronouns consist of the definite article + the long form of the possessive adjective.

b. The possessive pronoun agrees in number and gender with the noun it replaces, not with the possessor.

Mi bicicleta es más nueva que **la** (bicicleta) **suya.**   *My bicycle is newer than his.*

Esos papeles y **los** (papeles) **tuyos**   *These papers and yours*
son importantes.   *are important.*

NOTES:

1. The specific meaning of *el suyo* (*la suya, los suyos, las suyas*) may be made clear by replacing the possessive with the expressions *de Ud.* (*Uds.*), *de él* (*ella*), or *de ellos* (*ellas*) after the article.

   sus discos y los **de ella**   *his records and hers*

   mis monedas y las **de Uds.**   *my coins and yours*

2. After forms of *ser*, the article preceding the possessive pronoun is usually omitted.

   Este cinturón **es mío.**   *This belt is mine.*

   Aquellas bufandas **son suyas.**   *Those scarves are hers.*

EXERCISE J.   **Jerry likes to compare his possessions with those of his friends. Express what he says using the appropriate possessive pronouns.**

EXAMPLE: Mi casa es más grande que la casa de Federico.
La mía es más grande que **la suya (la de él).**

1. Mi computadora es más moderna que la computadora de Esteban.

_____

2. Mi equipo de fútbol gana más juegos que el equipo de mis primos.

_____

3. Hay más libros en español en mi biblioteca que en tu biblioteca.

_____

4. Mi mochila es más amplia que tus mochilas.

_____

5. Nuestra tienda de campaña es más grande que la tienda de campaña de ellos.

_____

6. Las uñas de mi hermana son más largas que las uñas de mi abuela.

_____

7. Mi cartera es de piel pero la cartera de Alberto es de plástico.

_____

8. Las bromas que yo hago son más divertidas que las bromas que hace José.

_____

EXERCISE K. Gina can never find what she is looking for. Using the cues provided, help her locate the items she needs.

EXAMPLE: No encuentro las fotografías de mis abuelos (*en el álbum*)
Las suyas están en el álbum.

1. ¿Dónde está mi toalla? (*detrás de la puerta del baño*)

   _____

2. Necesito una camiseta blanca. ¿Me prestas la tuya? (*en el armario*)

   _____

3. Aquí está el llavero de mi hermana. ¿Dónde está mi llavero? (*en tu mochila*)

   _____

4. ¿Dónde están los aretes de mi mamá? (*en el estuche*)

   _____

5. El carro de mi mamá está delante de la casa. ¿Y el carro de mi papá? (*en la gasolinera*)

   _____

6. Tengo todos los regalos menos uno para ti. (*en la tienda*)

   _____

7. No tienes tu cartera ni yo tampoco. (*en la mesa de la cocina*)

   _____

EXERCISE L. Neil always has to borrow things when he travels with his friends. Help him obtain what he needs.

EXAMPLE: ¿Pasta de dientes? Felipe puede prestarte **la suya.**

1. ¿Un peine? Yo puedo prestarte _____.

2. ¿Calcetines? Vicente puede prestarte _____.

3. ¿Champú? Carlos dejó _____ en la ducha. Allí está _____.

4. ¿Aspirinas? Jacques dejó _____ en el baño.

5. ¿El secador de pelo? Solamente hay uno que nosotros usamos. Puedes usar _____.

6. ¿Lentes de sol? Arturo tiene dos pares. Puedes usar _____.

MASTERY EXERCISES

EXERCISE M. Tommy likes to tell his friends what belongs to him, to his older brother, and what is theirs. Use the long form adjective to tell to whom each item belongs.

EXAMPLE: ¿De quién es el diccionario?
            El diccionario **es suyo.**

1. ¿De quién es el perro?   _____

2. ¿De quién es la calculadora?   _____

3. ¿De quién son los juegos electrónicos?   _____

4. ¿De quién es la casa?   _____

5. ¿De quién es la raqueta de tenis?   _____

6. ¿De quién es la pelota?   _____

7. ¿De quién son los MP3?   _____

8. ¿De quién es el guante de béisbol?   _____

9. ¿De quién es el televisor?   _____

10. ¿De quién es la tienda de campaña?   _____

EXERCISE N.   **Jan likes to compare her things with those of her friends. Using the cues provided, complete the sentences with the appropriate possessive.**

EXAMPLE: Los pantalones _____ son de algodón. _____ son de lana. _____ son de seda.
           (*Sarita / Gabi y Luz / yo*)

           Los pantalones **de Sarita** son de algodón. **Los de ellas (los suyos)** son de lana.
           Los míos son de seda.

1. La camiseta de talla mediana es _____ . _____ es talla pequeña. La talla grande es
        _____ . (*yo / tú / Rodolfo*)

2. _____ carro es negro. ¿De qué color es _____? _____ es azul. (*yo / Ud. / nosotros*)

3. Flor perdió las llaves _____ . ¿Tienes _____ ? Yo no encuentro _____ . (*Flor / ella / yo*)

4. _____ mochila es negra. _____ es azul. ¿De qué color es _____ ? (*tú / yo / Ana*)

5. El reloj _____ es elegante. _____ es para uso diario. _____ es modelo deportivo. (*Linda / Tere / yo*)

EXERCISE O.   In an e-mail to a friend in Peru, you describe your house and where you live. Use as many possessive adjectives and/or pronouns as you can in each sentence. You may wish to include the following:

- the size of your house

- with whom you live there

- a description of your house, including color, material, etc.

- a relative who lives on the same street

- a comparison of their house and yours, including the differences

- when your relatives like to swim in your pool

- other things you share with your relatives

ACTIVIDADES

You have just gotten a new gadget (piece of sports equipment, computer, cell phone, etc.) that you believe is superior to the one your friend has. Write ten statements in which you describe and compare yours and your friend's. Use as many possessive adjectives and pronouns as you can in each statement.

CHAPTER

27

Comparisons

◆ 1 ◆ COMPARISONS OF EQUALITY

a. *Tan* + adjective (or adverb) + *como* = as . . . as

Jorge es **tan fuerte como** tú.	*Jorge is as strong as you.*
Ellos son **tan alegres como** yo.	*They are as happy as I.*
Ella baila **tan bien como** su hermana.	*She dances as well as her sister.*

EXERCISE A. Grace is comparing herself to her friends and finds that they have many similarities. Express what she says.

EXAMPLE: Yo soy muy lista. Alicia es muy lista también.

  Yo soy **tan lista como** Alicia.

1. Imelda es muy cortés. Yo soy muy cortés también.

_____

2. Ruthie y Beatriz son simpáticas. Yo soy simpática también.

_____

3. Jeanne y yo somos atléticas. Tawny es atlética también.

_____

4. Silvia es delgada. Yo soy delgada también.

_____

5. Yo soy popular. María e Inés son populares también.

_____

6. Rosa es cómica. Sandra y yo somos cómicas también.

_____

7. Pedro es serio. Yo soy seria también.

_____

EXERCISE B. Jimmy is always comparing how well (sometimes how badly) he does things to his older brother and his friends. Express what he says.

EXAMPLE: correr rápidamente / mi hermano   Yo corro **tan rápidamente como** mi hermano.

1. jugar bien al béisbol / sus amigos   _____

2. reírse alegremente / mi hermano   _____

3. salir mal en los exámenes / mi hermano _____

4. cantar fuertemente / sus amigos _____

5. caminar lentamente / mi hermano _____

b. *Tanto* (*tanta, tantos, tantas*) + noun + *como* = as much (as many) . . . as

Tengo **tanto dinero como** tú.   *I have as much money as you.*

Él lee **tantos libros como** su amigo.   *He reads as many books as his friend.*

c. *Tanto* (tanta, tantos, tantas) + como = *as much (as many) . . . as*

¿Cuántas manzanas comió?   *How many apples did he eat?*
Comió **tantas como** Juan.   *He ate as many as John.*
Ella no hace **tanto como** yo.   *She doesn't do as much as I.*

EXERCISE C.   **Rogelio believes that he has to keep up with his cousin. Express what he says.**

EXAMPLE: películas   Yo tengo **tantos** discos compactos **como** mi primo.

1. amigos _____

2. juegos electrónicos _____

3. experiencia _____

4. suerte _____

5. dinero _____

6. fe _____

7. gorras _____

EXERCISE D.   **Janet is very competitive with her friends. Express what she did.**

EXAMPLE: correr millas   Ella corrió **tantas** millas **como** sus amigas.

1. comprar ropa _____

2. gastar dinero _____

3. leer novelas _____

4. tener notas buenas _____

5. ganar trofeos _____

6. visitar museos _____

7. organizar fiestas _____

◆ 2 ◆ COMPARISONS OF INEQUALITY

a. Adjectives are compared as follows:

POSITIVE	**alto (alta, altos, altas)**	*tall*
COMPARATIVE	**más (menos) alto (alta, altos, altas)**	*taller*
SUPERLATIVE	**el (la, los, las) ... más (menos) alto (alta, altos, altas)**	*the tallest*

Pedro es alto.   *Pedro is tall.*
Pedro **es más (menos) alto** que Andrés.   *Pedro is taller (less tall) than Andrés.*
Pedro **es el más (menos) alto** de la clase.   *Pedro is the tallest (least tall) in the class.*

NOTES:

1. Generally, *than* is equivalent to *que.*

   Juan es más cómico **que** Adán.   *Juan is funnier than Adán.*

2. When *than* precedes a number, it is expressed by *de*, except when the sentence is negative.

   Él gastó más **de** diez dólares.   *He spent more than ten dollars.*

   Cuesta menos **de** treinta centavos.   *It costs less than thirty cents.*

   BUT

   Él no gastó más **que** diez dólares.   *He spent only ten dollars. (He did not spend more than ten dollars.)*

3. In the superlative, the nouns stands between the article (*el, la, los, las*) and the adjective.

   Él es el profesor **más** popular.   *He is the most popular teacher.*

   Es la revista **menos** interesante.   *It's the least interesting magazine.*

4. After a superlative, *de* means *in.*

   Él es el alumno más inteligente **de** la clase.   *He is the most intelligent pupil in the class.*

EXERCISE E.   **Express your opinion about the following things, using *más* or *menos* and the adjective in parentheses.**

EXAMPLE: una biografía / un drama (*interesante*)
           Una biografía es **más (menos) interesante** que un drama.

1. la televisión / la radio (*divertido*)   _____

2. los discos compactos / las cintas (*práctico*)   _____

3. un carro / un avión (*rápido*)   _____

4. una bicicleta / una motocicleta (*peligroso*)   _____

5. un diccionario / una revista (*útil*)   _____

6. el helado / el pastel (*delicioso*)   _____

EXERCISE F. Compare the following pairs of people.

EXAMPLE: Miguel es diligente. (– / *Felipe*)   Sarita es bondadosa. (+ / *Flor*)
Miguel es **menos diligente que** Felipe.   Sarita es **más bondadosa que** Flor.

1. Stan es atlético. (+ / *Vinny*) _____

2. Estela es ambiciosa. (– / *Tomás*) _____

3. Larry es cómico. (+ / *Fred*) _____

4. Hugo es descortés. (+ / *Anita*) _____

5. Nilda es habladora. (– / *Carmen*) _____

6. Ari es nervioso. (– / *Greg*) _____

7. Sonia es orgullosa. (+ / *Norma*) _____

EXERCISE G. Use the following adjectives to describe your teachers.

simpático	justo	aburrido	bondadoso
paciente	cómico	interesante	exigente

EXAMPLES: Mi profesor de inglés es el más **estricto.**
Mi profesora de historia es la más **generosa.**

1. _____

2. _____

3. _____

4. _____

5. _____

6. _____

EXERCISE H. Express your opinion of the importance of the elements in each category.

EXAMPLE: una persona famosa (*el Papa, el presidente, la reina*)
El presidente **es una persona** famosa.
La reina **es una persona más** famosa.
El Papa **es la persona más** famosa.

1. un deporte peligroso (el motociclismo, montar a caballo, el fútbol americano)

_____

_____

_____

2. un animal feroz (el león, el lobo, el zorro)

_____

_____

_____

3. una profesión noble (ser médico, ser profesor, ser policía)

_____

_____

_____

4. una materia interesante (la química, la psicología, las matemáticas)

_____

_____

_____

5. un sueño alcanzable (visitar otros países, viajar a la luna, graduarse de la universidad)

_____

_____

_____

b. Adverbs are compared as follows:

POSITIVE	**lentamente**	*slowly*
COMPARATIVE	**más (menos) lentamente**	*more (less) slowly*
SUPERLATIVE	**más (menos) lentamente**	*more (less) slowly than*

NOTE: The superlative of adverbs is not distinguished from the comparative.

EXERCISE I.   **Tell how these people do different things.**

EXAMPLE: estudiar diligentemente / Gabriel (+) / Beto (-)
Gabriel estudia más diligentemente.
Beto estudia menos diligentemente.

1. cantar dulcemente / Carmen (–) / Clara (+)

_____

2. gritar fuertemente / el niño (+) / la niña (–)

_____

3. hablar claramente / Jorge (+) / Esteban (–)

_____

4. correr rápidamente / Neil (–) / Pablo (+)

_____

5. cocinar hábilmente / mi mamá (+) / mi tía (–)

_____

EXERCISE J.   Celia is telling a new aide at the daycare center about the children. Express what she says. Alternate the use of *más* and *menos*.

EXAMPLE: Felipe / dormir profundamente / Arturo

Felipe duerme **más** (**menos**) **profundamente** que Arturo.

1.   Leticia / llorar fácilmente / Susana y Heather

_____

2.   Janet / comer lentamente / su hermano

_____

3.   Amanda / actuar respetuosamente / Rebecca

_____

4.   Brian / colorear cuidadosamente / ese niño

_____

5.   Jennifer / reírse fácilmente / Nina

_____

◆ 3 ◆ IRREGULAR COMPARATIVES

POSITIVE	COMPARATIVE	SUPERLATIVE
bueno, -a, -os, -as *good*	**mejor, -es** *better*	**el / la mejor; los / las mejores** *the best*
malo, -a, -os, -as *bad*	**peor, -es** *worse*	**el / la peor; los / las peores** *the worst*
grande, -es *large(great)*	**mayor, -es** *greater, older*	**el / la mayor; los / las mayores** *greatest, oldest*
pequeño, -a, -os, -as *small*	**menor, -es** *lesser, younger*	**el / la menor; los / las menores** *least, youngest*

NOTES:

1.   *Mejor* and *peor* generally precede the nouns they modify.

   el mejor libro   *the best book*   **la peor película**   *the worst film*

2.   *Mayor* and *menor* usually follow the nouns they modify.

   el hijo mayor   *the oldest son*   **mi hermana menor**   *my youngest sister*

3.   The regular and irregular comparative forms of *grande* and *pequeño* have different meanings. *Más grande* and *más pequeño* compare differences in size or height (physical meaning); *mayor* and *menor* compare differences in age or status (figurative meaning).

   el hijo más pequeño   *the smaller (smallest) son*

   el hijo menor   *the younger (youngest) son*

   de mayor (menor) importancia   *of greater (lesser) importance*

EXERCISE K.   **Tell who does these things better or worse than you.**

EXAMPLE: bailar   Mi hermano baila **mejor** (**peor**) que yo.

1. nadar   _____

2. jugar al tenis   _____

3. esquiar   _____

4. correr   _____

5. cocinar   _____

6. conducir un carro   _____

7. hablar español   _____

EXERCISE L.   **You and a friend are discussing different things. For each one, give your opinion about which is the best and which is the worst.**

EXAMPLE: equipo de fútbol   El equipo de fútbol de la Argentina es **el mejor** equipo.
                                El equipo de fútbol de los Estados Unidos es **el peor** equipo.

1. película   _____

_____

2. disco compacto   _____

_____

3. carro   _____

_____

4. canción   _____

_____

5. grupo musical   _____

_____

6. atleta profesional   _____

_____

7. programa de televisión   _____

_____

◆ 4 ◆ THE ABSOLUTE SUPERLATIVE

To express an absolute superlative (when no comparison is involved), *-ísimo, ísima, ísimos, -ísimas* is often added to the adjective. The meaning is the same as *muy* + adjective.

un libro **muy popular**
un libro **popularísimo**   }   *a very popular book*

una casa **muy grande**
una casa **grandísima** ⎫ *an extremely large house*

NOTES:

1. Adjectives ending in a vowel drop that vowel before adding *-ísimo*.

2. *Muchísimo* = very much.

   Juan quiere **muchísimo** a su novia.   *Juan loves his girlfriend very much.*

3. Before adding *-ísimo*, adjectives ending in *co* change to *qu*; those ending in *go* change to *gu*; and those ending in *z* change to *c*.

   rico   →   riquísimo   *very rich*
   largo   →   larguísimo   *very long*
   feliz   →   felicísimo   *very happy*

EXERCISE M.   **Mrs. Soto is telling a friend about her family. Express what she says by adding *-ísimo* (*-a, -os, -as*) to the adjective given.**

EXAMPLE: (*grande*)   Mi hijo tiene un apetito **grandísimo**.

1. (*largo*)   Yo paso horas _____ en la cocina.

2. (*caro*)   La comida es _____.

3. (*temprano*)   Él siempre llega a casa _____.

4. (*poco*)   Mis otros hijos comen _____.

5. (*mucho / flaco*)   Aunque él come _____, él es _____.

6. (*dulce*)   Él prefiere los postres _____.

7. (*gordo*)   Si yo comiera como él, yo estaría _____.

8. (*feliz*)   Somos una familia _____.

MASTERY EXERCISES

EXERCISE N.   **Answer the questions a new student asks you.**

1. ¿Eres más alto / alta que tus compañeros?

_____

2. ¿Quién es el / la más inteligente de la clase de español?

_____

3. ¿Eres mayor que tu hermano(-a)?

_____

4. ¿Quién es el menor de tu familia?

_____

5. ¿Cómo se llama tu mejor amigo(-a)?

_____

6. ¿Tienes más de cincuenta dólares en el banco?

_____

7. ¿Cuál es el peor grupo de música en tu opinión?

_____

8. ¿Eres más aplicado / aplicada que los otros alumnos?

_____

9. ¿Cuál es la mejor estación del año?

_____

10. ¿Quién es el muchacho / la muchacha más popular de la escuela?

_____

(EXERCISE O.) **Mrs. Sosa received a card from a long lost friend. In her response, she describes her family. Complete her letter with the following comparatives.**

grandísima	más … de	más … que	más de
mayor	menor	menos … que	muchísimo
tan … como	tantas	tantos	tantos … como

Querida Antonia:

Me dio _____ 1. gusto recibir tu tarjeta. Han pasado _____ 2. años y _____ 3. cosas desde la última vez que nos vimos. ¡Hace _____ 4. veinticinco años! Estábamos en la universidad y teníamos _____ 5. años _____ 6. mis hijos tienen ahora.

Tengo tres hijos: Elvira, Alfredo y Sarita. Elvira tiene treinta años, es la _____ 7.; Alfredo tiene veintiocho y Sarita, la _____ 8., tiene veinticuatro. Elvira y Alfredo están casados y cada uno tiene dos hijos. Yo tengo _____ 9. nietos _____ 10. tú, cuatro. Los hijos de Elvira son _____ 11. simpáticos _____ 12. los de Alfredo. Elvira y su familia viven en una casa _____ 13. en el campo. Alfredo y su familia viven cerca de aquí en un apartamento que es _____ 14. grande _____ 15. la casa de Elvira: hay doce cuartos. Sarita sigue estudiando porque quiere llegar a ser médico. Ella es la _____ 16. inteligente _____ 17. mis hijos. Ella siempre ha trabajado _____ 18. para lograr sus metas. Escríbeme pronto. Recibe _____ 19. besos _____ 20. abrazos de mi parte.

Tu amiga,

Dolores

EXERCISE P.   **You describe your best friend at summer camp in an electronic message to a Spanish-speaking acquaintance. Include the following:**

- who is your best friend
- who is older/younger
- you have the same number of siblings
- something about the house he/she lives in
- if he/she is the oldest/youngest child
- his generosity compared to your other friends
- his sense of humor
- his worst/best trait

A C T I V I D A D E S

You are preparing a "show and tell" presentation for your Spanish class. Select an object that you can bring to class (sports equipment, MP3s of your favorite music group, a picture or photo of a larger object, etc.) and explain how it compares to a similar object. Use as many comparative expressions as possible.

EXAMPLE: una bicicleta

Esta bicicleta **es mejor que las otras.**

Es tan bonita como las otras pero no cuesta **tanto dinero como esas.**

Yo creo que **es la mejor bicicleta de todas.**

CHAPTER

28

Numbers

◆ 1 ◆ CARDINAL NUMBERS

0	cero	28	veintiocho (veinte y ocho)
1	uno	29	veintinueve (veinte y nueve)
2	dos	30	treinta
3	tres	31	treinta y uno
4	cuatro	40	cuarenta
5	cinco	50	cincuenta
6	seis	60	sesenta
7	siete	70	setenta
8	ocho	80	ochenta
9	nueve	90	noventa
10	diez	100	cien
11	once	101	ciento uno
12	doce	115	ciento quince
13	trece	116	ciento dieciséis
14	catorce	200	doscientos, -as
15	quince	300	trescientos, -as
16	dieciséis (diez y seis)	400	cuatrocientos, -as
17	diecisiete (diez y siete)	500	quinientos, -as
18	dieciocho (diez y ocho)	600	seiscientos, -as
19	diecinueve (diez y nueve)	700	setecientos, -as
20	veinte	800	ochocientos, -as
21	veintiuno (veinte y uno)	900	novecientos, -as
22	veintidós (veinte y dos)	1.000	mil
23	veintitrés (veinte y tres)	2.000	dos mil
24	veinticuatro (veinte y cuatro)	100.000	cien mil
25	veinticinco (veinte y cinco)	1.000.000	un millón (de)
26	veintiséis (veinte y seis)	2.000.000	dos millones (de)
27	veintisiete (veinte y siete)	100.000.000	cien millones (de)

NOTES:

1. Compound numbers 16 to 99 are connected by *y*.

2. Although numbers 16 to 19 and 21 to 29 may be connected by *y*, they are usually written as one word. Note the spelling changes that occur when these numbers are written as one word.

   diez y seis   →   **dieciséis**   **veinte** y dos   →   **veintidós**

3. *Uno* and combinations of *uno* (like *veintiuno* and *treinta y uno*) become *un* before masculine nouns and *una* before feminine nouns.

un periódico	*one (a) newspaper*	**una** silla	*one (a) chair*
veint**iún** lápices	*twenty-one pencils*	veint**iuna** blusas	*twenty-one blouses*
treinta y **un** alumnos	*thirty-one students*	treinta y **una** plumas	*thirty-one pens*

4. The only numerals that vary with gender are *uno* (*una, un*) and the compounds of *ciento* (*doscientos, -as; trescientos, -as*), and so on.

un alumno	*one (a) student*	quinientas mujeres	*five hundred women*
una alumna	*one (a) student*	veintiún centavos	*twenty-one cents*
trescientos hombres	*three hundred men*	cuarenta y una mesas	*forty-one tables*

5. *Cien* becomes *ciento* when it's followed by another number from one to ninety-nine.

cien bolívares   cien mil habitantes

BUT

ciento veinticinco dólares

6. *Un* is not used before *cien* or *mil. Un* is used before the noun *millón*. If another noun follows *millón, de* is placed between *millón* and the other noun.

ciento diez personas   mil cuatrocientos años   un millón de dólares

7. Spanish usually uses periods rather than commas to separate digits.

2.568.953 (Spanish)   2,568,953 (English)

8. Spanish vusually uses a comma in decimals where English uses a period.

$8,95 (Spanish) $8.95 (English)

(**EXERCISE A.**) **Use the chart below to answer the questions based on it. Write out the numbers in Spanish.**

BUENOS AIRES, ARGENTINA

Población
Ciudad	3.036.891	Suburbios	13.711.746

Clima en noviembre
Temperatura	alta	76°
	baja	56°
Días con lluvia		9

Hotel (tarifa diaria)
Cuarto para uno (con impuesto)	$319,00

Cena para uno
Con impuesto y propina	$28,00

Taxi
Al subir	$1,20
Cada kilómetro adicional	$0,85
Del aeropuerto	$47,00

Alquiler de carro por un día
Tamaño mediano, no automático con 150 o 200 kilómetros gratis	$86,00

---

1. ¿Cual es la población de la ciudad de Buenos Aires?

---

2. ¿Cuál es la población de los suburbios de Buenos Aires?

---

3. ¿Cuál es la temperatura alta en noviembre?

_____

4. ¿Cuál es la temperatura baja en noviembre?

_____

5. ¿Cuántos días de lluvia hay en el mes de noviembre?

_____

6. ¿Cuánto cuesta al día un cuarto en un hotel para una persona?

_____

7. ¿Cuánto cuesta una cena para una persona con propina?

_____

8. ¿Cuánto marca el taxímetro al subir?

_____

9. ¿Cuánto cuesta cada kilómetro adicional en el taxi?

_____

10. ¿Cuánto cuesta un taxi del aeropuerto al centro?

_____

11. ¿Cuánto cobran para alquilar un carro por un día?

_____

12. Por lo general, ¿cuántos kilómetros gratis dan al alquilar un carro?

_____

_____

EXERCISE B. As Norma prepares to apply to colleges, her parents want to know how many students attend each of the institutions she is considering. Tell the number of students that attend each one; the number of male students, and the number of female students.

UNIVERSIDAD	HOMBRES	MUJERES	TOTAL
Boston College	4,183	4,785	8,968
Brown	2,597	3,028	5,625
Columbia	1,884	1,845	3,729
Emory	2,558	3,231	5,789
Harvard	3,683	2,917	6,600
Northwestern	3,701	3,908	7,609
Notre Dame	4,250	3,450	7,700
Ohio State	15,845	14,434	30,279
Pennsylvania State	17,103	14,006	31,109
University of Maryland	10,744	10,251	20,995
University of Miami	3,556	3,816	7,372
University of Michigan	13,088	14,674	27,762

EXAMPLE: Brown   dos mil quinientos noventa y siete hombres; tres mil veintiocho mujeres;
cinco mil seiscientos veinticinco estudiantes

1. Harvard   _____

_____

2. University of Miami   _____

_____

3. University of Michigan   _____

_____

4. Pennsylvania State   _____

_____

5. University of Maryland   _____

_____

6. Boston College   _____

_____

7. Ohio State   _____

_____

8. Northwestern   _____

_____

9. Columbia   _____

_____

10. Notre Dame   _____

_____

(EXERCISE C.)   **You are helping your younger sister prepare for a test. Help her answer the following questions.**

1. ¿Cuántos zapatos hay en un par
de zapatos?   _____

2. ¿Cuántos jugadores hay en un equipo
de béisbol?   _____

3. ¿Cuántas letras hay en el alfabeto inglés?   _____

4. ¿Cuántos centavos hay en un dólar?   _____

5. ¿Cuántos estados hay en los Estados
Unidos?   _____

6. ¿Cuántos días hay en un año?   _____

7. ¿Cuántos días hay en el mes de marzo?   _____

8. ¿Cuántos días hay en el mes de febrero?   _____

9. ¿Cuántas preguntas hay en este ejercicio? _____

10. ¿En qué capítulo está este ejercicio? _____

11. ¿Cuántos años hay en un siglo? _____

12. ¿Cuántos dedos tiene una persona en
cada mano? _____

13. ¿Cuántas naranjas hay en una docena? _____

14. ¿Cuántas horas hay en un día? _____

15. ¿Cuántas estaciones hay en un año? _____

EXERCISE D. **Angelo is very interested in the maximum and minimum temperatures in different cities in Spanish America. Tell what the maximum and minimum temperatures are and help him calculate the difference between them. Write the numbers in Spanish.**

CUIDAD	TEMPERATURA MÁXIMA	TEMPERATURA MÍNIMA	GRADOS DE DIFERENCIA
Asunción	68	54	
Bogotá	66	49	
Caracas	88	75	
Chihuahua	95	64	
Guayaquil	89	66	
Montevideo	56	38	
Quito	76	44	
San Salvador	91	67	
Tegucigalpa	89	49	
Tierra del Fuego	39	30	

1. Asunción

Máxima _____

Mínima _____

Diferencia _____

2. Bogotá

Máxima _____

Mínima _____

Diferencia _____

3. Caracas

Máxima _____

Mínima _____

Diferencia _____

4. Chihuahua

Máxima _____

Mínima _____

Diferencia _____

5. Guayaquil

Máxima   _____

Mínima   _____

Diferencia   _____

6. Montevideo

Máxima   _____

Mínima   _____

Diferencia   _____

7. Quito

Máxima   _____

Mínima   _____

Diferencia   _____

8. San Salvador

Máxima   _____

Mínima   _____

Diferencia   _____

9. Tegucigalpa

Máxima   _____

Mínima   _____

Diferencia   _____

10. Tierra del Fuego

Máxima   _____

Mínima   _____

Diferencia   _____

◆ 2 ◆ ARITHMETIC EXPRESSIONS

The following expressions are used in arithmetic problems in Spanish:

y, más	*plus* (+)	**dividido por**	*divided by* (÷)
menos	*minus* (−)	**son, es igual a**	*equals* (=)
por	(*multiplied*) *by,* "*times*" (×)		

EXERCISE E.   **Express the following in Spanish.**

1. $7,632 + 895 = 8,527$ _____

2. $27 + 83 = 110$ _____

3. $800,000 − 300,000 = 500,000$ _____

4. $729 − 208 = 521$ _____

5. $910 \times 45 = 40,950$ _____

6. $763 \times 22 = 16,786$ _____

7. 9,000 ÷ 90 = 100 _____

8. 195 ÷ 13 = 15 _____

9. 1,000,000 ÷ 50 = 20,000 _____

10. 10,081 + 7,629 = 17,710 _____

11. 2,700,000 + 300,000 = 3,000,000 _____

12. 26 × 36 = 936 _____

13. 9,389 − 5,018 = 4,371 _____

14. 863 − 175 = 688 _____

15. 4,020 ÷ 12 = 335 _____

16. 280 + 21 = 301 _____

17. 1,100 − 82 = 1,018 _____

18. 777 × 20 = 15,540 _____

19. 64 × 80 = 5,120 _____

20. 1,250 ÷ 25 = 50 _____

(EXERCISE F.) **While the family is taking a car trip, the children are assigning a numerical value to everything they see. Tell what they say:**

EXAMPLE: 100   cien dólares

1. 500 _____

3. 1,000,000 _____

2. 41 _____

4. 101 _____

5. 700 _____

8. 109 _____

6. 81 _____

9. 2,331 _____

7. 92 _____

10. 230 _____

◆ 3 ◆ ORDINAL NUMBERS

1°	primero, -a; primer	*1st, first*	6°	sexto, -a	*6th, sixth*
2°	segundo, -a	*2nd, second*	7°	séptimo, -a	*7th, seventh*
3°	tercero, -a; tercer	*3rd, third*	8°	octavo, -a	*8th, eighth*
4°	cuarto, -a	*4th, fourth*	9°	noveno, -a	*9th, ninth*
5°	quinto, -a	*5th, fifth*	10°	décimo, -a	*10th, tenth*

NOTES:

1. All ordinal numbers agree in gender (m./f.) and number (sing./pl.) with the nouns to which they refer.

   el octavo día   *the eighth day*   la quinta semana   *the fifth week*

2. The numbers *primero* and *tercero* drop the final *-o* when they come before a masculine singular noun.

   el primer mes   *the first month*   el tercer piso   *the third floor*

   BUT

   la primera semana   *the first week*   la tercera estación   *the third season*

3. If a preposition comes between *primero* or *tercero* and the noun, the full form is used.

   el primero de septiembre   *September 1*

4. Ordinal numbers are generally used to express rank order only from the first to the tenth in a series. Numbers above ten also have ordinal forms, but they are seldom used. Instead, a cardinal number is placed after the noun, and the word *número* is understood.

| la quinta página | *the fifth page* |
| Carlos V (Carlos quinto) | *Charles the Fifth* |

BUT

| la lección quince | *the fifteenth lesson or lesson (number) fifteen* |
| Alfonso XII (Alfonso doce) | *Alfonso the Twelfth* |

EXERCISE G. You are looking at the directory in the hospital lobby. Tell to which floor you would go to do the various activities.

(Note: In most Spanish-speaking countries, the ground floor or first floor is called *la planta baja* (PB); the second floor, *primer piso*, and so forth.)

SERVICIO / DEPARTAMENTO	PISO
Cafetería	11
Caja	4
Cirugía	10
Consultorios de doctores	7
Farmacia	1
Información	PB
Maternidad	5
Oficinas ejecutivas	4
Ortopedía	3
Pediatría	2
Sala de Emergencia	PB
Tienda / Florería	PB

EXAMPLE: hablar con el director del hospital **el cuarto piso**

1. para visitar a un niño enfermo _____

2. para comer _____

3. para pedir información _____

4. para pagar una cuenta _____

5. para ver a un médico _____

6. para obtener medicina _____

7. en caso de accidente _____

8. para hablar con el director de las enfermeras _____

9. para visitar a un bebé recién nacido y a su mamá _____

10. para ver a un amigo que se ha roto una pierna _____

11. para ver a una persona a quien han operado _____

12. para comprar un regalo o flores _____

EXERCISE H. Pete has just learned that a Spanish calendar begins with Monday. Identify which day of the week each day is according to a Spanish calendar.

EXAMPLE: domingo **el séptimo día**

1. miércoles _____

2. sábado _____

3. viernes _____

4. lunes _____

5. jueves _____

6. martes _____

EXERCISE I. Write each number in parentheses as a Spanish word.

1. Enrique (6°) es un rey moderno. _____

2. Estamos en la (5°) ciudad de la excursión. _____

3. Tu dormitorio está en el (1°) piso de la casa. _____

4. Yo era la (9°) persona en la cola. _____

5. Este es el (3°) carro que compra mi papá este año. _____

6. Debo bajarme en la (2°) parada del autobús. _____

7. Es el (4°) verano que trabajo con mi hermano. _____

8. Celebro mi cumpleaños en el (8°) mes del año: agosto. _____

9. Esos señores acaban de celebrar su aniversario (47°). _____

10. Contesta la (1°) pregunta al final del examen. _____

◆ 4 ◆ FRACTIONS

½	un medio, medio, -a, una mitad de	(a/one) half, half of
⅓	un tercio, una tercera parte de	(a/one) third, the third part of
¼	un cuarto, una cuarta parte de	(a/one) fourth, a quarter of
⅔	dos tercios, dos terceras partes de	two-thirds, two-thirds of
¾	tres cuartos, tres cuartas partes de	three-fourths, three quarters of
⅘	cuatro quintos, cuatro quintas partes de	four -fifths of
⅒	un décimo, una décima parte de	(a/one) tenth, a tenth of

NOTES:

1. Except for *medio* and *tercio*, noun fractions are formed with ordinal numbers up through *décimo* (tenth). Thereafter, the ending *-avo* is usually added to the cardinal number to express fractions smaller than a tenth.

    $\frac{1}{12}$ un doceavo, una doceava parte de   *(a / one) twelfth of*

2. Fractions are masculine nouns.

    $3\frac{1}{3}$ tres y un tercio   *three and one-third*

When the fraction precedes the thing divided, it may be used with the feminine noun *parte*, unless a unit of measure is expressed.

una tercera parte (un tercio) del pan	*a third of the bread*
BUT	
un tercio de libra	*a third of a pound*

3. The adjective *medio, -a* means "half," while the noun *mitad* means "half (of)."

media docena de huevos	*half a dozen eggs*
la mitad del público	*half of the audience*

EXERCISE J.   You and some friends are going to spend the day at a picnic and you have to buy the food. Copy the following list, writing out the fractions as words in Spanish.

LISTA DE COMPRAS

1/2 libra de jamón
2 1/2 galones de refresco
1 1/2 sandía
1/2 galón de helado
3/4 libra de queso
1 1/4 libra de tomates
1/2 pan
1/2 docena de donas

1. _____
2. _____
3. _____
4. _____

5. _____
6 _____
7. _____
8. _____

◆ 5 ◆ MULTIPLES

Terms that indicate that one quantity is a multiple of another are used in the same manner as their English equivalents.

una vez	*once*	simple	*single, simple*
dos veces	*twice*	doble	*double*
tres veces	*thrice, three times*	triple	*triple*

Me habló una vez.	*He spoke to me once.*
Nos visitaron dos veces.	*They visited us twice.*
Leí el doble de lo que leíste tú.	*I read twice as much as you.*

NOTES:

1. Adverbial phrases explaining the number of times that an event occurs are formed by a cardinal number and the feminine noun *vez* (a time).

Lavé la ropa cuatro veces.   *I washed the clothes four times.*

2. Multiples like *doble, triple* may be either adjectives or nouns.

Es una máquina de doble motor.   *It's a double-motor machine.*

Este carro cuesta hoy el doble.   *This car costs twice as much today.*

EXERCISE K.   **Nick is telling some friends how many times he has done these things. Tell what he says using the cues in parentheses.**

EXAMPLE: comer en un restaurante japonés (*2*)

         Es la **segunda vez** que como en un restaurante japonés.

1. viajar en avión (*10*) _____

2. estudiar la literatura española (*1*) _____

3. trabajar después de las clases (*3*) _____

4. remar en el lago (*4*) _____

5. tocar el violín en un concierto (*8*) _____

6. ir a una fiesta de disfraces (*6*) _____

EXERCISE L.   **You and a friend are trying to decide what to do. Your friend is giving you a hard time because for every suggestion you make, your friend tells you how many times she has done that. Tell what he says using the cues in parentheses.**

EXAMPLE: ver la película «The Lion King» (*5*)

         Vi la película «The Lion King» **cinco veces.**

1. patinar en hielo (*10*) _____

2. correr en un maratón (*3*) _____

3. ir de compras (*100*) _____

4. ver la obra de teatro «Gatos» (*15*) _____

5. visitar el museo de ciencia y tecnología (*1*) _____

6. escuchar los MP3 (*1.000*) _____

◄ MASTERY EXERCISES ►

EXERCISE M.   **Solve these word problems in Spanish. Write out the numbers in Spanish.**

1. Alex tiene que leer una novela en quince días. La novela contiene 600 páginas.

   ¿Cuántas páginas debe leer Alex cada día para terminar a tiempo?

_____

2. Mi mamá tiene 3 cheques: uno por $ 1.000,00; el segundo por $ 750,00, y el tercero por $ 2.500,00. ¿Cuántos dólares tiene en total?

_____

3. José tiene $ 350,00. Va a la tienda y compra un suéter por $ 79,00, pantalones por $ 85,00 y zapatos por $60,00. ¿Cuánto gasta José en las compras y cuánto dinero le queda?

_____

4. Gloria quiere comprar una pulsera de oro que cuesta $ 270,00. Si ella ahorra $ 15,00 a la semana, ¿en cuántas semanas podrá Gloria comprar la pulsera?

_____

5. Mi familia piensa visitar a mis abuelos que viven en otro estado. Vamos a viajar en carro. Si tenemos que viajar 360 millas y seguimos una velocidad de 60 millas por hora, ¿en cuántas horas llegaremos? (Use la fórmula: distancia = velocidad x tiempo).

_____

6. Aníbal está trabajando en un almacén. Recibe una comisión del 10 por ciento en todo lo que vende. Si trabaja 5 días y vende $ 810.00 de mercancía cada día, ¿cuánta comisión recibirá al fin de la semana?

_____

(**EXERCISE N.**)   **Express the following in Spanish.**

1. No one answered the first time I called Julie.

_____

2. The second time I called, a machine answered.

_____

3. A voice said: "This is 34-72-89. Please leave a message."

_____

4. I said: "It's Fred. My telephone number is 96-61-45. Please call me."

_____

5. She called in 2 1/2 hours but it seemed like 100 hours.

_____

6. She said that there were 21 messages on the machine.

_____

7. She understood half the message.

_____

8. She told me that we had to read pages 267 to 331 for our English class.

_____

9. I said: "That's 65 pages! Why didn't he ask for 1,000 pages?"

_____

10. She heard that 1,000,000 people watched the marathon on television.

_____

11. Her cousin won sixth place in the race.

_____

12. One third of the people didn't complete the race.

_____

ACTIVIDADES

1. Select six of your favorite family members and write in Spanish the year in which each one was born. Then tell how old each person is.

2. Do the following word problem. Write the numbers in Spanish.

Un promedio de 4.7 personas vive en cada uno de los 66 apartamentos de este edificio. ¿Cuántas personas viven en el edificio?

Now create a word problem in Spanish and solve it.

3. You and your parents are planning to drive to several college campuses during a school vacation. Select three colleges that you will drive to and tell in Spanish how many miles each one is from the city in which you live. Then tell the total number of miles you travelled during this vacation.

Time and Dates

◆ 1 ◆ EXPRESSING TIME

a. *¿Qué hora es?* is equivalent to *What time is it?*

b. In expressing time, *it is* is equivalent to *es la* (for one o'clock) and *son las* for other hours (two o'clock, three o'clock, and so on.)

Es la una.	*It's one o'clock.*
Son las diez (once, . . .)	*It's ten (eleven, . . .) o'clock.*

c. Time after or past the hour (up to half past) is expressed by the hour + *y,* followed by the number of minutes. Half past is expressed by *y media;* a quarter past is expressed by *y cuarto.*

Es la una **y** veinte.	*It's twenty (minutes) after one. (It's 1:20.)*
Son las ocho **y media.**	*It's half past eight. (It's 8:30.)*
Son las dos **y cuarto.**	*It's a quarter after two. (It's 2:15.)*

d. After half past, the time is expressed in terms of the following hour minus (*menos*) the minutes.

Son las cuatro **menos** diez.	*It's ten (minutes) to four. (It's 3:50.)*
Son las once **menos** cuarto.	*It's a quarter to eleven. (It's 10:45.)*

e. The expression *de la mañana* corresponds to English A.M. (in the morning). *De la tarde* (in the afternoon) and *de la noche* (in the night) correspond to English P.M. *En punto* means "sharp" or "on the dot."

f. The twenty-four hour clock is used in many Spanish-speaking countries, especially in the announcement of television and theater presentations.

9.00	las nueve **de la mañana**	*nine in the morning*
12.00	el mediodía	*noon*
13.15	la una y quince de la tarde	*one fifteen in the afternoon*
19.00	las siete **de la noche**	*seven in the evening*
21.45	las diez menos cuarto **de la noche**	*nine forty-five in the night*
24.00	la medianoche en punto	*midnight sharp*

NOTES:

1. Instead of *media* and *cuarto*, the number of minutes may be used (*treinta, quince*).

Son las tres y treinta.	*It's three-thirty. It's half past three.*
Es la una y quince.	*It's one-fifteen. It's a quarter past one.*

2. It is not uncommon to hear times like 12:45 and 12:50 expressed with *y.*

Son las siete y cuarenta.	*It's seven forty.*
Son las siete y cincuenta y cinco.	*It's seven-fifty-five.*

g. Common Time Expressions

¿Qué hora es?	*What time is it?*	a eso de las siete	*at about seven o'clock*
¿A qué hora?	*At what time?*	Es mediodía.	*It's noon.*
a las dos (tres, etc.)	*at two (three, etc.) o'clock*	a mediodía	*at noon*
de la mañana	*in the morning, A.M.*	Es medianoche.	*It's midnight.*
de la tarde	*in the afternoon, P.M.*	a medianoche	*at midnight*
de la noche	*in the evening, P.M.*	Es temprano.	*It's early.*
en punto	*sharp, exactly*	Es tarde.	*It's late.*
a tiempo	*on time*		

EXERCISE A. You are in a clock store at the mall. Every clock shows a different time. Tell what time it is on each clock.

EXAMPLE: Son las **ocho menos veinticinco.**

1. _____

2. _____

3. _____

4. _____

5. _____

6. _____

7. _____

8. _____

9. _____

10. _____

11. _____

12. _____

13. _____

14. _____

15. _____

16. _____

17. _____

18. _____

19. _____   *20.* _____

EXERCISE B. Answer the questions a new friend asks you.

1. ¿A qué hora te levantas? _____

2. ¿A qué hora te desayunas? _____

3. ¿Cuándo llegas a la escuela? _____

4. ¿A qué hora comienzan las clases? _____

5. ¿A qué hora almuerzan tus amigos y tú? _____

6. ¿Cuándo sales de la escuela? _____

7. ¿A qué hora cena tu familia? _____

8. ¿Cuándo estudias tus lecciones? _____

9. ¿A qué hora terminan las clases? _____

10. ¿A qué hora te acuestas? _____

EXERCISE C. You are looking at a schedule of movies. Answer the questions based on the schedule.

• Comodidad • Sonido Stereo	• Pantallas Gigantes de Alta Definición • Las Mejores Salas de Cine	
GRAN REX	**EMPERATRIZ**	**LAMONTE**
Cenizas del paraíso	*Máxima velocidad*	*Hércules*
17:10 / 19:40 / 22:20	16:10 / 18:20 / 20:30 / 22:40	14:30 / 16:15 / 18:20

1. ¿A qué hora es la primera función del Cine Lamonte?

_____

2. ¿A qué hora es la última función en el Cine Emperatriz?

_____

3. ¿A qué hora es la tercera función de «Máxima velocidad»?

_____

4. Si yo quiero ver la película «Cenizas del paraíso» pero quiero llegar a casa antes de las nueve de la noche, ¿a qué función debo ir?

_____

5. Si voy a la última función de «Máxima velocidad» y la película dura dos horas, ¿a qué hora saldré del cine?

_____

◆ 2 ◆ EXPRESSING DATES

a. Days of the Week (*Los días de la semana*)

lunes	*Monday*	viernes	*Friday*
martes	*Tuesday*	sábado	*Saturday*
miércoles	*Wednesday*	domingo	*Sunday*
jueves	*Thursday*		

NOTES:

1. "On" before a day of the week is expressed by *el* for the singular and *los* for the plural.

el lunes	*on Monday*	los lunes	*on Mondays*
el martes	*on Tuesday*	los martes	*on Tuesdays*
el miércoles	*on Wednesday*	los miércoles	*on Wednesdays*
el sábado	*on Saturday*	los sábados	*on Saturdays*
el domingo	*on Sunday*	los domingos	*on Sundays*

2. Days of the week whose names end in *-s* do not change their form in the plural.

3. The days of the week are not capitalized in Spanish.

b. Months (*los meses*)

enero	*January*	mayo	*May*	septiembre	*September*
febrero	*February*	junio	*June*	octubre	*October*
marzo	*March*	julio	*July*	noviembre	*November*
abril	*April*	agosto	*August*	diciembre	*December*

NOTE: Like the days of the week, the months are not capitalized in Spanish.

c. Dates

¿Cuál es la fecha de hoy? ¿A cuántos estamos hoy?	*What is today's date?*
Es el primero de abril. Estamos a primero de abril.	*It's April 1.*
Es el dos de marzo.	*It's March 2.*
Es el cinco (seis) de mayo.	*It's May 5 (6).*
dos mil diez	*2010*
el cuatro de julio de mil setecientos setenta y seis	*July 4, 1776*

NOTES:

1. Cardinal numbers are used for all dates except for *primero* (first).

   el **primero** de enero   *January 1*
   el dos (tres, cuatro) de enero   *January 2 (3, 4)*

2. The year is expressed in Spanish by thousands and hundreds, not by hundreds alone as in English.

   mil ochocientos doce   *eighteen hundred twelve*

3. The date and month are connected by the preposition *de*. The month and the year are also connected by *de*.

   el veinte **de** agosto de **mil novecientos diez**   *(on) August 20, 1910*

4. With dates, *el* corresponds to "on".

EXERCISE D.   **Look at the excerpt from Julia's calendar and tell on which days she does the different activities.**

EXAMPLE: clase de piano   **Los lunes** Julia tiene clase de piano.

LUNES	MARTES	MIÉRCOLES	JUEVES
clase de piano	el gimnasio	cuidar al hermanito	clase de natación

VIERNES	SÁBADO	DOMINGO
libre	ayudar en casa	ir al cine

1. ir al cine   _____

2. practicar la gimnasia   _____

3. ayudar en casa   _____

4. no hacer nada   _____

5. cuidar al hermanito   _____

6. ir a la piscina   _____

EXERCISE E.   **Tell on which date these holidays are celebrated in the United States.**

EXAMPLE: Veteran's Day   Se celebra el **once de noviembre.**

1. Valentine's Day   _____

2. Christmas   _____

3. Independence Day   _____

4. Columbus Day   _____

5. Halloween   _____

6. Lincoln's birthday _____

7. Washington's birthday _____

8. April Fools Day _____

9. New Year's Day _____

EXERCISE F.   The dates listed below are of holidays that are usually celebrated in most Spanish-speaking countries. Express the dates in Spanish.

EXAMPLE: December 25   el **veinticinco de diciembre**

1. November 2 _____

2. January 1 _____

3. October 12 _____

4. January 6 _____

5. May 1 _____

EXERCISE G.   Express the following dates in Spanish.

1. December 7, 1942 _____

2. August 25, 1910 _____

3. February 1, 1458 _____

4. March 15, 1212 _____

5. May 5, 1808 _____

6. January 1, 2001 _____

7. September 20, 1647 _____

8. June 3, 1555 _____

9. April 23, 1616 _____

10. November 11, 1779 _____

EXERCISE H.   You are preparing a family tree that is based on the birth date of your family members. Tell the date of birth (including the year) of these members of your family.

EXAMPLE: tu padre   Mi padre nació el **ocho de julio de mil novecientos sesenta y dos.**

1. tu abuela materna _____

2. tu hermano / hermana _____

3. tú _____

4. tu abuelo paterno _____

5. un /una tío(-a) _____

6. un / una primo(-a) _____

7. tu madre _____

MASTERY EXERCISES

EXERCISE I. **Your mother left her daily calendar near the telephone. She calls from her cellular telephone. Answer the questions she asks about her schedule for the day.**

18 MARTES		**noviembre**
9:00		Sr. Mateo -- Marcas Finas
10:00		Banco Internacional
11:00	11:30	--- Reunión de vendedores
12:00		
1:00	1:15	Jack/Rosa - Restaurante del Lago
2:00		
3:00	3:45	llamada internacional --- Sr. Rupert
4:00		
5:00		Gimnasio
6:00	6:30	Cena y teatro

1. ¿A qué hora es la reunión de vendedores? _____

2. ¿Cuándo debo estar en el «Restaurante del Lago»? _____

3. ¿A qué hora tengo cita con el Sr. Mateo? _____

4. ¿A qué hora iré al gimnasio? _____

5. ¿A qué hora me llamará el señor Rupert? _____

6. ¿Cuándo debo estar en el «Banco Internacional»? _____

7. ¿A qué hora es la cena y el teatro? _____

EXERCISE J. You are preparing a birthday bulletin board for your Spanish class. Tell when these classmates celebrate their birthday. Include yourself at the end.

EXAMPLE: Rosalía / November 20   Rosalía celebra su cumpleaños el **veinte de noviembre.**

1. Abe y Peter / September 3   _____

2. Francisco / January 1   _____

3. Lucy / April 18   _____

4. Ricky / December 12   _____

5. Andrea / October 31   _____

6. Justino / August 27   _____

7. Emma / March 9   _____

8. Brian / November 15   _____

9. Carmen / July 21   _____

10. yo /   _____

EXERCISE K. You are studying for a Spanish test. Answer the questions that may appear on the test.

1. ¿Cuáles son los días del fin de la semana?   _____

2. ¿Qué meses del año tienen treinta y un días?   _____

3. Si hoy es jueves, ¿qué día fue ayer?   _____

4. ¿En qué días asistes a la escuela?   _____

5. ¿En qué días no vas a la escuela?   _____

6. ¿Cuál es el décimo mes del año?   _____

7. ¿En qué meses suele hacer mucho calor?   _____

8. ¿Cuál es el cuarto mes del año?   _____

9. ¿En qué mes celebras tu cumpleaños?   _____

10. ¿En qué mes terminan las clases?   _____

11. Si hoy es viernes, ¿qué día será mañana?   _____

12. ¿Cuál es el primer mes del año?   _____

13. ¿En qué meses hay treinta días?   _____

14. ¿En qué fecha celebramos el «Día de la Raza»? _____

15. ¿Cuál es la fecha de hoy?   _____

EXERCISE L.   You and a Spanish-speaking friend are planning to go to a concert. Send your friend an e-mail in which you give information about the concert. You may wish to include the following:

- the day and date of the concert
- when you bought the tickets
- the time the concerts begins
- the need to arrive on time
- when the doors will open
- the time you intend to arrive
- when the train arrives
- at what time you will meet him/her at the station
- the hour the concert should end
- when you can eat dinner

ACTIVIDADES

1. Prepare a journal entry in which you describe all of the activities that you did today. Be sure to include the time you began and ended each activity.

2. Select a month and prepare a calendar for it. Label the days of the week in Spanish and write out each day's date in numbers. Then list different activities for the month. Include special events, parties, sports activities, birthdays, holidays, etc.

3. It's time to move the clock forward (spring) or back (fall). Write a paragraph in Spanish in which you explain this concept and how it affects your activities, for example, "Now I can play ball in the park at 7:00 P.M. on Tuesdays." Refer to as many different times as you can.

CHAPTER

30

Adverbs and Adverbial Phrases

Adverbs describe the action expressed by a verb. They explain how, when, where, why, or in what way the action takes place. Adverbs also modify adjectives and other adverbs. They don't change form according to gender or number. An adverbial phrase is a group of words that together function as an adverb.

◆ 1 ◆ ADVERBS AND ADVERBIAL PHRASES OF MODE

a. Adverbs of mode (those answering the question how? or in what way?) are generally formed by adding *-mente* to the feminine singular form of an adjective.

ADJECTIVE		ADVERB	
clara	*clear*	**claramente**	*clearly*
cortés	*polite, courteous*	**cortésmente**	*politely, courteously*
inteligente	*intelligent*	**inteligentemente**	*intelligently*

NOTES:

1. Adjectives that have an accent mark keep the accent mark when they are changed to adverbs.

   rápida　→　rápidamente　　　　　fácil　→　fácilmente

2. In a series of two or more adverbs, the ending *-mente* is added only to the last one.

   Ella cantó clara y divinamente.　　　　　*She sang clearly and divinely.*

3. The adjectives *bueno* and *malo* have irregular adverb forms.

   bueno　*good*　　　　bien　*well*
   malo　*bad*　　　　　mal　*badly*
   Juan es un atleta **bueno**, pero　　　*Juan is a good athlete, but today*
   　hoy jugó **mal**.　　　　　　　　　*he played badly.*

4. Some adverbs have special forms:

   aprisa　*quickly*　　　　despacio　*slowly*

b. Adverbial phrases of mode are usually formed as follows:

de manera + adjective
Ella canta de manera cómica.　　　*She sings in a funny way.*

de modo + adjective
Ella canta de modo cómico.　　　*She sings in a funny way.*

c. Adverbial phrases may be formed by using *con* + noun.

El joven corrió **con rapidez** (rápidamente).	*The young man ran with rapidity (rapidly).*
El poeta escogió las palabras **con cuidado** (cuidadosamente).	*The poet chose the words with care (carefully).*
Salimos con nuestros amigos **con frecuencia** (frecuentemente).	*We go out with our friends with frequency (frequently).*

EXERCISE A.   **When Jack returned from a homestay in Venezuela, his parents wanted to know about the family with whom he stayed. Using the cues given in parentheses, answer his family's questions.**

EXAMPLE: ¿Cómo hablan ellos? (*rápido*)   Ellos hablan **rápidamente.**

1. ¿Cómo juegan al fútbol? (*hábil*) _____

2. ¿Cómo comen ellos? (*lento*) _____

3. ¿Cómo hablan inglés? (*mal*) _____

4. ¿Cómo tratan a los huéspedes? (*cortés*) _____

5. ¿Cómo te recibieron a ti? (*alegre*) _____

6. ¿Cómo se despidieron de ti? (*triste*) _____

7. ¿Piensan ellos visitarnos? (*probable*) _____

EXERCISE B.   **A group of friends took their driving test on the same day. Express what Sam tells about each one's performance.**

EXAMPLE: Yo conduje _____ . (*cuidadoso*)   Yo conduje **cuidadosamente.**

1. Felipe contestó las preguntas _____ . (*claro*)

2. Sarita sacó la licencia _____ . (*fácil*)

3. Esteban y Arturo condujeron _____ . (*lento*)

4. Félix frenó _____ . (*impulsivo*)

5. Josh y Laura aplaudieron _____ . (*fuerte*)

6. El inspector se portó _____ . (*profesional*)

EXERCISE C.   **Victor repeats, with a slight change, what his friend Jared says about the sports event they attended. Tell what Victor says using an adverbial phrase composed of *con* + noun.**

EXAMPLE: El equipo jugó el partido seriamente.
       Sí, el equipo jugó el partido **con seriedad.**

1. El equipo jugó enérgicamente.

2. Los otros miembros del equipo esperaron su turno para jugar pacientemente.

_____

3. Los árbitros trabajaron profesionalmente.

_____

4. Los aficionados aplaudieron al equipo locamente.

_____

5. Los locutores anunciaron el partido alegremente.

_____

6. Los ganadores salieron alegremente del campo de juego.

_____

7. Los oponentes dejaron el campo de juego tristemente.

_____

d. The words *más, menos, mucho, poco, mejor, peor*, and *demasiado* may be used either as adjectives or adverbs.

ADJECTIVE	ADVERB
Alicia tiene *menos* dinero que yo. *Alicia has less money than I do.*	**Ella es *más* pobre.** *She is poorer.*
La Sra. Goya tiene *demasiadas* joyas. *Mrs. Goya has too many jewels.*	**Ella es *demasiado* rica.** *She is too rich.*
Tu pintura es *peor* que la mía. *Your painting is worse than mine.*	**Yo pinto *mejor* que tú.** *I paint better than you.*

NOTE: As adjectives, *mucho, poco*, and *demasiado* vary in gender and number; as adverbs, they do not change.

EXERCISE D. **Express Martin's comments using the adverb and the appropriate form of the adjective in parentheses.**

1. Roberto tiene _____ amigos que yo porque yo soy _____ amistoso. (*más, menos*)

2. Freddy cree _____ supersticiones. Él es _____ supersticioso. (*demasiado, demasiado*)

3. La comida de mi mamá es _____ que la de mi abuela. Mi abuela cocina _____ que mi mamá. (*mejor, peor*)

4. Mi hermana tiene _____ ositos de peluche. Ella colecciona _____ . (*mucho, demasiado*)

5. Alex toca _____ el piano pero él va a dar _____ recitales. (*poco, demasiado*)

6. Jack y Berta no pelean _____ pero tienen _____ desacuerdos. (*mucho, demasiado*)

7. En el calendario hay _____ días festivos pero las personas los celebran _____ . (*mucho, poco*)

◆ 2 ◆ ADVERBS AND ADVERBIAL PHRASES OF TIME OR FREQUENCY

a. Adverbs of Time or Frequency (answering the question when?)

ahora	*now*	hoy	*today*	siempre	*always*
anoche	*last night*	luego	*then*	tarde	*late*
ayer	*yesterday*	nunca	*never*	temprano	*early*
entonces	*then*	pronto	*soon*	todavía	*still, yet*

b. Adverbial Phrases of Time or Frequency

algún día	*some day*	muchas veces	*often*
a veces	*sometimes*	pocas veces	*seldom*
esta noche	*tonight*	primero	*first*
este fin de semana	*this weekend*	todos los días	*every day*
más tarde	*later*		

EXERCISE E. Using the suggested adverb or adverbial phrase, tell when, or how frequently, you do, did, or will do the following things.

EXAMPLE: preparar la tarea / más tarde   **Yo prepararé la tarea más tarde.**

1. cantar en la calle / pocas veces   _____

2. ayudar a los padres / siempre   _____

3. practicar el esquí acuático / algún día   _____

4. montar a caballo / este fin de semana   _____

5. jugar al tenis / todos los días   _____

6. volver a ver una película / anoche   _____

7. entrar en el cine sin pagar / nunca   _____

8. usar la ropa del mejor amigo /
    muchas veces   _____

9. dejar la llave en casa / ayer   _____

10. faltar a una clase / a veces   _____

EXERCISE F. Tell when or how frequently these people do these activities. Use the expressions given.

a veces	nunca	siempre	tarde
muchas veces	pocas veces	temprano	todos los días

EXAMPLE: A Paco le gusta ver la salida del sol. Él se levanta **temprano.**

1. Rosa lee más de cien libros en un año. Ella lee _____ .

2. Alberto es un niño cortés. Él _____ dice «por favor» y «gracias».

3. A Ken le gusta estudiar las estrellas. Él se acuesta _____ .

4. Victoria no es partidaria de los deportes. Ella _____ practica ningún deporte.

5. Ricardo es tímido y no le gusta mucho bailar. Él baila _____ .

6. Cuando Elsa va de compras nunca tiene bastante dinero con ella. _____ ella pide dinero prestado a sus amigas.

7. A Gladys no le gustan los dulces pero _____ se le antoja un chocolate.

8. El señor Prado es muy puntual. Le gusta llegar _____ a sus citas.

◆ 3 ◆ ADVERBS AND ADVERBIAL PHRASES OF PLACE

a. Common Adverbs of Place (answering the question where?)

abajo	*below, downstairs*	dentro	*inside*
¿adónde?	*(to) where?*	derecho	*straight ahead*
allí	*there*	detrás	*behind*
aquí	*here*	¿dónde?	*where?*
arriba	*above, upstairs*	enfrente	*in front of, opposite*

b. Common Adverbial Phrases of Place

a la derecha	*to the right*	delante de	*in front of, ahead of*
a la izquierda	*to the left*	detrás de	*behind*
al lado de	*next to, alongside*	encima de	*on top of*
debajo de	*beneath*	frente a	*facing, in front of*

EXERCISE G.   **Tell the location of each one of the following.**

EXAMPLE: **El gato está debajo del sofá.**

1. Las llaves _____

_____ .

2. La pelota _____

_____ .

3. Los anteojos _____

_____ .

6. Susana _____

_____ .

4. Las sillas _____

_____ .

7. La mochila _____

_____ .

5. El dormitorio _____

_____ .

◆ 4 ◆ OTHER ADVERBIAL EXPRESSIONS

a. Some adverbial expressions are formed by combining prepositions with other words:

(1) Preposition + noun

a la vez	*at the same time*	de veras	*really, truly*
al fin	*finally*	en seguida	*immediately, at once*
de día	*by day*	por desgracia	*unfortunately*
de memoria	*by heart*	sin duda	*undoubtedly*
de noche	*by night*	sin embargo	*nevertheless*
de repente	*suddenly*		

(2) Preposition + adjective

a menudo	*often*	en general, por lo general	*generally*
de nuevo	*again*	por consiguiente	*consequently*
de pronto	*suddenly*	por supuesto	*of course*

(3) Preposition + adverb

al (a lo) menos	*at least*	en cuanto	*as soon as*

(4) Preposition + verb form

al amanecer	*at daybreak*	por escrito	*in writing*
al anochecer	*at nightfall*	por lo visto	*apparently, evidently*

(5) Preposition + adjective + noun

de buena (mala) gana	*(un)willingly*	en otra parte	*elsewhere*
en ninguna parte	*not anywhere, nowhere*	en todas partes	*everywhere*

b. The following are common adverbial expressions formed with several words:

ahora mismo	*right now*	hoy mismo	*this very day*
a pesar de	*in spite of*	junto a	*beside*
cada vez más	*more and more*	mientras tanto	*meanwhile*
cuanto antes	*as soon as possible*	rara vez	*seldom*
de cuando en cuando	*from time to time*	tal vez	*perhaps*
dentro de poco	*shortly*	tan pronto como	*as soon as*
hoy (en) día	*nowadays*	ya no	*no longer*

EXERCISE H. Michael likes to comment about everyone and everything. Complete his comments using the following adverbial expressions.

a la vez	de cuando en cuando	de repente	por lo visto
al amanecer	de día	en seguida	sin duda
al anochecer	de memoria	hoy mismo	sin embargo
al fin	de noche	por escrito	tal vez

1. _____ Marta viaja en autobús, pero _____ ella prefiere viajar en taxi.

2. Pilar se despierta _____ porque los pájaros comienzan a cantar.

3. A mi abuela le fascinan los colores que se ven en el cielo _____ .

4. Verónica nunca tarda en contestar cuando alguien le hace una pregunta. Ella responde _____ .

5. Los dos carros chocaron en la carretera porque el primer carro frenó _____ .

6. Enrique toca todas las canciones populares en la guitarra y no tiene que leer la música. Él las sabe _____ .

7. Tomás y David tenían un partido de fútbol ayer pero estaba lloviendo. _____ , ellos fueron al estadio listos para jugar.

8. Lina hace muchas cosas en un día porque tiene la habilidad de hacer dos cosas _____ .

9. Nina gasta mucho dinero cuando va de compras. _____ , sus padres son ricos.

10. El profesor no aceptó el perdón oral de Rodolfo. Rodolfo tiene que pedírselo _____ .

11. Estela y Marco andan juntos _____ . _____ , ellos son novios.

12. Me olvidé del cumpleaños de Antonia que fue ayer. _____ yo voy a llamarla para felicitarla.

13. Yo no soy gran partidario de las películas de ciencia-ficción. Pero, _____ yo veo una.

14. El cielo está muy nublado hoy. _____ va a llover.

15. _____ ayer terminaron la construcción en la escuela.

EXERCISE I. Complete the story that Linda wrote about her father by selecting the correct expression from those presented below for numbers 1-10 and then for number 11-20.

demasiado	por lo general	pocas veces	allí
arriba	de memoria	por consiguiente	juntos
nunca	ahora		

Yo no visito _____ el trabajo de mi padre. _____ él es el gerente de una gran tienda de
        1.   *2.*

ropa. El dueño de la tienda dijo que mi papá aprendió _____ los nombres de todos los empleados en
                                          3

media hora. _____ , él trabaja _____ y nosotros no podemos pasar tiempo _____ en la
           4.   *5.*   *6.*

tienda. _____ , cuando yo quiero hablar con él, lo llamo por teléfono. Su oficina está _____ , en el
      7.   *8.*

segundo piso. _____ lo encuentro _____ .
           9.   *10.*

abajo	en todas partes	cortésmente	mejor
al lado de	a pesar de	siempre	a menudo
diario	furiosamente		

Él _____ está _____ trabajando _____ los dependientes. Según su secretaria, él está
   11.   *12.*   *13.*

_____ . Él cree que los empleados trabajan _____ al verlo ayudándolos. Él trata a todo el
  14.   *15.*

mundo _____ , aun a los clientes que _____ le gritan _____ . _____ las
       16.   *17.*   *18.*   *19.*

horas largas y los problemas que se presentan _____ , le fascina su trabajo.
                                                   20.

⟨ MASTERY EXERCISES ⟩

EXERCISE J. Using adverbs in your responses, answer the questions a friend asks.

1. ¿A qué hora te levantas en general? _____

2. ¿Qué haces ahora mismo? _____

3. ¿Cómo patinas en hielo? _____

4. ¿Qué cosas haces de mala gana? _____

5. ¿Cómo tratas a tus hermanos? _____

6. ¿Siempre preparas la tarea con cuidado? _____

7. ¿Eres hábil cuando juegas a un deporte? _____

8. ¿Dónde estacionas tu carro? _____

9. ¿Todavía piensas estudiar en México
en el verano? _____

10. ¿Cúando vas a esquiar? _____

EXERCISE K.   **Complete the statements with an appropriate adverb.**

1. A mi mamá le fascina ir al teatro. Ella va allí _____ .

2. Yo traté de llamar a Juan por teléfono pero _____ tiene el mismo número.

3. _____ se ven menos expresiones de la cortesía.

4. Larry no supo dónde buscar un libro en la biblioteca. _____ , él va allí _____ .

5. _____ , diez alumnos van a participar en el concurso.

6. A Tere no le gustaba el tenis pero ahora parece que le gusta _____ .

7. Al ver la gravedad de la herida, el médico atendió al señor _____ .

8. El señor Molina ha viajado mucho y dice que _____ se habla español _____ .

9. Tengo muchísima hambre. Tengo que comer _____ .

10. Van a tardar _____ menos dos días en revelar las fotografías.

EXERCISE L.   **Your boss met with you today to discuss your performance and to indicate some areas for improvement. Prepare this summary of the meeting in Spanish and include and include it in your Spanish journal. You may wish to include the following using as many adverbs as possible.**

- when the meeting took place
- the tone of the meeting
- your self-evaluation of your work performance
- your self-evaluation of your areas of improvement
- how much and how easily you have learned new tasks
- a problem with your co-workers
- a possible solution that was suggested
- what you did immediately after meeting with your boss

◄⟅ A C T I V I D A D E S ⟆►

1. Write ten sentences in which you describe the manner in which you do different things.

2. Write a paragraph of six to ten sentences in which you describe your favorite activities. Tell how you do them and when.

3. Write a short sketch of ten to twelve sentences in which you describe an event or incident you witnessed recently. Include as many adverbs as possible in the description.

CHAPTER 31

Interrogative and Exclamatory Words

◆ 1 ◆ INTERROGATIVES

a. Common interrogative expressions

¿qué? *what?*

¿quién, –es? *who?*

¿a quién, –es *whom?, to whom?*

¿de quién? *whose?, of whom?*

¿con quién, –es? *with whom?*

¿cuál, –es? *which?, which one(s)?*

¿cuándo? *when?*

¿cuánto, –a? *how much?*

¿cuántos, –as? *how many?*

¿cómo? *how?*

¿por qué? *why?*

¿dónde? *where?*

¿de dónde? *(from) where?*

¿a dónde? *(to) where?*

NOTES:

1. All interrogative words have a written accent.

2. In Spanish, questions have an inverted question mark (¿) at the beginning and a standard one (?) at the end.

3. When interrogatives words such as *¿qué?, ¿cuándo?,* and *¿dónde?* are used in a question, the subject–verb order is reversed from the order in statements.

   ¿Qué hacen ellos?   *What are they doing?*

   Ellos comen.   *They are eating.*

   ¿Dónde está Enrique?   *Where is Henry?*

   Él está aquí.   *He is here.*

4. Both *¿qué?* and *¿cuál?* are equivalent to English *what?* and *which?*, but the two words are not usually interchangeable in Spanish.

   (a) *¿Qué?* seeks a description, definition, or explanation. It is used instead of *¿cuál?* before a noun.

   ¿Qué es esto?   *What is this?*

   ¿Qué vestido prefiere Ud.?   *Which dress do you prefer?*

   (b) *¿Cuál?* implies a choice or selection.

   ¿Cuál es la capital de México?   *What is the capital of Mexico?*

   ¿Cuáles son los productos importantes   *What are the important*

   de la Argentina?   *products of Argentina?*

   ¿Cuál de los vestidos prefiere Ud.?   *Which of the dresses do you prefer?*

5. *¿Adónde?* is used instead of *¿dónde?* to indicate motion to a place (to where).

   ¿Adónde va Ud.?   *Where are you going?*

EXERCISE A.   Ricardo doesn't listen carefully to his friends when they are talking and always has to ask about whom they are speaking. Express the questions he asks to find out who does the following.

EXAMPLE: Arturo y Vicki van al cine esta noche.   **¿Quiénes** van al cine esta noche?

1. Mario es miembro del equipo de béisbol.   _____

2. Sarita trabaja de salvavidas.   _____

3. Ali recibió un carro nuevo para su cumpleaños.   _____

4. Nosotros pensamos ir al parque de diversiones.   _____

5. Jacques piensa visitar a su familia en Francia.   _____

6. Yo tengo que cuidar a mi hermanito.   _____

7. Eliot y Víctor están en el estadio.   _____

EXERCISE B.   Your mother is telling you why she couldn't sleep last night. You ask her to repeat what she said.

EXAMPLE: Una sirena no dejó de sonar.   **¿Qué** no dejó de sonar?

1. Un teléfono sonó varias veces.   _____

2. Muchos carros tocaron la bocina.   _____

3. Entró mucha luz en el cuarto.   _____

4. Un farol se encendía y se apagaba.   _____

5. Los vecinos tocaron discos toda la noche.   _____

6. Cayó un relámpago.   _____

7. Oí muchos ruidos en la casa.   _____

EXERCISE C.   Alex was absent from school today. Complete the questions he asks with *¿qué?* or *¿quién / quiénes?*

1. ¿ _____ enseñó la clase de química?

2. ¿ _____ tarea dio el señor Vargas?

3. ¿ _____ más faltó a las clases hoy?

4. ¿ _____ hará el experimento pasadomañana?

5. ¿ _____ ayudaron al profesor?

6. ¿ _____ te acompañó durante el recreo?

7. ¿ _____ deporte jugaste en la clase de educación física?

8. ¿ _____ jugaron contigo?

9. ¿ _____ necesito llevar a la escuela mañana?

10. ¿ _____ fue elegido presidente del club?

EXERCISE D. **Your younger brother is looking through a book. He asks you to explain the words he doesn't understand. According to the answers given, express his questions.**

EXAMPLE: Un incendio es un fuego.   **¿Qué** es un incendio?

1. Una violeta es una flor.   _____

2. Una excursión es un viaje.   _____

3. Un ciprés es un árbol.   _____

4. Una ciruela es una fruta.   _____

5. Una enciclopedia es un libro.   _____

EXERCISE E. **Your teacher has asked you to prepare a series of questions to ask the class. Complete the following questions with *¿qué?* or *¿cuál /cuáles?*.**

1. ¿ _____ día es hoy?

2. ¿ _____ son los días de la semana?

3. ¿ _____ tiempo hace hoy?

4. ¿ _____ haces cuando llueve?

5. ¿ _____ es tu estación favorita?

6. ¿ _____ quieres recibir de regalo para tu cumpleaños?

7. ¿ _____ es el mejor equipo de fútbol?

8. ¿ _____ mes del año tiene sólo 28 días?

9. ¿ _____ deporte prefieres?

10. ¿ _____ de los grupos musicales es tu predilecto?

EXERCISE F. **You are helping your teacher clean the classroom on the last day of school. As she begins to put things in a box for the lost and found she wants to know to whom they belong. Express the question that she asks for each item.**

EXAMPLE: llaves   **¿De quién** son las llaves?

1. anteojos   _____

2. paraguas   _____

3. tarjetas de béisbol _____

4. mochila _____

5. patines _____

EXERCISE G. Based on the answers given, express the questions Jenny asks a new exchange student.

EXAMPLE: Les escribo a mis amigos por el correo electrónico.
¿A quiénes les escribes por el correo electrónico?

1. Llamo a mis padres por larga distancia. _____

2. Extraño más a mis hermanos. _____

3. Aquí llamo a mi amiga Lola. _____

4. Le mando una carta a diario a mi novio, Gerardo. _____

5. Visito a mis tíos a menudo. _____

EXERCISE H. Ricky is corresponding with a pen pal. From the paragraph below, express the questions Ricky asked him in his last e-mail.

EXAMPLE: **¿Dónde** está la escuela a la que asistes?

La escuela a la que asisto no está lejos de la casa. Mi mejor amigo, Hugo, vive a una cuadra de mi casa. Los cines están en el centro. Hay un parque cerca de la escuela. Mi restaurante favorito, un restaurante chino, está en el centro comercial. Mis amigos y yo nos reunimos en el centro comercial.

1. _____

2. _____

3. _____

4. _____

5. _____

EXERCISE I. A classmate wants to know where you and some of your friends went during the summer vacation. Express the questions she asks.

EXAMPLE: Lucinda   **¿Adónde** fue Lucinda durante las vacaciones?

1. Gregorio y Ralph _____

2. tú _____

3. Kamal _____

4. Jimmy y su familia _____

5. las gemelas Ortega _____

EXERCISE J.   Denise is visiting her aunt who just returned from a trip around the world. She wants to know where everything is from. Express her questions.

EXAMPLE: esta pintura   **¿De dónde** es esta pintura?

1. el calendario azteca   _____

2. las muñecas   _____

3. esta estatua   _____

4. el florero   _____

5. la caja de música   _____

6. los grabados en madera   _____

EXERCISE K.   Mr. Arenas is speaking to a travel agent about a proposed trip. Complete the questions he is asked by the travel agent with the appropriate question words.

1. ¿ _____ se llama Ud.?

2. ¿ _____ vive Ud.?

3. ¿ _____ es su número de teléfono?

4. ¿ _____ personas harán el viaje?

5. ¿ _____ piensan ir?

6. ¿ _____ es el propósito del viaje?

7. ¿ _____ días piensan estar allí?

8. ¿ _____ dinero quieren gastar?

9. ¿ _____ clase de viaje quieren hacer?

10. ¿ _____ ciudades quieren visitar?

11. ¿ _____ quieren conocer en cada ciudad?

12. ¿ _____ van a visitar en la última ciudad?

13. ¿ _____ no quieren pasar más días allí?

14. ¿ _____ piensan regresar?

◆ 2 ◆ EXCLAMATIONS

Exclamatory words, like interrogative words, have written accents. The most common exclamatory words are:

¡Qué... !	*What . . . !, What a . . . !, How . . . !*	**¡Qué grande es!**	*How large it is!*
¡Qué película!	*What a film!*	**¡Qué rica es la sopa!**	*How delicious the soup is!*
¡Cuánto, -a... !	*How much . . . !*	**¡Cuánta comida!**	*How much food!*
¡Cuántos, -as... !	*How many . . . !*	**¡Cuántos carros tienen!**	*How many cars they have!*

NOTES:

1. Exclamatory sentences have an inverted exclamation mark (¡) at the beginning and a standard one (!) at the end.

2. If there is an adjective next to a noun, the exclamation is made more intense by placing *tan* or *más* before the adjective.

   ¡Qué tren **más (tan)** rápido!   *What a fast train!*

EXERCISE L.   Alfredo and some friends are on a camping trip. Express what they exclaim upon seeing the following.

EXAMPLE: oso / grande   **¡Qué** oso **tan (más)** grande!

1. árbol / antiguo   _____

2. flores / bonitas   _____

3. arroyo / ancho   _____

4. ardillas / graciosas   _____

5. caverna / oscura   _____

6. pájaros / ruidosos   _____

7. choza / rústica   _____

8. tienda de campo / pequeña   _____

9. lago / tranquilo   _____

EXERCISE M.   You and several friends have mixed opinions about a musical comedy that you just saw. Express the comments you make as you leave the theater using *¡qué!, ¡cuánto!,* or *¡cuántos!*

EXAMPLE: música / viva   **¡Qué** música **tan (más)** viva!

1. vestuario / original   _____

2. bailarines / torpes   _____

3. argumento / ridículo   _____

4. cantantes / talentosos   _____

5. músicos / tocar / la orquesta   _____

6. intermedios / largos   _____

7. producción / aburrida   _____

8. sonido / espectacular   _____

MASTERY EXERCISES

EXERCISE N.   **Prepare as many questions as you can based on the following paragraphs.**

EXAMPLE: El sábado por la tarde, mientras Jorge estaba en la playa, conoció a Elena, una joven guatemalteca. Ella habla inglés muy bien y por eso no hablaron español.

¿A quién conoció Jorge?   *¿Qué lengua hablaron?*

¿Dónde estaba Jorge?   *¿Cómo habla Elena el inglés?*

¿Cuándo conoció Jorge a Elena?   *¿Por qué no hablaron español?*

1. Cada año Felipe espera con muchísimas ganas el día de su cumpleaños. Su familia suele darle un regalo colectivo que representa uno de sus pasatiempos favoritos. Este año Felipe recibió varios juegos electrónicos que puede usar en la computadora.

_____

_____

_____

_____

2. Los padres de Elisa están contentos porque Elisa tiene la costumbre de acostarse temprano. A ella le gusta leer en la cama antes de dormirse. Ahora ella lee una novela muy interesante y divertida. Su mamá se sorprendió porque Elisa no apagó la luz de su dormitorio hasta la medianoche.

_____

_____

_____

_____

EXERCISE O.   **You and several friends are spending the weekend in the country. Express what someone says when he/she hears the different comments.**

EXAMPLE: Es un día hermoso.   **¡Qué** día **más** hermoso!

1. Había muchas estrellas en el cielo. _____

2. El cielo es muy azul. _____

3. El paisaje es muy verde. _____

4. El ambiente es tranquilo. _____

5. El agua está muy fría. _____

6. Hay muchas montañas altas. _____

7. Hay poca gente aquí. _____

8. Es un lugar ideal. _____

EXERCISE P. The Spanish Club in your school is going to review short stories and novels in Spanish. You have been put in charge of this event. Prepare a list of questions in Spanish that each reviewer will have to cover in his/her review. Include the following:

- the title
- the author
- the author's nationality
- the setting of the story
- the principal and secondary characters
- the character development
- the time of the story
- your impression
- both positive and negative
- the ending
- the reason for your impression
- the message the story or novel conveys
- literary techniques employed
- your recommendation

ACTIVIDADES

1. Prepare a list of ten questions you would ask in each of the following situations:

   a. You are working in a department store for the summer. What would you ask a customer who wants to buy an article of clothing?

   b. You are interviewing an alumnus/alumna of your school to learn about their impressions of the school now that they have been graduated.

   c. You are going to spend the summer in a Spanish-speaking country. What questions will you ask to learn about the host family with whom you will live?

2. Prepare a list of positive comments (exclamatory expressions) you can use while living with the host family.

Word Study

CHAPTER

32

Word Building

One way to increase your Spanish vocabulary is to think of words as roots or word families. Learning specific patterns can help you to expand your Spanish vocabulary and read more effectively.

A. Some nouns drop their final vowel and add *-ero*, *-era* to indicate the person associated with the noun.

la aventura   *the adventure*   la cocina   *the kitchen*

el aventurero/la aventurera   *the adventurer*   el cocinero/la cocinera   *the cook*

EXERCISE A.   **Mr. Whitman is talking to a colleague in his company's office in Mexico. Complete the dialogue with the word that comes from the word in boldface.**

EXAMPLE: SR. WHITMAN: Espero **una carta** importante.
            EL COLEGA: **El cartero** llega a las diez.

1.   SR. WHITMAN: No he recibido ningún **mensaje.**

       EL COLEGA: _____ no ha venido hoy.

2.   SR. WHITMAN: ¿Cuándo van a terminar **la obra** de reparación?

       EL COLEGA: _____ la terminarán esta tarde.

3.   SR. WHITMAN: Tuve un problema en **la aduana.**

       EL COLEGA: _____ son muy estrictos .

4.   SR. WHITMAN: ¿Dónde puedo mandar a arreglar **los zapatos?**

                    _____ de la esquina hace un buen trabajo.

5.   SR. WHITMAN: ¿Cómo viajaré por la ciudad? Yo no tengo **coche.**

       EL COLEGA: _____ de la campañía lo llevará.

6.   SR. WHITMAN: Fue **un viaje** largo y pesado.

       EL COLEGA: _____ se cansan fácilmente.

B. Some nouns ending in *-ero* change to *-ería* to indicate the shop or store in which the person works.

el barbero   *the barber*   el librero   *the book seller*

la barbería   *the barber shop*   la librería   *the bookstore*

EXERCISE B.   Mrs. Andrade is telling a new neighbor where she can do her shopping. Write the name of the store based on the word in italics.

EXAMPLE: Nuestro vecino, el señor Vega, es **carnicero**. Su **carnicería** está en la Calle Londres.

1. Mi marido *es joyero* y trabaja en la _____ «Princesa».

2. *El lechero* ya no hace entrega a domicilio pero hay una buena _____ en la Calle Reforma.

3. El mejor *panadero* del vecindario es Humberto Flores. Su _____ está al lado de la carnicería.

4. Mi *peluquero* se llama Antonio y voy a su _____ mañana, si Ud. me quiere acompañar.

5. Hay *un zapatero* fabuloso muy cerca de aquí. Su _____ está en la esquina. También vende zapatos nuevos de última moda.

6. Yo soy una buena *repostera* pero prefiero comprar los pasteles en la _____ «La Francesa».

7. Venden *flores* frescas y bonitas en la _____ «El Jardín».

8. Si necesita reparar un reloj, el mejor *relojero* del barrio está en la _____ de la Calle Mayor.

C. Some nouns are derived from the past participle of the verb.

resultar *to result*	**oír** *to hear*	**decir** *to say*
el resultado *the result*	**el oído** *hearing*	**el dicho** *the saying*

EXERCISE C.   Estela often talks incessantly when she is with her friends. Complete her statements with the appropriate word from the suggestions provided.

SUGGESTIONS: asado   contenido   oído   vestido
cocido   dichos   pescado
conocidos   empleados   resultado

1. La explosión les afectó el _____ .

2. En la cocina de mi abuela hay muchos imanes con _____ chistosos.

3. Prefiero la carne y el pollo; no me gusta el _____ para nada.

4. Los _____ de esa tienda son muy amables. Siempre tratan bien a los clientes.

5. Para la boda de su hija, la señora Lozano piensa comprar un _____ carísimo.

6. Echaron a perder el _____ porque nadie lo cuidó en el horno.

7. Muchos _____ míos han recomendado esa película. Creo que nos gustará.

8. Antes de pedir en un restaurante, mi mamá quiere saber el _____ de todos los platos, especialmente el del _____ .

9. El _____ del partido de hoy fue un empate.

D. Some feminine nouns are formed from past participles by changing the *-o* ending to *-a.*

entrar *to enter*	**beber** *to drink*	**ver** *to see*
la entrada *the entrance*	**la bebida** *the drink, beverage*	**la vista** *the sight, view*

EXERCISE D.   **You are watching the nightly news. Complete the statements the news reporter makes basing your response on the word in italics.**

EXAMPLE: **Nevó** toda la noche al norte y tuvieron **una nevada** de doce pulgadas.

1. Es más económico *ir* a Roma si compramos un boleto de _____ y vuelta.

2. Muchas personas *comen* en el Restaurante Real porque la _____ es muy sabrosa y fresca.

3. Un niño fue *herido* en el accidente pero los médicos dicen que la _____ es superficial.

4. A la hora de *salir* del cine, los acomodadores abrieron todas las _____ .

5. El rey de España *llega* mañana. Todo el mundo espera su _____ con entusiasmo.

6. Los carros no deben *parar* en esa esquina porque es una _____ de autobús.

7. La maestra *miró* a los alumnos con seriedad. Es decir, ella tiene una _____ seria.

8. En muchos casos, cuando una persona se *cae*, la _____ es más embarazosa que dolorosa.

E. Some stem-changing verbs have a corresponding noun with a stem-change.

almorzar *to (eat) lunch*	**llover** *to rain*
el almuerzo *the lunch*	**la lluvia** *the rain*

EXERCISE E.   **Michael keeps a journal in his Spanish class. Complete the entry he made using the words provided.**

cuentos	vuelo	recuerdos	encuentro	prueba
sueño	gobierno	nieve	juegos	comienzo

Anoche tuve un _____ muy bonito. Tuve un _____ con unos amigos de mi niñez. Viajé
                        1.   2.

en avión al Canadá y el _____ fue corto y agradable. Aunque era el _____ del invierno, la
                              3.   4.

_____ blanca ya cubría las calles. Tuve que pasar por inmigración en el aeropuerto y el _____
        5.   6.

exige una _____ de la nacionalidad de los viajeros. Afortunadamente tenía mi pasaporte. Mis amigos y
              7.

yo contamos muchos _____ de la niñez: de los _____ infantiles que jugábamos y las bromas
                          8.   9.

que hacíamos. Me desperté con muchos _____ bonitos.
                                              10.

F. Some nouns are formed from verbs by dropping the *-ar* ending of the verb and adding *-amiento,* or dropping the *-er* or *-ir* ending of the verb and adding *-imiento.*

casar *to marry*	**establecer** *to establish*
el casamiento *the marriage*	**el establecimiento** *the establishment*

EXERCISE F.   Luke is preparing some statements for his classmates in his Spanish class. Complete each statement with a noun formed from the following verbs.

casar   consentir   nombrar   ofrecer
conocer   mover   nacer   descubrir

EXAMPLE: El 12 de octubre se conmemora el **descubrimiento** del Nuevo Mundo por Cristóbal Colón.

1. Rodolfo y su novia piensan casarse. _____ tendrá lugar el año próximo.

2. El romanticismo y el naturalismo son dos _____ literarios.

3. Un adorno tradicional de Navidad es el _____ .

4. El _____ de los ganadores del Premio Nobel siempre atrae mucha atención de la prensa.

5. Para quedar bien con sus dioses, los aztecas les hacían muchos _____ .

6. Un cirujano necesita el _____ del enfermo antes de operarlo.

7. Muchas personas mayores no tienen ningún _____ de computadoras.

G. Some nouns are derived from verbs by dropping the *-r* of the infinitive and adding *-ador* to the stem of *-ar* verbs, *-edor* to the stems of *-er*, and *-idor* to those of *-ir* verbs.

trabajar   *to work*   **comer**   *to eat*   **servir**   *to serve*
el trabajador   *the worker*   **el comedor**   *the dining room*   **el servidor**   *the servant*

EXERCISE G.   Using the verbs *conquistar, descubrir, explorar, fundar, pensar,* and *vencer,* form nouns and complete the statements.

EXAMPLE: *(gobernar)* En muchas de las repúblicas que se dividen en estados, cada estado elige a su propio **gobernador.**

1. En la batalla entre moros y cristianos en España en el siglo XI, el Cid fue el _____ .

2. De Soto y Ponce de León fueron dos _____ españoles.

3. Miguel de Unamuno fue uno de los grandes _____ de la «Generación del '98».

4. Thomas Edison fue el _____ de la electricidad.

5. Henry Ford fue el _____ de una empresa que fabrica automóviles,

6. Francisco Pizarro fue el _____ de los incas.

H. Some nouns are formed from adjectives by dropping the final vowel of the adjective and adding *-eza.*

bello   *beautiful*   **limpio**   *clean*
la belleza   *the beauty*   **la limpieza**   *the cleanliness*

EXERCISE H. Jim is helping a friend study for a vocabulary test. For each of the adjectives given, express the noun that comes from that adjective.

EXAMPLE: agudo   →   **agudeza**

1. ligero _____

2. noble _____

3. triste _____

4. puro _____

5. grande _____

6. rico _____

7. franco _____

8. pobre _____

I. Some English nouns ending in *-ty* are expressed in Spanish by changing the *-ty* to *-dad*.

brutality **la brutalidad**   *capacity* **la capacidad**

EXERCISE I. Giselle tells a friend some of the things she learned when she visited her sister at school. Complete her statements with the Spanish equivalent of the following words.

| activity | curiosity | humanity | society | university |
| brutality | generosity | prosperity | unity | |

EXAMPLE: Visité la **universidad** donde mi hermana estudia medicina.

1. Las guerras muestran la _____ en contra de la _____ .

2. La _____ intelectual es una característica buena.

3. Una persona tacaña no practica la _____ .

4. Para ganar una elección, muchos políticos prometen la _____ a los ciudadanos.

5. Ha habido muchos cambios en la _____ actual porque las costumbres han cambiado.

6. La _____ de una comunidad es un concepto básico e importante del ser humano.

7. Prefiero una _____ donde me ejercite activamente.

J. Some English nouns ending in *-tion* are expressed in Spanish by changing *-tion* to *-ción*.

invention **la invención**   *section* **la sección**

EXERCISE J. Based on the English words given below, complete each of the following statements with the appropriate Spanish word.

| construction | description | formation | invitation | operation |
| conversation | direction | intention | nation | |

EXAMPLE: Ésta es una **operación** difícil en la computadora.

1. Cada noche hay noticias sobre la _____ en el noticiero de las seis.

2. Para saber cómo era Carlos, Rita le pidió una _____ de sí mismo.

3. Recibí una _____ a la quinceañera de mi prima.

4. Mi mamá tuvo una _____ con mi maestra de matemáticas y ahora no puedo salir con mis amigos.

5. Yo no tengo ninguna _____ de trabajar durante las vacaciones de verano.

6. Se han vendido muchas casas en esta calle y ahora hay mucha _____ .

7. Ralph y Edward nunca caminan juntos. Edward siempre camina en _____ opuesta.

8. Los romanos contribuyeron mucho a la _____ de la cultura hispana.

K. **A number of adjectives are formed from nouns by adding** -oso **to the stem of the noun.**

| número | _the number_ | religión | _the religion_ |
| numeroso | _numerous_ | religioso | _religious_ |

EXERCISE K. **Complete the following statements using the italicized word to form an adjective.**

EXAMPLE: Dicen que una persona que muestra mucho **amor** es una persona **amorosa.**

1. El viento sopla afuera con mucha _furia_. Es un viento _____ .

2. Este actor tiene _fama_ mundial. Es decir, es muy _____ .

3. Cuando hay hielo en la calle hay mucho _peligro_. Es _____ caminar allí.

4. La paella es una _delicia_ de la cocina española. Me gusta porque es _____ .

5. El partido político que tiene más _poder_ que el otro es el más _____ .

6. Hay mucho _silencio_ en el jardín porque el vecino está dentro de la casa. Por fin es una tarde _____ .

Chapter 32

Synonyms and Antonyms

◆ *1* ◆ SYNONYMS

a. Nouns

afecto, cariño, amor   *affection, love*
alumno, estudiante   *student, pupil*
amo, dueño, propietario   *master, owner, boss*
batalla, combate, lucha   *battle, fight, struggle*
broma, chiste   *joke, trick*
buque, barco, vapor   *ship, boat*
cabello, pelo   *hair*
cara, rostro   *face*
cuarto, habitación   *room*
cura, sacerdote   *priest*

demonio, diablo   *devil*
error, falta   *error, mistake*
esposo, marido   *husband*
idioma, lengua   *language*
lugar, sitio   *place*
maestro, profesor   *teacher*
miedo, temor   *fear*
país, nación   *country, nation*
pájaro, ave   *bird*

b. Adjectives

alegre, feliz, contento   *happy, merry, content*
antiguo, viejo   *old, ancient*
aplicado, diligente, trabajador   *industrious, diligent, hard-working*
bastante, suficiente   *enough, sufficient*
bello, hermoso   *beautiful*
bonito, lindo   *pretty*
célebre, famoso, ilustre   *famous*

corto, breve   *short*
delgado, flaco   *thin, slender*
diferente, distinto   *different*
grave, serio   *serious*
igual, semejante   *similar, alike*
tonto, necio   *foolish, stupid*

c. Verbs

acabar, terminar, concluir (y)   *to finish, to end, to conclude*
acordarse (ue) de, recordar (ue)   *to remember*
aguardar, esperar   *to wait (for)*
alzar (c), elevar, levantar   *to raise*
andar, caminar   *to walk*
asustar, espantar   *to frighten, to scare*
atravesar (ie), cruzar (c)   *to cross*
colocar (qu), poner (g)   *to put, to place*
comprender, entender (ie)   *to understand*
conseguir (i, gu), obtener (ie, g)   *to get, to obtain*
contestar, responder   *to answer, to reply*

dejar, permitir   *to let, to allow, to permit*
desear, querer (ie)   *to want, to wish*
detenerse (ie, g), pararse   *to stop*
echar, arrojar, lanzar (c), tirar   *to throw*
empezar (ie), principiar, comenzar (ie)   *to begin*
enfadarse, enojarse   *to become angry*
enviar (í), mandar   *to send*
hallar, encontrar (ue)   *to find*
invitar, convidar to   *invite*
irse, marcharse   *to go away*
mostrar (ue), enseñar   *to show*
quedarse, permanecer (zc)   *to remain*

rogar (ue, gu), suplicar (qu)   *to beg,*
  to implore

romper, quebrar (ie)   *to break*

seguir (i, gu), continuar (ú)   *to continue*

sorprender, asombrar   *to surprise*

suceder, ocurrir   *to happen, to occur*

sufrir, padecer (zc)   *to suffer*

volver (ue), regresar   *to return*

d. Adverbs

aun, todavía   *still, yet*

despacio, lentamente   *slowly*

jamás, nunca   *never*

solo, solamente   *only*

EXERCISE A.   **Susan and her family are on a cruise. Rewrite the text message she sends to a friend with synonyms for the words in italic.**

Querida amiga:

Te *envío* este mensaje desde el *barco* en que viajo por el Mar Caribe. *Quiero* compartir contigo algunas de mis observaciones. Estoy muy *alegre* porque estoy divirtiéndome mucho. Hemos visitado tres islas *hermosas*. Cada isla es muy *diferente*. En una isla vi muchas *aves* exóticas. La tripulación del crucero es muy amable y todos hablan varios *idiomas*. Hay un novelista *célebre* en el crucero pero él prefiere *permanecer* en su *cuarto*. Cada mañana mi mamá y yo *andamos* a lo largo del barco. Conocí a un joven *delgado* de *cabello* rubio. Es el hijo del *propietario* de una tienda del barco. Mis padres me *permiten* participar en muchas de las actividades a bordo. *Aun* faltan tres días en el mar. El tiempo en el crucero pasa *despacio*. El crucero *termina* el sábado.

Con *afecto,*

Susan

EXERCISE B.   **Joey is preparing a word game for his Spanish class. Complete the choices he will offer his classmates by writing the appropriate synonym for the initial words given.**

EXAMPLE: *trabajador:* alegre, **diligente,** bello

1. *aguardar:* terminar, _____ , dejar

2. *broma:* barco, sacerdote, _____

3. *alzar:* cruzar, _____ , caminar

4. *lucha:* _____ , vapor, amor

5. *bastante:* antiguo, _____ , grave

6. *concluir:* atravesar, recordar, _____

7. *corto:* feliz, _____ , aplicado

8. *obtener:* _____ , comprender, principiar

9. *asustar:* lanzar, padecer, _____

10. *poner:* _____ , desear, rogar

11. *sorprender:* suceder, volver, _____

12. *jamás:* _____ , solo, todavía

13. *romper:* sufrir, mostrar, _____

14. *país:* demonio, _____ , dueño

15. *falta:* lengua, sitio, _____

(EXERCISE C.)   **Describe this bullfighter, giving a synonym for the words in italic.**

1. Conocí a un torero muy *famoso.*

_____

2. También es *dueño* de una estancia en la que crían toros.

_____

3. Los toros no lo *asustan.*

_____

4. Los toros no son ni *delgados* ni *bellos.*

_____

5. Los toros no le dan *temor* a él.

_____

6. Él ya no lidia; es *maestro* de la tauromaquia.

_____

7. Él *comprende* bien el inglés.

_____

8. Él habla cuatro *lenguas.*

_____

9. *Todavía* pasa cada domingo en la plaza de toros.

_____

10. Siempre hablaba con un *cura* antes de lidiar en una corrida de toros.

_____

11. La plaza de toros es un *lugar* de mucho espectáculo y valentía.

_____

◆ *2* ◆ ANTONYMS

a. Nouns

algo	*something*	**nada**	*nothing*
alguien	*someone, somebody*	**nadie**	*no one, nobody*

amigo *friend*	enemigo *enemy*
amo *master*	esclavo *slave*
amor *love*	odio *hate*
caballero *gentleman*	dama *lady*
cielo *heaven, sky*	tierra *earth, ground*
día *day*	noche *night*
entrada *entrance*	salida *exit*
este *east*	oeste *west*
éxito *success*	fracaso *failure*
fin *end*	principio *beginning*
guerra *war*	paz *peace*
héroe *hero*	heroína *heroine*
hombre *man*	mujer *woman*
madre *mother*	padre *father*
marido *husband*	esposa *wife*
muerte *death*	vida *life*
norte *north*	sur *south*
príncipe *prince*	princesa *princess*
respuesta *answer*	pregunta *question*
rey *king*	reina *queen*
ruido *noise*	silencio *silence*
verano *summer*	invierno *winter*
verdad *truth*	mentira *lie*
vicio *vice*	virtud *virtue*

b. Adjectives

alegre *happy*	triste *sad*
alguno *some*	ninguno *none*
alto *high, tall*	bajo *low, short*
amargo *bitter*	dulce *sweet*
ancho *wide*	estrecho *narrow*
antiguo *old, ancient*	moderno *modern*
barato *cheap*	caro *dear, expensive*
blanco *white*	negro *black*
común *common*	raro *rare*
corto *short*	largo *long*
débil *weak*	fuerte *strong*
difícil *difficult*	fácil *easy*
duro *hard*	blando *soft*
feliz *happy*	triste *sad*
flaco *thin*	gordo *fat*
frío *cold*	caliente *hot*
grande *large*	pequeño *small*
hermoso *beautiful*	feo *ugly*
inteligente *intelligent*	estúpido *stupid*
ligero *light*	pesado *heavy*

limpio	*clean*	sucio	*dirty*
lleno	*full*	vacío	*empty*
mayor	*older*	menor	*younger*
mejor	*better*	peor	*worse*
mismo	*same*	diferente	*different*
mucho, –s	*much (many)*	poco, –s	*little (few)*
oscuro	*dark*	claro	*light*
perezoso	*lazy*	trabajador, aplicado	*hard-working*
pobre	*poor*	rico	*rich*
posible	*possible*	imposible	*impossible*
primero	*first*	último	*last*
rubio	*blond*	moreno	*brunette*
sabio	*wise*	tonto	*foolish*
tarde	*late*	temprano	*early*
todo	*everything*	nada	*nothing*
valiente	*brave*	cobarde	*cowardly*
viejo	*old*	joven	*young*
		nuevo	*new*
vivo	*alive*	muerto	*dead*

c. Verbs

acercarse (qu) (a)	*to approach*	alejarse (de)	*to move away (from)*
acordarse (ue) de	*to remember*	olvidarse de	*to forget*
aparecer (zc)	*to appear*	desaparecer (za)	*to disappear*
bajar	*to go down*	subir	*to go up*
callarse	*to keep quiet*	hablar	*to speak*
comprar	*to buy*	vender	*to sell*
contestar	*to answer*	preguntar	*to ask*
dar	*to give*	tomar	*to take*
		recibir	*to receive*
despertarse (ie)	*to wake up*	dormirse (ue, u)	*to fall asleep*
empezar (ie, c)	*to begin*	acabar, terminar	*to end*
encender (ie)	*to light, to ignite*	apagar (gu)	*to put out, to extinguish*
ir	*to go*	venir (ie, g)	*to come*
levantarse	*to get up*	sentarse (ie)	*to sit down*
		acostarse (ue)	*to go to bed*
llorar	*to cry*	reír (í)	*to laugh*
mentir (ie, i)	*to lie*	decir (i, g) la verdad	*to tell the truth*
meter	*to put (in)*	sacar (qu)	*to take out*
morir (ue, u)	*to die*	vivir	*to live*
perder (ie)	*to lose*	ganar	*to win*
		hallar	*to find*
permitir	*to permit*	prohibir	*to prohibit*
ponerse (g)	*to put on*	quitarse	*to take off*
prestar	*to lend*	pedir prestado	*to borrow*
recoger (j)	*to pick up*	dejar caer	*to drop*
salir (g) (de)	*to leave*	entrar (en)	*to enter*

d. Adverbs

abajo *below, downstairs*	arriba *above, upstairs*
allí *there*	aquí *here*
anoche *last night*	esta noche *tonight*
antes (de) *before*	después (de) *after*
aprisa *quickly*	despacio *slowly*
ausente *absent*	presente *present*
bien *well*	mal *badly, poorly*
cerca de *near*	lejos de *far from*
debajo (de) *under*	encima (de) *on top*
delante de *in front of*	detrás de *in back of, behind*
fuera *outside*	dentro *inside*
hoy *today*	mañana *tomorrow*
	ayer *yesterday*
más *more*	menos *less*
no *no*	sí *yes*
siempre *always*	nunca *never*
tarde *late*	temprano *early*

e. Prepositions

con *with*	sin *without*
	contra *against*

EXERCISE D.   Ruth is preparing a crossword puzzle to help her improve her Spanish vocabulary. Complete the crossword puzzle with the appropriate antonym for the words given.

HORIZONTAL	VERTICAL
2. tarde	1. fuera
4. ir	3. hoy
7. sabio	5. dar
8. valiente	6. contestar
9. posible	7. empezar
12. siempre	10. rubio
13. ganar	11. peor
15. último	14. delante
16. entrada	15. madre
17. diligente	16. limpio

EXERCISE E. You like to annoy your brother by saying the opposite of what he says. Express what you tell him using an antonym for the word in italic.

EXAMPLE: Hay mucho **ruido** aquí.   No, hay mucho **silencio** aquí.

1. Víctor *tomó* noventa dólares por la bicicleta.

_____

2. El plato está *lleno*.

_____

3. Hay *más* nieve hoy que había el año pasado.

_____

4. Luis *se acuesta* temprano.

_____

5. Es *fácil* entrar al estadio cuando hay un partido.

_____

6. El lago está ochenta millas al *oeste*.

_____

7. La mujer *ríe* sin cesar.

_____

8. El perro *se despierta*.

_____

9. *Algo* extraordinario ocurrió *hoy*.

_____

10. *Apagaron* la luz.

_____

11. Los zapatos están *debajo* de la mesa.

_____

12. No me gustan los panecillos *calientes*.

_____

13. Todas las calles del centro son *anchas*.

_____

14. Nunca escuchas la *respuesta*.

_____

15. El carro está *sucio*.

_____

EXERCISE F. Alex answers negatively each question his mother asks him. Express his responses by replacing the word in italic with an antonym.

EXAMPLE: ¿Es **pequeña** la casa de Enrique?
No, la casa de Enrique es **grande**.

EXAMPLE: ¿Siempre **te olvidas de** traer tus libros?
No, siempre **me acuerdo de** traer mis libros.

1. ¿Es *amargo* el jugo de naranja? _____

2. ¿Contestas *siempre* en voz *alta*? _____

3. ¿Te gustan las películas *antiguas*? _____

4. ¿Te lavas las manos *con* jabón? _____

5. ¿Estuvo *ausente* el profesor el jueves
pasado? _____

6. ¿Son *cortas* las vacaciones de invierno? _____

7. ¿Son *baratos* los patines? _____

8. ¿Es *blanco* el carbón? _____

9. ¿Tienes muchos *amigos*? _____

10. ¿*Subes* la escalera para llegar al
piso bajo? _____

EXERCISE G. Correct the statements a younger cousin tells you by providing the antonym of the word in italic.

1. España está al *oeste* de Portugal. _____

2. Yo soy *mayor* que mi hermano. _____

3. Dar limosna a los pobres es *un vicio*. _____

4. Generalmente los héroes son *cobardes*. _____

5. Hoy día *se permite* fumar en los restaurantes. _____

6. La última novela del autor fue *un fracaso*; solo
se vendieron tres millones de ejemplares. _____

7. Una mujer de cien años de edad es *joven*. _____

8. Cuando dos naciones tienen conflictos
grandes, están en estado de *paz*. _____

9. Hace frío en *el verano*. _____

10. Un rascacielos es un edificio *bajo*. _____

11. El sótano está *encima* de la casa.   _____

12. Las piedras son *blandas.*   _____

13. Las aguas de los ríos son *calientes.*   _____

14. Una persona se siente *fuerte* cuando tiene
    un resfriado.   _____

15. Las estrellas se distinguen por *el día.*   _____

MASTERY EXERCISES

EXERCISE H.   Complete each analogy with the word that is missing:

EXAMPLE: pequeño : grande :: ancho : estrecho
             buque : barco :: batalla : lucha

1. esposo : marido :: maestro : _____

2. antiguo : viejo :: corto : _____

3. andar : caminar :: dejar : _____

4. dar : recibir :: comprar : _____

5. ligero : pesado :: flaco : _____

6. permitir : prohibir :: ganar : _____

7. sabio : tonto :: rico : _____

8. cielo : tierra :: vida : _____

9. colocar : poner :: arrojar : _____

10. limpio : sucio :: vacío : _____

11. sufrir : padecer :: mostrar : _____

12. alegre : contento :: bonito : _____

13. hoy : ayer :: esta noche : _____

14. aun : todavía :: nunca : _____

15. tarde : temprano :: bien : _____

16. cura : sacerdote :: ave : _____

17. dulce : amargo :: alegre _____

18. fuera : dentro :: cerca : _____

19. pelo : cabello : rostro _____

20. afecto : amor :: broma : _____

EXERCISE I.   **Express the synonyms or antonyms for each set of drawings.**

EXAMPLE: caminar   ;   correr

1. _____   ;   _____

2. _____   ;   _____

3. _____   ;   _____

4. _____   ;   _____

5. _____ ; _____

6. _____ ; _____

7. _____ ; _____

8. _____ ; _____

9. _____ ; _____

10. _____ ; _____

> **EXERCISE J.**   **Express what Raquel says about herself and her family.**

- a physical description of your parents and/or siblings

- differences in your personality

- how you feel at different times of the year, for example, the changing of the seasons

- what your parents believe that expresses their basic family philosophy

- food choices at different times of year

- awakening and sleeping times

- gift giving and receiving

- your sibling's and your friends

ACTIVIDADES

1. Write a brief description of yourself and a description of a friend who is very similar. Use as many synonyms as you can.

2. Describe an acquaintance or relative and explain how he/she differs from you. Use as many antonyms as you can.

3. Your family is planning to relocate from the city to the country, or vice versa. Prepare a list of arguments you can use to explain why the country or the city is better using synonyms and antonyms.

Thematic Vocabulary

◆ 1 ◆ LA IDENTIFICACIÓN PERSONAL / *Personal Identification*

a. La información biográfica / *Biographical information*

(1) La nacionalidad / *Nationality*

alemán *German*	**guyanés** *Guianan*
argentino *Argentinean*	**haitiano** *Haitian*
asiático *Asian*	**hondureño** *Honduran*
boliviano *Bolivian*	**indio** *Indian*
brasileño *Brazilian*	**inglés** *English*
canadiense *Canadian*	**italiano** *Italian*
centroamericano *Central American*	**jamaiquino** *Jamaican*
chileno *Chilean*	**japonés** *Japanese*
chino *Chinese*	**mexicano** *Mexican*
colombiano *Colombian*	**nicaragüense** *Nicaraguan*
coreano *Korean*	**norteamericano** *North American*
costarricense *Costa Rican*	**panameño** *Panamanian*
cubano *Cuban*	**paraguayo** *Paraguayan*
dominicano *Dominican*	**peruano** *Peruvian*
ecuatoriano *Ecuadorean*	**puertorriqueño** *Puerto Rican*
español *Spanish*	**salvadoreño** *El Salvadorian*
europeo *European*	**sudamericano** *South American*
francés *French*	**uruguayo** *Uruguayan*
griego *Greek*	**venezolano** *Venezuelan*
guatemalteco *Guatemalan*	**vietnamita** *Vietnamese*

(2) La familia / *Family*

la abuela *grandmother*	**los hijos** *children, sons and daughters*
el abuelo *grandfather*	**la madrastra** *stepmother*
los abuelos *grandfathers, grandparents (grandfather and grandmother)*	**la madre** *mother*
	la madrina *godmother*
el cuñado *brother-in-law*	**la mamá** *mom, mother*
la cuñada *sister-in-law*	**la nieta** *granddaughter*
la esposa *wife*	**el nieto** *grandson*
el esposo *husband*	**la niña** *girl*
la familia *family*	**el niño** *boy*
la hermana *sister*	**la nuera** *daughter-in-law*
el hermano *brother*	**el padrastro** *stepfather*
los hermanos *brothers, brothers and sisters*	**el padre** *father*
	los padres *fathers, parents (father and mother)*
la hija *daughter*	**el padrino** *godfather*
el hijo *son*	**los padrinos** *godparents*

los papás *fathers, parents (father and mother)*
el pariente *relative*
la prima *cousin*
el primo *cousin*
la sobrina *niece*
el sobrino *nephew*
la suegra *mother-in-law*

el suegro *father-in-law*
los suegros *fathers-in-law; in-laws*
    (father-in-law and mother-in-law)
la tía *aunt*
el tío *uncle*
los tíos *uncles, aunts and uncles*
el yerno *son-in-law*

b. Las características físicas / *Physical characteristics*

alto *tall*
bajo *short*
bonito *pretty, beautiful*
calvo *bald*
ciego *blind, visually-impaired*
débil *weak*
delgado *thin*
feo *ugly*

flaco *skinny*
fuerte *strong*
gordo *fat*
hermoso *handsome, beautiful*
joven *young*
minusválido *handicapped*
sordo *deaf, hearing-impaired*
viejo *old*

tener . . . años
tener los ojos azules
tener los ojos cafés
tener los ojos negros
tener los ojos verdes
tener el pelo rubio
tener el pelo moreno
tener el pelo castaño
tener el pelo negro
tener el pelo rojo
tener el pelo risado
tener el pelo ondulado
tener el pelo lacio

to be . . . years old
to have blue eyes
to have brown eyes
to have black eyes
to have green eyes
to have blond hair
to have dark hair
to have brown hair
to have black hair
to have red hair
to have curly hair
to have wavy hair
to have straight hair

c. Las características sicológicas / *Psychological characteristics*

activo *active*
alegre *happy*
amable *friendly*
ambicioso *ambitious*
antipático *unpleasant*
atlético *athletic*
bondadoso *kind*
cómico *funny*
contento *happy*
cortés *polite*
cruel *cruel*

curioso *curious*
descontento *unhappy*
divertido *fun*
egoísta *selfish*
franco *frank*
furioso *furious*
generoso *generous*
honesto *honest*
imaginativo *imaginative*
impulsivo *impulsive*
ingenuo *naive*

inteligente *intelligent*
interesante *interesting*
orgulloso *proud*
perezoso *lazy*
serio *serious*
simpático *nice, congenial*
supersticioso *supersticious*
triste *sad*
valiente *brave*

d. Las emociones y los sentimientos / *Emotions and feelings*

la **alegría** *joy*	la **lealtad** *loyalty*	la **piedad** *pity*
el **amor** *love*	el **miedo** *fear*	la **tristeza** *sadness*
la **envidia** *envy*	el **odio** *hate*	la **valentía** *bravery*
la **felicidad** *happiness*	el **orgullo** *pride*	la **vergüenza** *shame*
el **gusto** *pleasure*	la **pasión** *passion*	

(EXERCISE A.)   Write a letter to a new Spanish-speaking pen pal, in which you introduce yourself
and your family and describe your physical and psychological characteristics.

_____

_____

_____

_____

_____

_____

_____

_____

◆ 2 ◆ LA CASA Y EL HOGAR / *House and Home*

a. Las casa y los cuartos / *House and rooms*

el **alquiler** *rent*	el **fregadero** *kitchen sink*
el **apartamento** *apartment*	el **garaje** *garage*
el **armario** *wardrobe, closet*	la **habitación** *room*
el **ascensor** *elevator*	el **inquilino** *tenant*
el **balcón** *balcony*	el **jardín** *garden*
la **casa** *house*	la **pared** *wall*
el **césped** *lawn*	el **pasillo** *hall*
la **chimenea** *fireplace*	el **patio** *patio*
la **cocina** *kitchen*	el **piso** *floor, story*
el **comedor** *dining room*	la **planta baja** *ground floor*
el **contrato** *lease*	el **propietario** *owner*
el **cuarto** *room*	la **puerta** *door*
el **cuarto de baño** *bathroom*	la **sala** *living room*
el **desván** *attic*	el **sótano** *basement*
el **dormitorio** *bedroom*	el **techo** *ceiling, roof*
el **edificio de apartamentos** *apartment house*	la **terraza** *terrace*
la **escalera** *stairs*	la **ventana** *window*
el **estudio** *study, den*	

b. Los muebles y los aparatos domésticos / *Furniture and appliances*

la alfombra *rug, carpet*	el lavaplatos *dishwasher*
la almohada *pillow*	el librero *bookcase*
el armario *wardrobe, closet*	la mesa *table*
la aspiradora *vacuum cleaner*	el mueble *piece of furniture*
el buró *night stand*	el ordenador *computer*
la butaca *armchair (upholstered)*	el piano *piano*
la cama *bed*	la pintura *painting*
la cómoda *dresser*	el refrigerador *refrigerator*
la computadora *computer*	el reloj *clock*
el congelador *freezer*	despertador *alarm clock*
la cortina *curtain*	el reproductor de blu ray *blu ray player*
el cuadro *painting*	de MP3 *MP3 player*
el espejo *mirror*	la secadora *clothes dryer*
el estéreo *stereo*	la silla *chair*
la estufa *stove*	el sillón *armchair*
el horno *oven*	el sofá *sofa*
de microondas *microwave oven*	el televisor *TV set*
la lámpara *lamp*	el tocador *dresser*
la lavadora *washing machine*	

c. Los quehaceres del hogar / *Housework*

cocinar *to cook*	pasar la aspiradora *to vacuum*
cortar el césped *to mow the lawn*	planchar la ropa *to iron the clothing*
cuidar a los niños *to babysit*	poner la mesa *to set the table*
ir de compras *to go shopping*	quitar la mesa *to clear the table*
lavar los platos *to wash dishes*	sacar la basura *to throw out the garbage*
limpiar la casa *to clean the house*	sacudir los muebles *to dust the furniture*

EXERCISE B. **Describe what you see in each room.**

1. Yo veo _____

_____

_____

_____

_____

2. Yo veo _____

_____

_____

_____

_____

EXERCISE C.   **Express what household chore each person does.**

EXAMPLE: Felipe / lavar platos   Felipe **lava los platos.**

1. mi abuela / cocinar   _____

2. Papá / pasar la aspiradora   _____

3. tú / poner la mesa   _____

4. nosotros / sacar la basura   _____

5. Mamá / sacudir los muebles   _____

6. Uds. / quitar la mesa   _____

7. Papá / ir de compras   _____

8. Laura / cuidar a los niños   _____

> **EXERCISE D.**   Complete each statement with the appropriate word.

1. Para limpiar la alfombra se usa _____ .

2. La comida se prepara en _____ .

3. Los cuadros se cuelgan en _____ .

4. En un edificio alto de apartamentos se usa _____ para ir de un piso a otro.

5. Muchos apartamentos tienen _____ donde las personas pueden sentarse al aire libre.

6. En una casa particular se guardan las cosas que no se usan a menudo en _____ o en
   _____ .

7. En los Estados Unidos, el primer piso es equivalente a _____ en España.

8. La parte más fría del refrigerador es _____ .

9. Un contrato es un documento legal entre un propietario y _____ .

10. Un pavo se asa un en _____ .

11. En los días feriados se sirve una comida elegante en _____ de la casa.

12. Las plantas y las flores se cultivan en _____ .

◆ 3 ◆ LA COMUNIDAD; EL VECINDARIO; LOS ALREDEDORES / *Community; Neighborhood; Physical Environment*

a. La ciudad / *city*

la acera	*sidewalk*	el correo	*post office*
el aeropuerto	*airport*	la corte	*court (house)*
la aldea	*village*	el edificio	*building*
el almacén	*department store*	la escuela	*school*
la avenida	*avenue*	la estación	*(train) station*
el ayuntamiento	*town hall*	el estadio	*stadium*
el banco	*bank*	la fábrica	*factory*
el barrio	*neighborhood*	la farmacia	*drugstore, pharmacy*
la biblioteca	*library*	la ferretería	*hardware store*
la bodega	*grocery store*	la florería	*florist*
el café	*cafe*	la frutería	*fruit store*
la calle	*street*	la gasolinera	*gas station*
la carnicería	*butcher shop*	el hospital	*hospital*
la catedral	*cathedral*	el hotel	*hotel*
el centro	*commercial mall*	la iglesia	*church*
el centro juvenil	*youth center*	el jardín	*garden*
el cine	*movies (movie theater)*	la joyería	*jewelry store*
el cuartel de policía	*police precinct*	la lavandería	*laundry*

la librería *bookstore*	el restaurante *restaurant*
el mercado *market*	la sinagoga *synagogue*
el monumento *monument*	el suburbio *suburbs*
el museo *museum*	el supermercado *supermarket*
la panadería *bakery*	el teatro *theater*
el parque *park*	el templo *temple*
la estación de bomberos *fire station*	la terminal de autobuses *bus terminal*
la pastelería *pastry shop*	la tienda *store*
la perfumería *perfume shop*	la tienda de ropa *clothing store*
la piscina *swimming pool*	la tintorería *dry cleaners*
la plaza *square*	la universidad *university*
el pueblo *town*	el vecindario *neighborhood*
el puente *bridge*	la zapatería *shoe store*
el rascacielos *skyscraper*	

EXERCISE E.   **Tell what you can buy in the following stores.**

EXAMPLE: Se compran medicinas en una **farmacia.**

1. _____

_____ .

3. _____

_____ .

2. _____

_____ .

4. _____

_____ .

5. _____

_____ .

6. _____

_____ .

7. _____

_____ .

8. _____

_____ .

b. Materiales de construcción / _Building materials_

el acero _steel_	**la madera** _wood_	**el hierro** _iron_	**el vidrio** _glass_
el cemento _cement_	**el ladrillo** _brick_	**la piedra** _stone_	

EXERCISE F.   **Tell what each of the things shown is made of.**

EXAMPLE: La casa es **de piedra.**

1. _____

_____ .

2. _____

_____ .

3. _____

_____ .

5. _____

_____ .

4. _____

_____ .

c. La naturaleza / _Nature_

el árbol _tree_	**la isla** _island_	**el planeta** _planet_
la arena _sand_	**el lago** _lake_	**la planta** _plant_
el arroyo _stream_	**la laguna** _lagoon_	**la playa** _beach_
el bosque _woods_	**la lluvia** _rain_	**la ribera** _shore, bank (of a river)_
el campo _country, field_	**la luna** _moon_	**el río** _river_
el cielo _sky_	**el/la mar** _sea_	**la selva** _forest_
la colina _hill_	**la montaña** _mountain_	**el sol** _sun_
la costa _coast_	**el mundo** _world_	**la tierra** _earth_
el desierto _desert_	**la niebla** _fog_	**el viento** _wind_
la estrella _star_	**la nieve** _snow_	**el volcán** _volcano_
la flor _flower_	**la nube** _cloud_	
la hierba _grass_	**el océano** _ocean_	
la hoja _leaf_	**el paisaje** _landscape_	

EXERCISE G. You are traveling cross-country by train. As you look out of the window at the changing landscape, make a list of ten things you see.

EXAMPLE: un río, una colina, etc.

1. _____

2. _____

3. _____

4. _____

5. _____

6. _____

7. _____

8. _____

9. _____

10. _____

d. Los animales / *Animals*

la **abeja** *bee*	el **conejo** *rabbit*	el **pájaro** *bird*
la **araña** *spider*	el **elefante** *elephant*	la **pantera** *panther*
la **ardilla** *squirrel*	la **gallina** *hen*	el **pavo** *turkey*
la **ballena** *whale*	el **gallo** *rooster*	el **perro** *dog*
el **buey** *ox*	el **gato** *cat*	el **pez** *fish*
el **burro** *donkey*	la **jirafa** *giraffe*	el **pollo** *chicken*
el **caballo** *horse*	el **león** *lion*	la **serpiente** *snake*
la **cabra** *goat*	el **leopardo** *leopard*	el **tigre** *tiger*
el **canguro** *kangaroo*	el **lobo** *wolf*	el **tiburón** *shark*
la **cebra** *zebra*	el **mono** *monkey*	la **tortuga** *turtle*
el **cisne** *swan*	el **murciélago** *bat*	la **vaca** *cow*
el **cochino** *pig*	el **oso** *bear*	el **zorro** *fox*
el **cocodrilo** *crocodile*	la **oveja** *sheep*	

EXERCISE H.   Name five animals you see in each of these sites.

1. En el campo: _____

2. En la jungla: _____

3. Cerca del mar: _____

4. En el parque zoológico: _____

◆ 4 ◆ LAS COMIDAS; LA COMIDA; LAS BEBIDAS / *Meals; Food; Drinks*

a. Las comidas / *Meals*

el **almuerzo** *lunch*	la **cena** *dinner, supper*	el **desayuno** *breakfast*
el **apetito** *appetite*	la **comida** *meal, food*	el **menú** *menu*
la **botella** *bottle*	la **cuenta** *check*	la **propina** *tip*

b. Los cubiertos / *Utensils (Cutlery)*

la cuchara *spoon*   el mantel *tablecloth*   la taza *cup*
la cucharita *teaspoon*   el plato *plate, dish*   el tenedor *fork*
el cuchillo *knife*   la servilleta *napkin*   el vaso *glass*

c. La comida / *Food*

el agua mineral *mineral water*   el jamón *ham*   la papa *potato*
el arroz *rice*   las judías verdes *green beans*   las papas fritas *French fries*
el azúcar *sugar*   el jugo *juice*   el pastel *cake*
el biftec *steak*   el ketchup *ketchup*   la pera *pear*
el café *coffee*   la leche *milk*   el pescado *fish*
la carne *meat*   la lechuga *lettuce*   la pimienta *pepper*
la carne de res *beef*   las legumbres *vegetables*   la pizza *pizza*
el cereal *cereal*   el limón *lemon*   el plátano *plantain*
la cereza *cherry*   la limonada *lemonade*   el pollo *chicken*
el chícharo *pea*   la mantequilla *butter*   el queso *cheese*
el chocolate *chocolate*   la manzana *apple*   la sal *salt*
el cordero *lamb*   los mariscos *seafood*   la salchicha *sausage*
los dulces *candies*   la mayonesa *mayonnaise*   el sándwich *sandwich*
el elote *green bean*   el melocotón *peach*   la sopa *soup*
la ensalada *salad*   la mermelada *jam, marmalade* el té *tea*
la espinaca *spinach*   la mostaza *mustard*   la ternera *veal*
la fresa *strawberry*   el pan *bread*   el tomate *tomato*
la fruta *fruit*   el pan tostado *toast*   la uva *grape*
la hamburguesa *hamburger*   el panecillo *roll*   las verduras *greens, vegetables*
el helado *ice cream*   la zanahoria *carrot*
el huevo *egg*

EXERCISE I.   **A friend has invited you to spend a weekend at his house. He wants to be a good host and asks you to list the foods you like and those you dislike. Prepare the list for him.**

ME GUSTA(N):   NO ME GUSTA(N):

_____   _____

_____   _____

_____   _____

_____   _____

_____   _____

_____   _____

EXERCISE J. You are celebrating your birthday at an elegant restaurant. Describe what you see on the table.

_____

_____

_____

_____

_____

_____

◆ 5 ◆ LA SALUD Y EL BIENESTAR / _Health and Well-being_

a. El cuerpo / _The body_

la barba _beard_	el dedo del pie _toe_	el ojo _eye_
la barbilla _chin_	el diente _tooth_	la oreja _(outer) ear_
el bigote _moustache_	la espalda _back_	la pantorrilla _calf_
la boca _mouth_	el estómago _stomach_	el párpado _eyelid_
el brazo _arm_	la frente _forehead_	el pecho _chest_
el cabello _hair_	la garganta _throat_	el pelo _hair_
la cabeza _head_	el hombro _shoulder_	las pestañas _eyelashes_
la cara _face_	el labio _lip_	el pie _foot_
las cejas _eyebrows_	la lengua _tongue_	la piel _skin_
el codo _elbow_	la mano _hand_	la pierna _leg_
el corazón _heart_	la mejilla _cheek_	la rodilla _knee_
el cuello _neck_	la muela _molar_	el rostro _face_
el cuerpo _body_	la nariz _nose_	la sangre _blood_
el dedo _finger_	el oído _(inner) ear_	el tobillo _ankle_

b. Las enfermedades / *Illnesses*

tener dolor de cabeza *to have a headache*
tener dolor de estómago *to have a stomachache*
tener dolor de garganta *to have a sore throat*
tener dolor de pie *to have foot pain*

la apendicitis *appendicitis*	**la gripe** *flu*	**el resfriado** *cold (illness)*
el asma (f.) *asthma*	**la infección** *infection*	**la rotura** *fracture*
el dolor *pain*	**la neumonía** *pneumonia*	**el sarampión** *measles*
la energía *energy*	**las paperas** *mumps*	**la tos** *cough*
la fiebre *fever*	**la pulmonía** *pneumonia*	**la urgencia** *emergency*
la fractura *fracture*	**la quemadura** *burn*	**la varicela** *chicken pox*
la fuerza *strength*		

c. Palabras relacionadas / *Related words*

el accidente *accident*	**la enfermera** *nurse*	**la salud** *health*
la ambulancia *ambulance*	**el enfermo** *patient*	**el sudor** *sweat*
la aspirina *aspirin*	**la medicina** *medicine*	**la temperatura** *temperature*
el cuidado *care*	**la pomada** *salve*	**el tratamiento** *treatment*
la cura *cure*	**el reposo** *rest*	**la vacuna** *vaccine*

EXERCISE K. Complete the drawing by labeling the different parts of the body.

1. _____	15. _____
2. _____	16. _____
3. _____	17. _____
4. _____	18. _____
5. _____	19. _____
6. _____	20. _____
7. _____	21. _____
8. _____	22. _____
9. _____	23. _____
10. _____	24. _____
11. _____	25. _____
12. _____	26. _____
13. _____	27. _____
14. _____	

EXERCISE L.   A new pen pal has asked you to describe yourself. Write a detailed description of yourself.

_____

_____

_____

_____

_____

_____

EXERCISE M.   You are completing the application for a summer internship program. List the illnesses you have had.

_____

_____

_____

_____

_____

_____

◆ 6 ◆ EDUCACIÓN / *Education*

a. La escuela / *School*

el alumno *pupil*	la escuela primaria *elementary school*
la aula *classroom*	la escuela secundaria *high school*
el banco *bench*	el estudiante *student, pupil*
el bolígrafo *ballpoint pen*	el estudio *study*
la calculadora *calculator*	el examen *test*
el calendario *calendar*	la explicación *explanation*
la clase *class*	la falta *error*
el colegio *school, academy*	la fila *line (of people)*
el consejero *counselor*	la frase *sentence*
el cuaderno *notebook*	la goma de borrar *eraser*
el diccionario *dictionary*	la gramática *grammar*
el dictado *dictation*	el horario de clases *class schedule*
el director *principal*	el lápiz *pencil*
el ejercicio *exercise*	la lección *lesson*
el error *error*	la lectura *reading*
la escuela *school*	el libro *book*

el maestro *teacher*

el mapa *map*

la materia *subject*

la mochila *knapsack, backpack, bookbag*

la nota *grade*

la oración *sentence*

la página *page*

la palabra *word*

el papel *paper*

el patio *patio; schoolyard*

la pizarra *chalkboard*

la pluma *pen*

la poesía *poetry*

la pregunta *question*

el profesor *teacher*

el pupitre *(student) desk*

la regla *ruler*

la respuesta *answer*

el resumen *summary*

la sala de clases *classroom*

la tarea *homework*

las tijeras *scissors*

el timbre *bell*

la tiza *chalk*

el trabajo *work*

los útiles *school supplies*

el vocabulario *vocabulary*

b. Las materias / *School subjects*

el álgebra *algebra*

las artes industriales *shop*

la artesanía *arts and crafts*

el inglés *English*

la biología *biology*

la química *chemistry*

el diseño *drawing*

la educación física *physical education*

el español *Spanish*

la geografía *geography*

la historia *history*

la informática *computer science*

el latín *Latin*

las matemáticas *math*

la física *physics*

la ciencia *science*

la technología *technology*

c. Las actividades escolares / *School activities*

la banda *band*

el círculo *club*

el círculo de matemáticas *math club*

el círculo dramático *drama club*

el círculo español *Spanish club*

el círculo internacional *international club*

el coro *chorus*

el equipo *team*

el equipo de béisbol *baseball team*

el equipo de fútbol *soccer team*

la excursión *field trip*

la orquesta *orchestra*

(EXERCISE N.) **Prepare a list of the school supplies you will need to purchase for the new school year.**

_____

_____

_____

_____

_____

_____

EXERCISE O. You are sending a friend photographs you took in your school. Label each one to tell your friend the subject.

EXAMPLE: Es el equipo de fútbol.

1. _____

2. _____

3. _____

4. _____

5. _____

6. _____

7. _____

8. _____

◆ 7 ◆ OFICIOS Y PROFESIONES / *Trades and Professions*

el/la abogado(-a) *lawyer*

el actor *actor*

la actriz *actress*

el/la atleta *athlete*

el/la artista *artist, performer*

el/la bombero(-a) *firefighter*

el/la campesino(-a) *farmer*

el/la carnicero(-a) *butcher*

el/la cartero(-a) *mail carrier*

el/la científico(-a) *scientist*

el/la cocinero(-a) *chef*

el/la comerciante *merchant*

el/la dentista *dentist*

el/la dependiente *salesperson*

el/la director(-ora) *manager, principal*

el/la diseñador(-ora) *designer*

el/la enfermero(-a) *nurse*

el/la escritor(-ora) *writer*

el/la farmacéutico(-a) *pharmacist*

el/la gerente *manager*

el/la ingeniero(-a) *engineer*

el investigador *researcher*

el/la juez(-a) *judge*

el/la médico(-a) *doctor*

el/la mesero(-a) *waiter*

el/la mozo(-a) *waiter, server*

el/la músico *musician*

el/la obrero(-a) *laborer, worker*

el/la panadero(-a) *baker*

el/la peluquero(-a) *barber, hair stylist*

el/la piloto(-a) *pilot*

el/la pintor(-ora) *painter*

el poeta *poet*

la poetisa *poet*

el/la policía *police officer*

el/la presidente(-a) *president*

la profesión *profession*

el/la profesor(-ora) *teacher*

el/la programador(-ora) *programmer*

el/la secretario(-a) *secretary*

el/la soldado(-a) *soldier*

EXERCISE P.   **Use the following clues to identify the professions described.**

1. Soy muy creativa. Mis dibujos cambian el estilo de ropa de cada estación.

_____

2. Reparo las sandalias y los zapatos de las personas.

_____

3. Creo nuevos programas para la computadora.

_____

4. Me gusta escribir cuentos y publicarlos en forma de libro.

_____

5. Para mí los dientes son una parte muy importante de la buena salud.

_____

6. Sigo las instrucciones de los médicos cuando cuido a los enfermos.

_____

7. Reparto la correspondencia que las personas y las compañías reciben cada día.

_____

8. Apago los incendios y trato de salvar la vida y las propiedades de las personas.

_____

9. Siempre busco nuevas maneras de preparar la comida. Todo el mundo quiere mis recetas.

_____

10. Defiendo a mis clientes en la corte.

_____

11. Ayudo a las personas cuando van de compras a un almacén.

_____

12. Trabajo en la corte y dirijo los juicios. Estudié leyes. Llevo una túnica negra.

_____

13. Me gusta trabajar a solas en un laboratorio y descubrir nuevas cosas.

_____

14. Paso mucho tiempo corrigiendo exámenes. Uso la tinta roja pero no es mi color favorito.

_____

◆ 8 ◆ EL TIEMPO LIBRE / _Leisure_

a. Los pasatiempos / _Hobbies; leisure activities_

el baile _dance_	la montaña _mountain_
el campo _country_	el museo _museum_
el centro comercial _mall_	los naipes _cards_
el cine _movies_	la ópera _opera_
el concierto _concert_	el parque nacional _national park_
el deporte _sport_	el parque zoológico _zoo_
el día feriado _legal holiday_	el partido _game, match_
el día libre _day off_	el paseo _walk_
la discoteca _discotheque_	la pelota _ball_
el estadio _stadium_	la playa _beach_
la exposición _exhibit, show_	el teatro _theater_
la feria _fair_	la televisión _television_
la fiesta _holiday, celebration, party_	las vacaciones (pl.) _vacation_
la isla tropical _tropical island_	

b. Los deportes / _Sports_

el alpinismo _mountain climbing_	los bolos _bowling_
el atletismo _athletics_	el buceo _diving_
el barco de vela _sailboat_	la carrera _track_
el béisbol _baseball_	el esquí _skiing_
el esquí acuático _waterskiing_	el golf _golf_
el fútbol _soccer_	el hockey
el fútbol americano _football_	la natación _swimming_

la pesca *fishing*   el voleibol *volleyball*
el tenis *tennis*

EXERCISE Q.   You will be visiting a friend in another city for a long weekend. In preparation for your visit, write a note in which you remind him/her of the leisure activities you like to do and those you dislike doing.

EXAMPLE: **Me gusta ir al cine. Visitar un museo es aburrido.**

_____

_____

_____

_____

_____

EXERCISE R.   Identify the pastimes described below.

1. Las montañas me llaman la atención. Me gusta caminar y cuando el terreno es duro y la montaña es alta, tanto mejor.

_____

2. Me gusta el mar, especialmente cuando el agua está muy clara y hay mucha profundidad.

_____

3. Me gusta moverme al compás de la música. Es divertido ir a las discotecas con mis amigos.

_____

4. El único juego que no me gusta es el «solitario». Prefiero jugar con mis amigos.

_____

5. Mi abuelo es muy partidario de este deporte. Desde niño me ha gustado acompañarlo en su barco. Si tenemos suerte, comemos bien en la noche.

_____

6. Estoy aprendiendo a ser un buen jugador porque mi equipo participa en una competencia. Es difícil lanzar la pelota y derribar todos los bolos.

_____

7. Correr es una buena actividad y un buen ejercicio. Cada día corro más rápidamente.

_____

8. A mi papá le gusta este deporte porque hay que caminar. A veces voy con él, pero quisiera que alquilara un carrito para ir de un hoyo en otro.

_____

9. Me gusta este deporte porque hay que saltar para pegarle a la pelota con las manos y pasarla por encima de una red alta.

_____

10. No sé tocar ningún instrumento musical pero me gusta sentarme en un teatro y escuchar mientras una orquesta toca una obra sinfónica.

_____

◆ 9 ◆ SERVICIOS PÚBLICOS Y PRIVADOS / _Public and Private Services_

a. El teléfono / _Telephone_

la cabina telefónica _telephone booth_	la llamada _call_
el carnet telefónico _calling card_	el/la contestador/a _answering machine_
colgar (ue, gu) _to hang up_	marcar (qu) _to dial_
descolgar _to pick up (the phone)_	el número equivocado _wrong number_
el fonobuzón _voicemail_	ocupado _busy_
la guía telefónica _telephone book_	el receptor _receiver_
larga distancia _long distance_	

b. El correo / _Post Office_

el apartado postal _post office box_	el giro _money order_
el buzón _mailbox_	el paquete _package_
la carta _letter_	por avión _air mail_
el cartero _mail carrier_	el sobre _envelope_
el código postal _Zip Code_	la tarjeta postal _postcard_
el correo _mail_	el telegrama _telegram_
la dirección _address_	la ventanilla _(service) window_
la estampilla _stamp_	

c. El banco / _Bank_

el billete _bill_	depositar _to deposit_
la caja _cash register, teller's window_	el depósito _deposit_
el/la cajero(-a) _cashier, teller_	el dinero _money_
la caja fuerte _safe_	el efectivo _cash_
el cajero automático _ATM_	el giro _money order_
el cambio _exchange rate_	la moneda _coin, currency_
el cheque de viajero _traveler's check_	retirar _to withdraw_
la cuenta de ahorros _saving account_	el retiro _withdrawal_
la cuenta de cheques _checking account_	la transferencia electrónica _electronic transfer_

d. Otros servicios / _Other services_

la aduana _customs_
el aduanero _customs official_
el Seguro Social _Social Security_

EXERCISE S.   Express what Jamie says about his grandfather by writing the correct word or expression in the space provided.

cuenta de cheques	depósito	cuenta de ahorros	cajero
seguro social	efectivo	cheque	retiro
banco	correo		

Mi abuelo prefiere hacer todo a la antigua. Cada mes él recibe su _____ de _____ por
                                                                          1.   2.

_____ . No le gusta el _____ directo. Él prefiere llevarlo al _____ para
       3.   4.   5.

depositarlo en su _____ . También tiene que hacer _____ de su _____
                         6.   7.   8.

porque necesita dinero en _____ . Los _____ ya lo conocen y siempre lo saludan muy
                                  9.   10.

cordialmente.

EXERCISE T.   In each group, select the word that is not related to the other three.

1. buzón, carta, paquete, llamada   _____

2. marcar, colgar, retirar, descolgar   _____

3. cuenta, correo, caja, retiro   _____

4. caja fuerte, cabina telefónica, guía telefónica, número equivocado   _____

5. apartado postal, operadora, código postal, estampillas   _____

6. efectivo, moneda, cambio, telegrama   _____

7. ahorros, receptor, cheques, cajero   _____

◆ 10 ◆   LAS COMPRAS / *SHOPPING*

a. La ropa / *Clothing*

el abrigo *overcoat*	**la corbata** *tie*	**el saco** *jacket*
la blusa *blouse*	**la falda** *skirt*	**las sandalias** *sandals*
el bolsillo *pocket*	**la gorra** *cap*	**el sombrero** *hat*
las botas *boots*	**los guantes** *gloves*	**el suéter** *sweater*
la bufanda *scarf*	**el impermeable** *raincoat*	**los tenis** *sneakers*
el calcetín *sock*	**el pantalón** *pants*	**los tirantes** *suspenders*
la camisa *shirt*	**el pantalón corto** *shorts*	**el traje** *suit*
la camiseta *T-shirt*	**las pantimedias** *pantyhose*	**el traje de baño** *bathing suit*
el chaleco *vest*	**el pañuelo** *handkerchief*	**el vestido** *dress*
la chaqueta *jacket*	**la ropa** *clothing*	**el zapato** *shoe*
el cinturón *belt*		

b. Los colores / *Colors*

amarillo *yellow*	**blanco** *white*	**marrón** *brown*
anaranjado *orange*	**café** *brown*	**morado** *purple*
azul *blue*	**gris** *gray*	**negro** *black*

rojo *red*   verde *green*
rosado *pink*   violeta *purple*

c. Las telas y los materiales / *Fabrics and materials*

el algodón *cotton*   la lana *wool*   el poliéster *polyester*
el encaje *lace*   el lino *linen*   el raso *satin*
el fieltro *felt*   el nilón *nylon*   la seda *silk*
la franela *flannel*   la piel *leather, fur*   el terciopelo *velvet*
la gamusa *suede*

d. La joyería / *Jewelry*

el anillo *ring*   la cadena *chain*   la pulsera *bracelet*
el arete *earring*   el collar *necklace*   el reloj *watch*
la argolla *wedding band* el prendedor *pin*   la sortija *ring*
el broche *brooch, pin*

e. Piedras preciosas y metales / *Gems and metals*

el brillante *diamond*   el rubí *ruby*   el oro *gold*
el diamante *diamond*   el safiro *sapphire*   la plata *silver*
la esmeralda *emerald*   el topacio *topaz*   el platino *platinum*
la perla *pearl*

EXERCISE U. **Describe what you and your date will wear in the following circumstances. Include the articles of clothing, accessories, colors, and materials of each item.**

EXAMPLE: ir a la escuela
    YO: una blusa verde de algodón, pantalones blancos de algodón, tenis blanco de piel
    ÉL / ELLA: una camisa azul de algodón, pantalones azules de lana, zapatos negros de piel

1. ir a la playa

YO: _____

ÉL/ELLA: _____

2. ir a una fiesta

YO: _____

ÉL/ELLA: _____

3. ir a trabajar en una oficina

YO: _____

ÉL/ELLA: _____

4. descansar en casa

YO: _____

ÉL/ELLA: _____

5. ir a una boda

YO: _____

ÉL/ELLA: _____

◆ 11 ◆ EL VIAJE Y LA TRANSPORTACIÓN / *Travel and Transportation*

el aeropuerto *airport*	**el carro** *car*	**el peaje** *toll*
el alojamiento *lodging*	**el compartamiento** *compartment*	**la parada** *stop, bus stop*
el asiento *seat*	**el despegue** *takeoff*	**el pasajero** *passenger*
el aterrizaje *landing*	**el equipaje** *luggage*	**la posada** *inn*
el autobús *bus*	**la escala** *stop (air travel)*	**la puerta** *gate*
el automóvil *car*	**la estación** *train station*	**la ruta** *route*
la autopista *highway*	**el ferrocarril** *railroad*	**la salida** *departure*
el avión *airplane*	**el guía** *guide*	**la tarifa** *rate, price*
el barco *boat*	**el horario** *schedule*	**el taxi** *taxi*
el baúl *trunk*	**el huésped** *guest*	**la terminal de autobuses** *bus terminal*
la bicicleta *bicycle*	**el itinerario** *itinerary*	
el billete *ticket*	**la llegada** *arrival*	**el tranvía** *streetcar*
el boleto *ticket*	**la maleta** *suitcase*	**el tren** *train*
la brújula *compass*	**el medio de transporte** *means of transportation*	**el vapor** *steamship*
la calle *street*		**la ventanilla** *ticket window*
el camarote *cabin*	**el metro** *subway*	**el viaje** *trip*
el camino *road*	**la motocicleta (la moto)** *motorcycle*	**el viajero** *traveler*
el camión *truck*		**el vuelo** *flight*
la camioneta *van*	**el muelle** *pier*	
la carretera *road*		

EXERCISE V.   **Complete each statement with the appropriate word.**

1. Un instrumento importante para los pilotos es _____.

2. Las posadas y los hoteles son dos formas de _____.

3. Por lo general, a los choferes no les importa pagar un peaje para conducir en _____ porque es más rápida y segura.

4. Para saber la hora de salida o llegada de un avión o un tren, debo consultar _____.

5. Hay muchas personas que temen _____ y _____ de los aviones.

6. Prefiero un vuelo directo sin _____.

7. Los barcos embarcan y desembarcan en _____.

8. Puesto que mi papá no es muy aficionado a conducir mucho, él prefiere siempre tomar _____ más directa y corta.

9. Cuando hay una demora o una huelga en el aeropuerto, _____ se ponen furiosos.

10. El tren, el autobús y el taxi son tres _____ públicos de una ciudad grande.

◆ 12 ◆ EVENTOS DE ACTUALIDAD / *Current Events*

a.   La política / *Politics*

el/la alcalde (-esa) *mayor*

la asamblea *assembly*

el/la ayudante militar *military aide*

el ayuntamiento *town hall*

la cámara de diputados *house of representatives*

el/la candidato(-a) *candidate*

la conferencia *conference*

el congreso *congress*

la democracia *democracy*

los derechos *rights*

el desempleo *unemployment*

el/la dictador(-ora) *dictator*

la dictadura *dictatorship*

el/la diputado(-a) *representative*

la economía *economy*

el ejército *army*

la embajada *embassy*

el/la embajador(-ora) *ambassador*

la entrevista *interview*

la frontera *border*

el gabinete *cabinet*

el gobierno *government*

el/la gobernador(-ora) *governor*

la guerra *war*

el/la guerrillero(-a) *guerrilla fighter*

la inflación *inflation*

la insurrección *rebellion*

el/la jefe(-a) de estado *head of state*

la mayoría *majority*

el/la ministro(-a) *minister*

la minoría *minority*

las noticias *news*

el noticiero *news broadcast*

el parlamento *parliament*

el partido *party*

el periódico *newspaper*

el/la periodista *journalist*

el plazo *term*

el poder ejecutivo *executive power*

el/la político(-a) *politician*

el/la presidente(-a) *president*

el/la primer(-a) ministro(-a) *Prime Minister*

la primera dama *the first lady*

el programa *program, platform*

la rebeldía *rebellion, revolt*

la recesión *recession*

la reina *queen*

la república *republic*

la revista *magazine*

la revolución *revolution*

el rey *king*

el senado *senate*

el/la senador(-ora) *senator*

los titulares *headlines*

el tratado *treaty*

el/la vice-presidente(-a) *vice-president*

EXERCISE W.   **You are explaining the United States government to a new pen pal. Complete each statement with the appropriate word.**

congreso	gobierno	plazo	titulares
políticos	inflación	estado	la primera
el presidente	senado	alcalde	desempleo
partidos	embajadores	gobernador	noticieros
economía	derechos	gabinete	cámara de diputados

En los Estados Unidos hay dos _____ políticos: los demócratas y los republicanos. El
                                    1.

_____ de _____ elegidos es de cuatro años. El _____ federal se divide
        2.   3.   4.

en dos secciones: _____ y _____ . _____ nombra a los miembros
                              5.   6.   7.

de su _____ . También nombra a _____ , pero su nombramiento tiene que
              8.   9.

ser aprobado por _____. _____ es importante porque ella se interesa en las
_{10.}   _{11.}

causas sociales como _____ humanos. Casi todos los días se puede ver el nombre del presidente
_{12.}

en _____ de los periódicos o en _____ de radio o televisión. Cada _____
_{13.}   _{14.}   _{15.}

tiene su propio _____ y cada ciudad o pueblo tiene su propio _____. Todos tienen
_{16.}   _{17.}

interés en mantener _____ próspera y estable mientras trabajan para disminuir _____ y
_{18.}   _{19.}

_____.
_{20.}

b. La vida cultural / *Cultural life*

el/la acomodador(-ora) *usher*
el acto *act*
las artes *arts*
el/la artista *artist, performer*
el auditorio *auditorium*
el ballet *ballet*
la cola *line (of people)*
la comedia *comedy*
el/la compositor(-ora) *composer*
el concierto *concert*
la cultura *culture*
el/la dramaturgo(-a) *playwright*
la escena *scene*
el/la escultor(-ora) *sculptor*
la escultura *sculpture*
el espectáculo *show*
la estrella *star*

la exposición *exhibit, exposition*
la fila *row*
la función *performance, showing (movie)*
la música *music*
el músico *musician*
la obra de teatro *play*
la ópera *opera*
la orquesta *orchestra*
el personaje *character*
el/la pintor(-ora) *painter*
la pintura *painting*
la poesía *poetry*
el poeta *poet*
la poetisa *poet*
el reparto *cast (theater, film)*
la taquilla *box office*
el teatro *theater*

EXERCISE X.   **Complete each statement with the appropriate word.**

1. Generalmente una obra de teatro se divide en dos o tres _____.

2. Para comprar boletos para el cine, hay que hacer _____ en _____.

3. En un teatro _____ conduce a las personas a sus asientos.

4. Cuando una persona va a _____, espera escuchar música.

5. La persona que escribe obras de teatro es _____.

6. En una ópera, los _____ cantan.

7. Los actores de una película u obra de teatro forman _____.

8. Una persona que escribe frases cortas sin o con rima es _____.

9. En el arte, una forma tridimensional es _____.

10. Las personas inventadas por el autor de una novela o un drama son _____.

MASTERY EXERCISES

EXERCISE Y. Complete each statement with an appropriate word.

1. Las personas usan _____ para respirar y oler.

2. Mi padre es _____ de mi madre.

3. En una pastelería se venden _____ .

4. Antes de la cena, la madre _____ la mesa.

5. Muchos hombres llevan _____ entre la nariz y el labio superior.

6. _____ gobierna sin el apoyo del pueblo e impone muchas restricciones a los derechos de los ciudadanos.

7. Hoy día _____ son muy populares porque hay un surtido de tiendas en un solo lugar.

8. En una oficina _____ contesta el teléfono y escribe las cartas de su jefe en la computadora.

9. Las obras de arte valiosas se exhiben en _____ .

10. Una persona a quien no le gusta trabajar es _____ .

11. Lo contrario del amor es _____ .

12. Para ir de un piso a otro en una casa particular se usa _____ .

13. Muchas madres se ponen furiosas cuando sus hijos dejan los vasos sucios en _____ sin lavarlos.

14. Se guarda la ropa en _____ .

15. Para verse, una persona usa _____ .

16. Para quitar las arrugas a una prenda de ropa, hay que _____ la prenda.

17. La parte central de muchos pueblos y ciudades hispanos es _____ .

18. La nubes, el sol, la luna y las estrellas están en _____ .

19. En el otoño _____ caen de los árboles.

20. Un terreno árido con arena y muy pocas plantas es _____ .

21. Los magos siempre sacan _____ de su sombrero.

22. _____ es un animal que camina muy despacio.

23. Se encuentra el significado de las palabras en _____ .

24. Para cortar papel se usan _____.

25. Muchos vestidos de novia son de _____ fino y bonito.

EXERCISE Z.   The King and Queen of Spain visited your city. You are writing a description of their visit on your Spanish blog. You may wish to include the following:

- who visited your city
- the location of your city
- a description of the royal couple
- how they arrived and traveled in the city
- the places they visited (for example, a school, hospital, daycare center, etc.) and with whom they interacted
- something special they did (for example, buy gift, see a monument, etc.)
- who attended those events
- a description of how the students were dressed
- their evening activity (for example, a formal dinner, etc.)
- the numerous photos taken
- your opinion of the event and its popularity

ACTIVIDADES

1. Prepare a food pyramid in Spanish for display in your classroom.

2. Prepare the school's breakfast and lunch menus in Spanish for a week.

3. Prepare a description of the club or extracurricular program in your school for a group of Spanish-speaking visitors.

4. Your school is planning a week to celebrate the arts. Prepare several flyers that highlight the activities the Spanish Club will organize for this event.

5. Research the Spanish-speaking nations and prepare a report that includes such things as the type of government, name of the head of state, election term, voting age, etc.

6. Prepare a mini-handbook about your school for new Spanish-speaking students.

PART

5

Spanish and Spanish-American Civilizations

35

La geografía de España

LOCALIZACIÓN DE ESPAÑA

España está situada en el sudoeste de Europa. Ocupa el 80 por ciento de la Península Ibérica, que comparte con Portugal.

EXTENSIÓN Y POBLACIÓN

Su extensión es de unas 200 millas cuadradas, (cuatro veces más grande que la del estado de Nueva York). Tiene una población de unos 47.265.000 de habitantes.

MONTAÑAS

España es un país muy montañoso.
1. Los Montes Pirineos están en el nordeste y marcan la frontera entre España y Francia.
2. La Cordillera Cantábrica está en el noroeste.
3. La Sierra de Guadarrama está en el centro, cerca de Madrid.
4. La Sierra Nevada y la Sierra Morena están en el sur.

RÍOS

1. El Ebro, en el nordeste, desemboca en el Mar Mediterráneo.
2. El Tajo, en la región central, es el río más largo. Pasa por la ciudad de Toledo.
3. El Guadalquivir, en el sur, es el río más profundo y navegable de España. Pasa por las ciudades de Sevilla y Córdoba.

INDUSTRIAS Y PRODUCTOS PRINCIPALES

1. España es un país agrícola e industrial.
2. Los productos principales agrícolas son aceitunas, naranjas, uvas, trigo, limones y corcho.
3. España es uno de los mayores productores de vino en el mundo. Los centros principales de la producción de vinos son Málaga y Jerez.
4. España es uno de los productores principales del aceite de oliva del mundo.

5. Sus recursos minerales incluyen carbón, hierro, mercurio, plomo y cobre.

REGIONES

España está dividida en quince regiones:
Cantabria, en el norte;
Galicia, en el noroeste;
Asturias, en el norte al este de Galicia;
el País Vasco, en el norte, con frontera en los Pirineos;
Navarra, en el norte;
Aragón, en el nordeste, al este de Navarra;
Cataluña, en el nordeste;
La Rioja, en el centro al sur de Navarra;
Castilla y León, en el noroeste-centro;
Castilla-La Mancha, en el centro, al sur de Castilla y León;
Madrid, en el centro, al norte de Castilla-La Mancha;
Valencia, en el este;
Extremadura, en el norte, entre Portugal y Castilla-La Mancha;
Murcia, en el sudeste;
Andalucía, en el sur.

POSESIONES ULTRAMARINAS

1. **Las Islas Baleares** están en el Mar Mediterráneo. Mallorca es la isla más grande del grupo.
2. **Las Islas Canarias** están en el Océano Atlántico, cerca de la costa noroeste de Africa.
3. **Ceuta y Melilla** son dos puertos de Marruecos, África.

IDIOMAS

1. El **español** (también llamado el castellano) es el idioma principal de España.
2. El **gallego** es un dialecto que se habla en Galicia.
3. El **catalán** es la lengua de Cataluña.
4. El **vascuence** es la lengua de los vascos, que viven en el País Vasco.

CIUDADES IMPORTANTES

Madrid es la capital y la ciudad más grande de España. Tiene una población de unos 6.499.000 de habitantes. En Madrid y en sus alrededores existen varios lugares de interés.

1. **El Retiro** es un parque famoso.
2. **La Puerta del Sol** es la plaza principal de Madrid. De allí se extienden muchas calles que conducen a todas partes de la ciudad.
3. **El Museo del Prado** es un museo de bellas artes de fama mundial.
4. **El Escorial** está situado cerca de Madrid. Es un edificio enorme que tiene un monasterio, un palacio, una biblioteca y un mausoleo para reyes españoles. Fue construido por orden del rey Felipe II entre 1563 y 1584.
5. **El Valle de los Caídos** también está situado cerca de Madrid. Es un monumento grandísimo dedicado a la memoria de los soldados que murieron en la Guerra Civil española (1936-1939). El dictador Francisco Franco está enterrado allí.

Barcelona, en la región de Cataluña, es el puerto principal y la ciudad más industrial de España. Tiene unos 5.552.000 de habitantes. Cerca de la ciudad está el famoso Monasterio de Montserrat.

Sevilla, en la región de Andalucía, es la ciudad más pintoresca y romántica. Está situada a orillas del río Guadalquivir. Entre sus lugares de interés se encuentran:

a. **La Catedral de Sevilla,** la catedral más grande de España.
b. **La Giralda,** una torre de la catedral, es un admirable ejemplo de la arquitectura árabe.
c. **El Alcázar** que es un famoso palacio moro.

Valencia es la ciudad principal de la región del mismo nombre. Esta región se llama «la huerta de España» y es famosa por las naranjas que produce.

Bilbao, en el norte, es famosa por su producción de hierro y acero.

Toledo es una antigua ciudad situada en el Río Tajo. Es famosa por sus productos de acero y de metales preciosos. También es conocida por ser la casa del pintor famoso El Greco. Muchas de sus pinturas se exhiben allí.

Granada, en la región de Andalucía, tiene la famosa Alhambra, y también otro palacio moro, el Generalife. Granada fue la última posesión de los moros en España. La volvieron a ganar los cristianos en 1492.

Córdoba, también en Andalucía y situada en el Río Guadalquivir, tiene la famosa **Mezquita** (Mosque), un antiguo templo de la época de los moros, que fue convertido en una catedral católica en 1238. Durante los siglos X y XI Córdoba fue la capital mora de España y uno de los centros culturales de Europa.

Burgos, que se encuentra en Castilla y León, es la ciudad natal del Cid, el héroe nacional de España. Su tumba está en la Catedral de Burgos.

Salamanca es famosa por su universidad. Establecida en el siglo XIII, la **Universidad de Salamanca** es la más antigua de España y una de las más prestigiosas de Europa.

Segovia es una antigua ciudad situada en la parte central de España. Es famosa por el acueducto romano, construido bajo el emperador romano Trajano (A.D. 53-117). El acueducto funciona aun hoy en día.

EXERCISE A. Relacione ambas columnas. En el espacio provisto, escriba la letra con la expresión correspondiente a cada punto de la columna A.

	A		B
_____	1. la Península Ibérica	*a.*	lengua hablada en Cataluña
_____	2. la Sierra de Guadarrama	*b.*	río más navegable
_____	3. la Puerta del Sol	*c.*	construido por orden de Felipe II
_____	4. el Tajo	*d.*	las Islas Baleares
_____	5. Córdoba	*e.*	el Cid
_____	6. el catalán	*f.*	España y Portugal
_____	7. Málaga	*g.*	región situada en el sur
_____	8. El Escorial	*h.*	Sevilla
_____	9. los Pirineos	*i.*	el río más largo
_____	10. el Guadalquivir	*j.*	centro de la producción de vinos
_____	11. Andalucía	*k.*	plaza principal de Madrid
_____	12. Burgos	*l.*	cerca de Madrid
_____	13. Mallorca	*m.*	puerto de Marruecos
_____	14. Ceuta	*n.*	la Mezquita
_____	15. La Giralda	*o.*	frontera entre España y Francia

EXERCISE B. Escoja las frases que completen correctamente las oraciones.

1. La frontera que separa a España de Francia es (la Sierra de Guadarrama, la Sierra Nevada, los Pirineos).

_____

2. España está situada en la parte (sudoeste, nordeste, central) de Europa.

_____

3. Una región del norte de España es (Valencia, Extremadura, Galicia).

_____

4. En (Madrid, Segovia, Valencia) se encuentra un acueducto romano.

_____

5. Andalucía es (una ciudad, un río, una región) de España.

_____

6. Las ciudades de Jerez y Málaga son famosas por sus (aceitunas, vinos, naranjas).

_____

7. (El Generalife, El Escorial, La Mezquita) es un palacio moro.

_____

8. Mallorca es una de (las Islas Baleares, las Islas Canarias, los Cantábricos).

_____

9. La población de España es de aproximadamente (47.000.000, 25.000.000, 37.000.000) de habitantes.

_____

10. La catedral más grande de España se encuentra en (Madrid, Burgos, Sevilla).

_____

11. Un dialecto que se habla en Galicia es el (vascuence, catalán, gallego).

_____

12. Salamanca es famosa por su (catedral, universidad, acueducto).

_____

13. Los recursos minerales de España incluyen el (estaño, mercurio, oro).

_____

14. El río más navegable de España es el (Guadalquivir, Tajo, Ebro).

_____

15. Al Greco se lo relaciona con la ciudad de (Burgos, Córdoba, Toledo).

_____

EXERCISE C. **Lea cada oración e indique si es cierta o falsa. Si es falsa, cámbiela para hacerla cierta.**

1. El río Tajo desemboca en el Mar Mediterráneo.

_____

2. La Cordillera Cantábrica marca la frontera entre España y Francia.

_____

3. El Cid, el héroe nacional, nació en la ciudad de Toledo.

_____

4. España tiene una población de más de cuarenta y siete millones de habitantes.

_____

5. El tabaco es uno de los principales productos agrícolas de España.

_____

6. La Universidad de Salamanca se estableció en el siglo XIII.

_____

7. Jerez y Málaga son los centros de la producción de vinos.

_____

8. Galicia está en el noroeste del país.

_____

9. Barcelona es el puerto principal de España.

_____

10. Hay veinte regiones tradicionales en España.

_____

11. El vascuence es el idioma principal de España.

_____

12. La Giralda era un templo antiguo de la época de los moros.

_____

13. Las Islas Canarias están en el Mar Mediterráneo.

_____

14. España es un productor principal de jugo de naranja del mundo.

_____

15. Bilbao es la ciudad conocida por su producción de hierro y acero.

_____

EXERCISE D.   **Complete las siguientes oraciones.**

1. El gallego es el idioma de _____ .

2. En _____ , hay dos ciudades españolas en la costa de Marruecos.

3. Los vascos hablan _____ además del español.

4. Los Pirineos separan a España de _____ .

5. El río más navegable de España es el _____ .

6. Un famoso palacio moro de Sevilla es _____ .

7. El monasterio de Montserrat se encuentra cerca de la ciudad de _____ .

8. La región central de España se llama _____ .

9. El río más grande de España es el _____ .

10. España ocupa la mayor parte de la _____ .

11. La última posesión de los moros en España fue _____ .

12. Durante los siglos X y XI _____ fue la capital mora de España.

13. Dos posesiones ultramarinas de España son _____ y _____ .

14. Dos riquezas mineras de España son _____ y _____ .

15. El museo famoso de Madrid es _____ .

La historia de España

HABITANTES PRIMITIVOS

1. Los **iberos** y los **celtas** fueron los primeros habitantes de España. De los iberos y los celtas se formó la raza celtíbera, precursora de los españoles de hoy.

2. Los **fenicios** fueron una nación de marineros. Fundaron la ciudad de Cádiz. Los **griegos** fundaron colonias en la costa oriental de España. Estos dos grupos estaban en España del siglo once al siglo ocho, antes de Cristo, aproximadamente.

3. Los **cartagineses** invadieron a España en el siglo III antes de Cristo. Constituían una nación guerrera que venció a los celtíberos durante las Guerras Púnicas.

4. Los **romanos** vencieron a los cartagineses alrededor del año 200 antes de Cristo y reinaron en España durante seis siglos (hasta el año 400 después de Cristo, aproximadamente). Tuvieron mucha influencia en España: dieron a España la religión cristiana, las leyes romanas, y su lengua (el castellano se deriva del latín). También construyeron puentes, acueductos y caminos.

5. Los **visigodos**, una tribu germánica, vencieron a los romanos e invadieron a España por el año 409 después de Cristo. Reinaron hasta la invasión de los moros.

6. Los **moros** invadieron España y vencieron a los visigodos en 711. Permanecieron en España por siete siglos, hasta 1492, y dominaron el país durante gran parte de ese período. Tuvieron mucha influencia en la vida española. Esta influencia morisca incluye la introducción de la noria para regar los campos, la introducción de las ciencias (matemáticas, medicina, astronomía, filosofía, etc.), la construcción de palacios, alcázares y mezquitas, y la introducción de nuevas palabras en el idioma español, sobre todo palabras que comienzan con al- (algodón, alcalde, álgebra, etc.).

RECONQUISTA DE ESPAÑA

1. **Pelayo** venció a los moros en la batalla de Covadonga en 718.

2. **El Cid** (Rodrigo Díaz de Vivar), el héroe nacional de España, capturó la ciudad de Valencia de los moros en 1094.

3. En 1492, después de más de siete siglos de lucha, los españoles, bajo **Fernando** e **Isabel** (los Reyes Católicos), vencieron finalmente a los últimos moros, en Granada. Así terminó la Reconquista.

ESPAÑA, UN PAÍS PODEROSO

Los Reyes Católicos —Fernando, el rey de Aragón, e Isabel, la reina de Castilla— terminaron la Reconquista de España y empezaron su unificación. Bajo su reinado, España llegó a ser la primera nación de Europa. Ayudaron al navegante genovés Cristóbal Colón a culminar su empresa y le dieron tres carabelas, la Niña, la Pinta y la Santa María. Colón y sus marineros pisaron tierra el 12 de octubre en una isla que llamaron San Salvador. Con el descubrimiento del Nuevo Mundo empezó el gran imperio español.

Carlos V (1516-1556), nieto de Fernando e Isabel, fue uno de los reyes más poderosos de España. Durante su reinado, la época de los grandes descubrimientos y conquistas, España llegó a tener posesiones en Europa y en el Nuevo Mundo.

Felipe II fue el hijo de Carlos V. Durante su reinado España participó en muchas guerras. Venció a los turcos en la batalla de Lepanto (1571). Su «Armada Invencible» fue vencida por Inglaterra en 1588.

DECADENCIA DE ESPAÑA (SIGLO XVIII)

La decadencia de España se debió, entre muchas cosas, a las guerras, los altos impuestos y a los reyes débiles que gobernaron al país durante esa época.

LOS SIGLOS XIX, XX Y XXI

1. La **Guerra de la Independencia** (1808-1814), comenzó el 2 de mayo de 1808 con una rebelión contra los franceses (Napoleón). Esta fecha se convirtió en la fiesta nacional del país. Lograron expulsar a las fuerzas francesas en 1814.

2. Las **Guerras Carlistas** (1833-39; 1872-76) fueron largas guerras civiles en las cuales Carlos, hermano de Fernando VII, trató de quitarle el trono del país a Isabel, hija de Fernando VII.

3. La **Guerra Hispanoamericana** entre España y los Estados Unidos tuvo lugar en 1898. España fue vencida y perdió sus posesiones ultramarinas de Cuba, Guam, Puerto Rico, y las Islas Filipinas.

4. La Primera República fue establecida en 1873, y duró solamente un año. Alfonso XII estableció otra vez la monarquía. Su hijo, Alfonso XIII, fue rey de España hasta 1931. Durante su reinado, estableció una dictadura bajo Primo de Rivera. La segunda república fue establecida el 14 de abril de 1931.

5. En 1936 estalló una guerra civil que duró hasta 1939. El general Francisco Franco venció a las fuerzas de la república y estableció una dictadura. Franco rigió el país hasta su muerte en 1975. El gobierno actual es una monarquía constitucional. En 1975, Juan Carlos I fue proclamado rey por las Cortes. En 1982, Felipe González Márquez llegó a ser presidente del Gobierno. A partir de 1985, España es miembro de la Comunidad Económica Europea (C.E.E.). Adoptó su moneda única, el euro, y abandonó la peseta.

6. Al final de la primera década del siglo XXI, España experimentó una crisis económica que aumentó el desempleo en el país y afectó el sistema nacional bancario y la vida diaria de los habitantes.

7. El 2 de junio de 2014, Juan Carlos I anunció su intención de abdicar al trono de España. El 18 de junio, el Congreso de Diputados aprobó la decisión del rey. Al día siguiente se celebró el juramento y la proclamación del nuevo rey, Felipe VI, hijo de don Juan Carlos y doña Sofía.

EXERCISE A. Relacione ambas columnas en el espacio provisto, escriba la letra con la expresión correspondiente a cada punto de la columna A.

A	B
_____ 1. Pelayo	*a.* el Cid
_____ 2. los Reyes Católicos	*b.* Napoleón
_____ 3. Rodrigo Díaz de Vivar	*c.* rey de España hasta 1931
_____ 4. Felipe II	*d.* Guerra Hispanoamericana
_____ 5. Dos de Mayo	*e.* Fernando e Isabel
_____ 6. Alfonso XIII	*f.* antigua moneda española
_____ 7. guerra que ocurrió al fin del siglo XIX	*g.* Guerra de Independencia
_____ 8. peseta	*h.* 14 de abril de 1931
_____ 9. la segunda república	*i.* dictador español
_____ 10. Francisco Franco	*j.* inició la Reconquista

EXERCISE B. Escoja la palabra o expresión que complete correctamente cada frase.

1. Los primeros habitantes de España fueron los (iberos, moros, romanos).

_____

2. La segunda república española se estableció en el año (718, 1931, 1808).

_____

3. Muchos puentes y acueductos fueron construidos por los (fenicios, romanos, moros).

_____

4. Muchas palabras españolas que comienzan con "al-" son de origen (romano, árabe, ibero).

_____

5. Las guerras entre los moros y los españoles se llamaron (las Guerras Civiles, las Guerras Carlistas, la Reconquista).

_____

6. España perdió a Cuba, Puerto Rico, y las Filipinas en (la guerra civil, la guerra con los Estados Unidos, la guerra de independencia).

_____

7. Pelayo venció a los moros en la batalla de (Covadonga, Lepanto, Sagunto).

_____

8. Los visigodos vencieron a los (moros, romanos, fenicios).

_____

9. El dictador de España bajo Alfonso XIII fue (Francisco Franco, Primo de Rivera, Pelayo).

_____

10. El hijo de Carlos V fue (Fernando VII, Felipe II, Alfonso XIII).

_____

EXERCISE C. **Lea cada oración e indique si es cierta o falsa. Si es falsa, cámbiela para hacerla cierta.**

1. Los romanos reinaron hasta la invasión de los moros.

_____

2. Se debe la introducción de la noria a los cartagineses.

_____

3. Pelayo venció a los moros en la batalla de Sagunto.

_____

4. Los españoles vencieron a los turcos en la batalla de Lepanto.

_____

5. España llegó a tener muchas posesiones ultramarinas durante el reinado de Fernando e Isabel.

_____

6. La «Armada Invencible» fue vencida por los ingleses en 1588.

_____

7. Durante los primeros años del siglo XXI, España experimentó gran prosperidad económica.

_____

8. La decadencia de España se debió a muchas guerras, reyes débiles, y la expulsión de los judíos y los moros.

_____

9. La Guerra Civil comenzó en 1936 y no terminó hasta 1941.

_____

10. En la actualidad el gobierno de España es una monarquía constitucional.

_____

(EXERCISE D.) **Complete las siguientes oraciones.**

1. El español se deriva del _____ .

2. El día de la independencia española se celebra _____ .

3. Los cartagineses vencieron a los celtíberos en la batalla de _____ .

4. La Reconquista fue terminada por _____ .

5. Los moros introdujeron _____ en España.

6. España sufrió una decadencia completa en el siglo _____ .

7. Los fenicios fundaron la ciudad de _____ .

8. A principios del siglo XXI, España sufrió _____ .

9. El héroe nacional de España es _____ .

10. Las guerras entre la reina Isabel y Carlos se conocen como _____ .

La vida y las costumbres de España

En la actualidad, la vida diaria de España es muy semejante a la vida diaria de los Estados Unidos. Sin embargo, cada país tiene algo de particular. En España existen muchas costumbres y tradiciones interesantes.

LA CASA Y LA FAMILIA

Las casas de las ciudades grandes se parecen a las de las otras ciudades del mundo. Hay edificios de apartamentos y casas particulares. Muchos españoles viven en su condominio o piso que forma parte de un edificio alto.

En los pueblos pequeños, las ciudades antiguas y en las partes antiguas de las ciudades grandes las casas están en calles estrechas. Generalmente, estas casas son de un solo piso, con balcones, ventanas con rejas y pintorescos patios interiores. En muchas casas, las paredes están cubiertas de azulejos.

LOS NOMBRES Y LOS APELLIDOS

Los nombres españoles son diferentes a los de los anglosajones, y esta costumbre de los nombres se extiende a todos los países hispanos. Además del nombre de pila, los españoles e hispanos llevan dos apellidos (el apellido del padre seguido del apellido de la madre): por ejemplo, Rafael *Hernández Silva*. Este nombre se archiva bajo «H» porque se considera más importante el apellido del padre.

Cuando una mujer se casa, ella retiene el apellido de su padre y añade el «de» seguido por el apellido de su esposo. Por ejemplo, si Rafael se casa con Marisa Trujillo Rodríguez, su nombre sería Marisa Trujillo de Hernández. Ella no usa ninguno de los apellidos maternos.

Por lo general, el nombre de pila de la mayoría de los españoles (y de los hispanoamericanos) es el nombre de un santo. Además de su propio cumpleaños, celebran el día del santo.

TIPOS PINTORESCOS

La tuna es un grupo de músicos ambulantes que ha sido parte de la vida estudiantil universitaria desde el siglo XVI. Los tunos usan un traje tradicional de color negro y una capa. Tocan música romántica y alegre. Sus instrumentos incluyen el laúd, la bandurria, el requinto, la guitarra y la pandereta.

Los gitanos viven en el sur de España, principalmente cerca de las ciudades de Sevilla y Granada. Conservan muchas de sus tradiciones dentro de las que la música y el baile son muy importantes. Hablan un idioma llamado romaní.

COSTUMBRES

La vida social es muy importante para los españoles. Son muy sociables y amigables. Les gusta pasar mucho tiempo charlando con los amigos en los cafés y en los bares. Cenan mucho más tarde que en nuestro país, y por consiguiente, se acuestan más tarde.

En muchas ciudades hay un **ateneo,** un club intelectual donde se reúnen grupos literarios y científicos.

La tertulia es una reunión informal con el propósito de charlar y divertirse. Muchas veces no termina hasta después de la medianoche.

La siesta es la tradición de acostarse por la tarde durante las horas de mayor calor. Las tiendas y las oficinas cierran, y los trabajadores regresan a sus casas para comer, descansar o dormir la siesta. Después de la siesta, las tiendas y oficinas vuelven a abrir y quedan abiertas hasta muy tarde. La tradición de la siesta ha ido desapareciendo en las ciudades grandes.

La lotería es dirigida por el gobierno y es muy popular. Las ganancias de la lotería se usan para el beneficio de las personas pobres y los niños huérfanos. El sorteo tiene lugar tres veces al mes y hay muchos premios. El premio mayor se llama «el premio gordo».

«Pelar la pava» es una tradición antigua que se usaba cuando el novio cortejaba a la novia. El novio le hablaba a la novia a través de una reja. Él parado afuera y ella sentada dentro de la casa. Con el pasar del tiempo, muchas de estas costumbres han ido desapareciendo, especialmente en las ciudades grandes.

COMIDAS Y BEBIDAS

La tradición de comer tres comidas al día existe tanto en España como en los Estados Unidos. Principalmente, la diferencia está en el horario. En España existe la costumbre de comer más tarde. El desayuno se toma a eso de las ocho de la mañana y generalmente consiste en café con leche o chocolate y pan con mantequilla y mermelada o panecillos. La comida se come a eso de las dos de la tarde y la cena no se toma hasta después de las ocho o nueve de la noche. Estas dos comidas son comidas completas. Pueden consistir en sopa, ensalada, carne con arroz o verduras y postre. Alrededor de las seis de la tarde los españoles toman la merienda, algo ligero como un sándwich. Se acostumbra comer bocados que llaman «tapas» cuando toman el aperitivo antes de la cena.

España tiene una gastronomía variada, interesante y deliciosa. Entre los platos tradicionales está el **puchero** que es considerado quizás el plato nacional de España. Es un guisado que se sirve casi a diario, especialmente entre los campesinos. Se llama también olla o cocido.

El plato más conocido de España es el **arroz con pollo.** En Valencia añaden mariscos y otros ingredientes al arroz con pollo y lo llaman paella.

Las bebidas que toman los españoles incluyen el **café,** el **té,** la **leche** y los **refrescos.** La **horchata** es una bebida tradicional hecha de almendras, agua y azúcar. La horchata se toma fría en el verano como refresco. El **chocolate caliente** es una bebida popular del desayuno y de la merienda. Lo preparan muy espeso y lo toman muy caliente con **panecillos, bizcochos** o **churros.**

LA ROPA

La ropa de los españoles se parece a la del resto de Europa. Sin embargo, existen prendas tradicionales. La **mantilla** es un pañuelo grande de seda y encajes que la mujer lleva en la cabeza. Debajo de la **mantilla** se usa un peine alto y muy adornado, llamado **peineta.** El **mantón** es un chal grande y, generalmente, bordado a mano. Sirve de adorno o de abrigo. La **boina** es una gorra de lana redonda parecida al «beret» francés. Las **alpargatas** son una especie de sandalia hecha de lona. Son comunes entre los trabajadores en muchas partes de España.

FIESTAS RELIGIOSAS

Puesto que la mayoría de los españoles practican la religión católica, las fiestas religiosas son muy importantes en el país.

1. La **Navidad** se celebra el 25 de diciembre y es la fiesta más importante del año. Desde principios de diciembre en cada casa se preparan los **Nacimientos** (grupos de figuras que representan el nacimiento de Jesucristo). La **Nochebuena** (*Christmas Eve*) la gente asiste a la **misa del gallo** (midnight mass) en las iglesias. Grupos de personas caminan por las calles cantando villancicos (Christmas carols). También se acostumbra dar regalos, llamados aguinaldos, a las personas que han servido a la familia durante el año (el cartero, los criados y otros). Los niños reciben sus regalos el 6 de enero, que se llama el **Día de los Reyes Magos.** Los Reyes Magos corresponden a nuestro Santa Claus.

2. El **Carnaval** es un período de tres días de diversión antes del Miércoles de Ceniza, que comienza la **Cuaresma** (Lent). La Cuaresma son los cuarenta días que siguen. Termina el domingo de Resurrección, la **Pascua Florida.** La **Semana Santa,** que precede a la Pascua Florida, se celebra con mucha solemnidad y devoción, sobre todo en Sevilla. El **Viernes Santo** hay procesiones religiosas en muchos pueblos y ciudades.

   Cada pueblo tiene su santo patrón, cuyo día se celebra con una fiesta. La noche anterior se celebra una **verbena** (evening festival). El día del santo hay **romerías** (religious picnics) a la tumba del santo.

3. El **Día de los Difuntos o Muertos** (All Souls' Day) se celebra el 2 de noviembre, en memoria de los muertos.

FIESTAS NACIONALES

1. El **dos de mayo** es la fiesta nacional de España. Conmemora un suceso patriótico, el comienzo de la resistencia contra los franceses en 1808.

2. El **Día de la Raza,** que se celebra el 12 de octubre, corresponde a nuestro «Columbus Day». Se celebra esta fiesta en todo el mundo hispano.

DEPORTES Y DIVERSIONES

1. La **corrida de toros** es un espectáculo muy típico de España. Generalmente hay corridas los domingos por la tarde y los días de fiesta. Tiene lugar en la plaza de toros. La corrida comienza con un desfile de todos los participantes por la arena, mientras se escucha la música de pasodobles.

   La corrida tiene tres partes o lo que llaman suertes. Los picadores entran, montados a caballo en la primera suerte. Llevan picas largas. Los banderilleros entran a pie en la segunda suerte. Ellos llevan banderillas. En la tercera suerte el matador (el torero final), armado de una espada de acero muy fina, y llevando una pequeña muleta roja, exhibe su arte y su valor. Ejecuta varios pases con la muleta, hasta que el momento ideal llega para matar al toro.

2. El **jai-alai** es un juego de pelota de origen vasco que se juega con una pelota dura en un gran frontón de tres paredes. Es semejante al «handball» pero el jugador usa una cesta larga y estrecha, que está atada a la muñeca, para tirar y coger la pelota.

3. El **fútbol** es muy popular no sólo en España, sino también en el resto de Europa y en Latinoamérica. Se puede decir que es el deporte nacional de la mayoría de esos países.

LA EDUCACIÓN

La educación es un derecho constitucional de los ciudadanos españoles. La educación básica española es obligatoria y gratuita. Consiste en la **educación primaria** (seis años) y la **educación secundaria obligatoria** (cuatro años) y se desarrolla usualmente entre los seis y los dieciséis años de edad.

EXERCISE A.   Indique si cada una de las siguientes palabras es una bebida, prenda de vestir, fiesta religiosa, o costumbre social.

1. boina _____

2. verbena _____

3. paella _____

4. tertulia _____

5. cocido _____

6. romería _____

7. horchata _____

8. el Día de los Difuntos _____

9. alpargatas _____

10. arroz con pollo _____

11. mantilla _____

12. Carnaval _____

13. merienda _____

14. peineta _____

15. chocolate _____

EXERCISE B.   Relacione ambas columnas. En el espacio provisto, escriba la letra con la expresión correspondiente a cada punto de la columna A.

	A		B
_____ 1.	apellido	a.	premio gordo
_____ 2.	pelar la pava	b.	frontón
_____ 3.	lotería	c.	sandalias
_____ 4.	Nochebuena	d.	músicos ambulantes
_____ 5.	banderillero	e.	reja
_____ 6.	jai-alai	f.	nombre
_____ 7.	día del santo patrón	g.	alimento

_____ 8. puchero   *h.* Navidad

_____ 9. tuna   *i.* corrida de toros

_____ 10. alpargatas   *j.* verbena

EXERCISE C.   **Complete las siguientes oraciones.**

1. Antonio Moreno Villa está casado con Luisa Gómez Vega, y tienen un hijo, Juan. El nombre completo del hijo es Juan _____ .

2. Un alimento popular en Valencia, hecho de arroz, pollo y mariscos se llama _____ .

3. La fiesta nacional de España se celebra _____ .

4. Los niños españoles reciben regalos el 6 de enero, el Día de los _____ .

5. El torero que va montado a caballo se llama el _____ .

6. El 12 de octubre se celebra _____ .

7. En vez de celebrar su cumpleaños, los niños españoles celebran su _____ .

8. _____ es el nombre que se da a un club científico y literario.

9. La horchata es una bebida fría que se hace de _____ .

10. El jai-alai es un deporte que se juega en un _____ .

EXERCISE D.   **Explique el significado de cada uno de los siguientes conceptos.**

1. Día de los Muertos _____

2. matador _____

3. Semana Santa _____

4. azulejos _____

5. verbena _____

6. Pascua Florida _____

7. romería _____

8. villancicos _____

9. nacimiento _____

10. Misa del Gallo _____

La contribución española a la literatura, las artes, la música y las ciencias

LITERATURA

España siempre ha tenido una presencia en la literatura mundial.

La Edad Media

El más antiguo poema épico y la primera obra importante de la literatura española, es el **«Poema (Cantar) de Mío Cid».** De escritor anónimo, fue compuesto hacia el año 1140. El poema celebra la vida y las hazañas de Rodrigo Díaz de Vivar, el héroe nacional de España. **Alfonso X,** El Sabio (1221-1284), hizo mucho para impulsar la literatura de España. Compiló una colección de leyes y costumbres de la época, **«Las siete partidas»** y escribió varias obras de poesía. Además, reunió en su corte a los hombres más cultos de la época para estudiar, traducir y escribir textos en distintas áreas.

En el siglo XV, el **Renacimiento** comenzó una renovación de la poesía en España. Los romances, poemas narrativos épico-líricos que se cantan, tuvieron su origen en este siglo. Un autor que se destacó en la poesía lírica fue Jorge Manrique, quien escribió **«Las Coplas»,** una bella poesía escrita en memoria de la muerte de su padre. Esta poesía fue traducida al inglés por el poeta norteamericano Henry Wadsworth Longfellow.

Antonio de Nebrija fue el autor del primer libro de gramática española, escrito en 1492.

El Siglo de Oro (1535-1680)

En el siglo XVI aparece un género literario narrativo de tipo realista y satírico, conocido como «la novela picaresca». Describe la vida de un pícaro, una persona que trata de vivir sin trabajar. Es una sátira de la vida y de la sociedad de la época. La primera y la más famosa de las novelas picarescas es **«El Lazarillo de Tormes»,** escrita por un autor anónimo.

1. **Miguel de Cervantes** (1547-1616) fue el novelista principal de España y es quizás el más conocido. Su obra más famosa es **«Don Quijote de la Mancha»,** uno de los libros más leídos en todos los idiomas. Los personajes principales son don Quijote y Sancho Panza, su escudero y criado. Cervantes también escribió una colección de cuentos, las «Novelas ejemplares». Su obra literaria también incluye poesías y obras de teatro.

2. **Lope de Vega** (1562-1635) fue el dramaturgo más importante del Siglo de Oro. Escribió centenares de obras de teatro. Se le considera el padre del teatro español. Dos de sus obras teatrales más famosas son «Fuenteovejuna» y «Peribáñez y el Comendador de Ocaña».

3. **Tirso de Molina** (1584-1648) es famoso por haber creado el personaje de don Juan en su drama «El burlador de Sevilla».

4. **Pedro Calderón de la Barca** (1600-1681) fue el último de los grandes dramaturgos del Siglo de Oro. Fue autor de «La vida es sueño». Con su muerte se considera terminado el Siglo de Oro.

Siglos XVIII y XIX

Durante este período hubo poca producción literaria de valor en España. El estilo más popular imitaba en español a los escritores franceses. En España, el **«Romanticismo»** comenzó cuando muchos de los escritores que habían salido del país durante el reinado de Fernando VII, regresaron.

José Zorrilla (1817-1893) escribió obras de teatro inspiradas en las leyendas de España. Su obra principal, **«Don Juan Tenorio»,** se representa anualmente en los teatros de todo el mundo hispano el 2 de noviembre, el Día de los Muertos.

Otro movimiento literario, el **«Realismo»,** siguió al **Romanticismo.** El **Realismo** pretendía representar la realidad sin idealizarla.

Benito Pérez Galdós (1843-1920), fue el novelista principal del siglo XIX. Fue gran enemigo de la intolerancia religiosa y de la injusticia social. Una de sus mejores novelas, **«Doña Perfecta»,** ataca el fanatismo.

Armando Palacio Valdés (1853-1938) fue un novelista muy popular. Entre sus obras debe mencionarse **«José»** que trata de los pescadores de Asturias.

Vicente Blasco Ibáñez (1867-1928) escribió novelas sobre los campesinos de Valencia. Su obra principal es **«La barraca».** También escribió **«Los cuatro jinetes del Apocalipsis»** (*The Four Horsemen* *of the Apocalypse*), sobre la primera Guerra Mundial, y **«Sangre y arena»**, (*Blood and Sand*), sobre la corrida de toros.

La «Generación del 98»

La guerra contra los Estados Unidos en 1898 resultó un desastre para España. Como resultado de la guerra, muchos escritores y filósofos se dedicaron a examinar y modernizar la cultura del país. Estos escritores, que representan todos los géneros literarios, se conocen hoy con el título de la «Generación del 98».

1. **Miguel de Unamuno** (1864-1936) es la figura más dominante de la Generación del 98. Fue filósofo y ensayista. Su ensayo más conocido es **«Del sentimiento trágico de la vida»**.

2. **Jacinto Benavente** (1866-1954) fue un dramaturgo ganador del Premio Nobel de Literatura en 1922. Sus obras más importantes son **«La malquerida»** y **«Los intereses creados»**.

3. **Ramón Menéndez Pidal** (1869-1968) fue un erudito famoso. Hizo estudios profundos sobre la lengua y la literatura medievales de España.

4. **Pío Baroja** (1872-1956) fue un novelista. Entre sus obras más importantes se destacan **«El árbol de la ciencia»** y **«Camino de perfección»**.

5. **José Martínez Ruiz** (1873-1967), llamado Azorín, fue un gran ensayista y novelista. Entre sus obras principales deben mencionarse **«La voluntad»** y **«Los valores literarios»**.

6. **Antonio Machado** (1875-1939) fue uno de los mejores poetas de este siglo. Su obra **«Campos de Castilla»** es muy conocida y tiene por tema el paisaje austero de su país.

Otros autores modernos

1. **José Ortega y Gasset** (1883-1955) fue un filósofo y ensayista. Dos de sus obras principales son **«La rebelión de las masas»** y **«Meditaciones del Quijote»**.

La época de la Guerra Civil de España (1936-1939) afectó la literatura. Muchos escritores se opusieron a la dictadura que Franco estableció al terminar la guerra y salieron del país para vivir en el extranjero. Otros fueron encarcelados o condenados a muerte.

2. **Juan Ramón Jiménez** (1881-1958) además de ser poeta, escribió libros en prosa. El más conocido de sus libros en prosa es **«Platero y yo».** Ganó el Premio Nobel de Literatura en 1956.

3. **Gregorio Martínez Sierra** (1881-1947) fue un dramaturgo que logró crear notables personajes femeninos en sus obras dramáticas. Escribió **«Canción de cuna».**

4. **Federico García Lorca** (1898-1936) fue un notable poeta y dramaturgo. Escribió los dramas **«Bodas de sangre»** y **«La casa de Bernarda Alba»** que se representan mucho en los teatros hoy. Murió en circunstancias trágicas durante la Guerra Civil.

5. **Vicente Aleixandre** (1898-1984) fue ensayista y poeta. Escribió **«Pasión de la tierra».** Ganó el Premio Nobel de Literatura en 1977.

6. **Camilo José Cela** (1916-2002) fue novelista. Escribió **«La familia de Pascual Duarte».** Ganó el Premio Nobel de Literatura en 1989.

7. **Carmen Laforet** (1920-2004) fue una escritora que trata el tema de la España de la posguerra. Recibió un premio por su novela **«Nada»** que se publicó en 1946.

8. **Ana María Matute** (1925-2014) es una escritora contemporánea cuyas novelas han recibido muchos premios nacionales. Su obra incluye **«Fiesta al noroeste», «Los hijos muertos»** y **«Primera memoria».**

EXERCISE A. Identifique a cada escritor como novelista, dramaturgo, poeta o ensayista.

1. Miguel de Cervantes _____

2. Jacinto Benavente _____

3. José Ortega y Gasset _____

4. Pío Baroja _____

5. Antonio Machado _____

6. Lope de Vega _____

7. José Martínez Ruiz _____

8. Miguel de Unamuno _____

9. Pedro Calderón de la Barca _____

10. Juan Ramón Jiménez _____

EXERCISE B. Relacione ambas columnas. En el espacio provisto, escriba la letra de la obra asociada a cada escritor de la columna A.

A	B
_____ 1. Federico García Lorca	*a.* Don Quijote de la Mancha
_____ 2. Vicente Blasco Ibáñez	*b.* El burlador de Sevilla
_____ 3. Tirso de Molina	*c.* Bodas de sangre
_____ 4. Alfonso X	*d.* Doña Perfecta
_____ 5. Miguel de Cervantes	*e.* Sangre y arena
_____ 6. José Zorrilla	*f.* La vida es sueño
_____ 7. Jorge Manrique	*g.* Las siete partidas
_____ 8. Pedro Calderón de la Barca	*h.* Don JuanTenorio
_____ 9. Antonio de Nebrija	*i.* gramática de la lengua castellana
_____ 10. Benito Pérez Galdós	*j.* Coplas

EXERCISE C. Complete las siguientes oraciones.

1. El escudero de don Quijote se llamaba _____ .

2. La novela «José» fue escrita por _____ .

3. Un dramaturgo que ganó el Premio Nobel fue _____ .

4. La más famosa de las novelas picarescas es _____ .

5. El fundador del drama nacional español fue _____ .

6. La primera obra importante de la literatura española fue un poema épico, _____ .

7. El último de los grandes escritores del Siglo de Oro fue _____ .

8. _____ fue un rey español que compiló una colección de leyes.

9. _____ creó el personaje de don Juan.

10. Un drama que se representa en el Día de los Difuntos en todos los países hispanos es

_____ .

PINTURA

España tiene una tradición amplia y rica en la pintura. Hay cuadros de famosos pintores españoles en casi todos los museos importantes del mundo. El museo principal de España es el Prado en Madrid. Entre los pintores españoles más distinguidos y conocidos están los siguientes:

1. **Doménico Theotocopulos** (1541-1614), conocido como **el Greco,** era de origen griego pero vivió en Toledo en el siglo XVI. Sus obras tienen un profundo tono religioso. Su obra maestra es «El entierro del conde de Orgaz».

2. **Diego Velázquez** (1599-1660) es considerado el más importante de los pintores españoles. Fue pintor de cámara del Rey Felipe IV, y pintó muchos retratos de la familia real. Su obra maestra es «Las meninas». También pintó «La rendición de Bredá», llamada también «Las lanzas».

3. **Francisco Goya** (1746-1828) fue el pintor más importante de los siglos XVIII y XIX. Fue pintor de cámara del rey Carlos IV. En sus obras ataca la decadencia social y política de España. Entre sus obras principales deben mencionarse «Los fusilamientos del dos de mayo», y «Los caprichos».

4. **Joaquín Sorolla** (1863-1923) es el pintor de «Sol y color.» Pintó las costumbres y los trajes de las varias regiones de España. Muchos de sus cuadros se encuentran en el Museo de la Sociedad Hispánica, en Nueva York.

5. **José María Sert** (1876-1945) fue pintor de murales, muchos de los cuales se encuentran en el Rockefeller Center y en el Salón Sert del Hotel Waldorf-Astoria, en Nueva York.

6. **Pablo Picasso** (1881-1973) fue uno de los fundadores del cubismo, estilo de pintura en el cual figuras geométricas representan figuras humanas.

7. **Joan Miró** (1893-1983) fue uno de los mejores pintores del arte abstracto unido a la fantasía surrealista.

8. **Salvador Dalí** (1904-1989) fue uno de los fundadores del surrealismo en la pintura. El artista trató de pintar los pensamientos y los sueños.

LA ARQUITECTURA

Tanto los romanos como los moros y los españoles dejaron ejemplos de su arquitectura en España. De los romanos existen todavía puentes y acueductos, como el acueducto de Segovia. Los moros dejaron mezquitas, alcázares y el famoso palacio de la Alhambra, en Granada.

De la Edad Media se conservan muchas catedrales de estilo románico, como la de Santiago de Compostela, y de estilo gótico, como las catedrales de Burgos, Sevilla y Toledo.

De los tiempos posteriores hay que mencionar El Escorial, cuyo arquitecto principal fue Juan de Herrera (1530-1597). Un arquitecto famoso del siglo XVIII, José de Churriguera, introdujo el estilo barroco. El llamado «estilo churrigueresco» mezcla elementos góticos y barrocos. Un importante arquitecto modernista de principios del siglo XX fue el barcelonés Antonio Gaudí (1852-1926). La mayoría de sus obras se hallan por toda la ciudad de Barcelona. Sus edificios se destacan por líneas curvas y exhuberantes de piedra y de metal, adornados con pintorescos frescos y mosaicos. Entre sus obras principales están «La pedrera» y «El parque». Otra de sus creaciones es «La sagrada familia», una iglesia cuya construcción permanece incompleta aun actualmente. Aunque nunca se terminó de construir, la iglesia es un patrimonio de la humanidad (*world heritage site*) de Unesco. En 2010 el Papa Benedicto XVI consagró la iglesia y la nombró una basílica menor.

El arquitecto español contemporáneo más conocido es Santiago de Calatrava (1954-). Nacido en Valencia, es arquitecto, escultor e ingeniero. Su obra es prolífica e incluye puentes, museos, teatros y una variedad de edificios. Entre sus puentes y edificios más famosos, se debe mencionar la **Ciutat de les Arts i les Ciències**, en Valencia, España. De Calatrava también ha diseñado una estación central de tren en el *World Trade Center* de Nueva York, que se estrenará con la apertura de ese edificio.

MÚSICOS Y COMPOSITORES

1. **Isaac Albéniz** (1860-1909) compuso música para el piano. Entre sus composiciones están **«Iberia»** y **«El Albaicín».**

2. **Enrique Granados** (1867-1916) también compuso música para el piano. Escribió la ópera «Goyescas», basada en las obras de Goya.

3. **Manuel de Falla** (1876-1946) fue el más importante de los compositores españoles. Compuso «La vida breve» y «El amor brujo».

4. **José Iturbi** (1896-1980) fue un pianista y compositor famoso.

5. **Andrés Segovia** (1893-1987) fue uno de los guitarristas más famosos del mundo.

6. **Pablo Casals** (1876-1973) fue uno de los mejores violoncelistas del mundo.

Entre los cantantes del género operático que se han destacado por todo el mundo son las sopranos **Victoria de los Angeles** y **Monserrat Caballé,** y los tenores **Plácido Domingo, Alfredo Krauss** y **José Carreras.**

Muchos cantantes españoles de la música popular han logrado fama mundial. Entre ellos se encuentran **Sarita Montiel, Julio Iglesias, Raphael, Camilo Sexto,**

Rocío Jurado, Lolita, Joan Manuel Serrat y **Rocío Dúrcal.** También hay otros cantantes jóvenes españoles que han alcanzado éxitos internacionales como **Enrique Iglesias** y **Alejandro Sanz Rosario.**

EL BAILE

Casi cada región de España tiene sus propios bailes. De Andalucía viene un gran número de bailes, tales como el **bolero**, el **fandango**, el **jaleo**, y el **flamenco.** De Aragón viene la **jota**, de Cataluña la **sardana** y de Galicia la **muñeira.**

Muchos intérpretes del baile flamenco han logrado fama mundial. Entre ellos se hallan **Vicente Escudero, Carmen Amaya,** la pareja **Antonio** y **Rosario** y **Antonio Gades.**

INSTRUMENTOS

El instrumento típico de España es la guitarra. Además, en Galicia se emplea la gaita. La pandereta y las castañuelas son instrumentos de percusión que se emplean para acompañar la música y el baile.

CIENTÍFICOS

Varios científicos de fama mundial han venido de España. **Santiago Ramón y Cajal** (1852-1934) recibió el Premio Nobel de Medicina en 1906 por sus estudios sobre las funciones del sistema nervioso. **Juan de la Cierva** (1895-1936) inventó el autogiro, el precursor del helicóptero. **Severo Ochoa** (1905-1993) ganó el Premio Nobel de Medicina en 1959 por sus estudios de genética.

(EXERCISE D.)   **Identifique a cada una de las siguientes personas como bailarín, pintor, científico, arquitecto o músico.**

1. El Greco _____

2. Santiago Ramón y Cajal _____

3. Severo Ochoa _____

4. Vicente Escudero _____

5. José Iturbi _____

6. Santiago de Calatrava _____

7. Manuel de Falla _____

8. Juan de la Cierva _____

9. Antonio Gaudí _____

10. Francisco Goya _____

11. Juan de Herrera _____

12. Pablo Casals _____

13. Joaquín Sorolla _____

14. Andrés Segovia _____

15. Salvador Dalí _____

16. José de Churriguera _____

17. Enrique Granados _____

EXERCISE E. Relacione ambas columnas. En el espacio provisto, escriba la letra de la expresion asociada a cada artista de la columna A.

	A		B
_____	*1.* Francisco Goya	*a.*	pintor de «Las meninas»
_____	*2.* El Greco	*b.*	pintor de murales
_____	*3.* Diego Velázquez	*c.*	Doménico Theotocopulos
_____	*4.* Juan de la Cierva	*d.*	guitarrista
_____	*5.* Manuel de Falla	*e.*	violoncelista
_____	*6.* Isaac Albéniz	*f.*	«La vida breve»
_____	*7.* Pablo Picasso	*g.*	autogiro
_____	*8.* Pablo Casals	*h.*	Iberia
_____	*9.* Andrés Segovia	*i.*	cubismo
_____	*10.* José María Sert	*j.*	«Los fusilamientos del dos de mayo»

EXERCISE F. Complete las oraciones con un nombre o una palabra.

1. Diego Velázquez fue el pintor de cámara de _____ .

2. El _____ es un baile de Andalucía.

3. Santiago Ramón y Cajal fue un gran _____ español.

4. «La rendición de Bredá» se llama también _____ .

5. _____ compuso música basada en las obras de un gran pintor.

6. Para acompañar la música se emplean las _____ .

7. _____ fue un gran compositor español.

8. _____ pintó «El entierro del conde de Orgaz».

9. El baile regional de Cataluña es la _____ .

10. _____ fue el pintor de cámara de Carlos IV.

11. Muchas de las obras de _____ se hallan en el Waldorf-Astoria y el Rockefeller Center.

12. Los aragoneses bailan mucho la _____ .

13. _____ fue un famoso pintor surrealista.

14. _____ pintor el «sol y color» de España.

15. En Galicia se oye mucha música producida en la _____ .

CHAPTER

39

La geografía de Hispanoamérica

Al sur de los Estados Unidos, viven alrededor de trescientos setenta millones de personas que constituyen la llamada América Española, o sea lugares donde el idioma oficial es el español. La América Española consta de diecinueve países, situados en tres regiones distintas: (1) la América del Norte, (2) la América Central y las Antillas y (3) la América del Sur.

AMÉRICA DEL NORTE

a. Extensión y población

México está al sur de los Estados Unidos en la parte sur de la América del Norte. Los límites de México son: al norte el **Río Bravo** (nosotros lo llamamos el Río Grande), que separa a México del estado de Texas, al oeste el **Océano Pacífico**, al este el **Golfo de México**, y al sur **Guatemala** y **Belice**.

Su extensión territorial es la cuarta parte de la de los Estados Unidos. México tiene más de 112 millones de habitantes.

b. Montañas y volcanes

Hay dos cordilleras que cruzan a México de norte a sur: la **Sierra Madre Oriental** y la **Sierra Madre Occidental**. También hay varios volcanes, tales como el **Orizaba**, el **Popocatépetl**, el **Ixtaccíhuatl**, y el **Paracutín**.

c. Productos

La agricultura y la industria minera son importantes. Los minerales principales son la plata y el petróleo. Los productos agrícolas principales son el trigo, el maíz y el ganado.

d. Ciudades principales

La Ciudad de México (el Distrito Federal) es la capital y está situada en una meseta a unos 7.000 pies de altura. Fue la antigua capital de los aztecas, quienes la llamaban Tenochtitlán. Entre los puntos de interés principales de la capital se encuentran:

el **Castillo de Chapultepec,** actualmente un museo de historia colonial;

el **Palacio de Bellas Artes,** el teatro más grande del país, es también un museo con una colección impresionante de pinturas mexicanas;

la **Basílica de Guadalupe,** una iglesia fundada en honor de la Virgen de la Guadalupe, santa patrona del país;

el **Zócalo,** la plaza principal de la ciudad de México. A un lado de la plaza esta la Catedral de México, la catedral más grande y más antigua del continente;

el **Museo de Antropología,** donde se puede aprender la historia y admirar la cultura y el arte de las tribus indígenas de la región;

los **jardines flotantes de Xochimilco** y los templos y **pirámides de Teotihuacán,** situados a poca distancia de la capital;

Guadalajara, la segunda ciudad de México y el centro principal de la agricultura y la ganadería;

Tampico y Veracruz, puertos del Golfo de México. Tampico es el centro de la industria petrolera, Veracruz es un importante centro cultural y turístico;

Acapulco y Puerto Vallarta, puertos en el Océano Pacífico. Son famosos por sus playas hermosas;

Taxco, una ciudad antigua, un monumento nacional a la arquitectura colonial y el centro de la industria de la plata;

Chichén-Itzá, la antigua ciudad maya en el norte de la península de Yucatán donde hay notables ruinas mayas y toltecas.

EXERCISE A.   Complete las siguientes oraciones.

1. La capital de México fue fundada sobre la antigua ciudad azteca de _____ .

2. _____ es un producto importante de México.

3. _____ es una sierra del este de México.

4. El Orizaba y el Paricutín son _____ .

5. La segunda ciudad de México es _____ .

6. _____ y _____ son dos puertos del Golfo de México.

7. En los Estados Unidos el Río Bravo es conocido como el _____ .

8. _____ es una ciudad industrial de México.

9. El _____ es un hermoso teatro y museo en la Ciudad de México.

10. La santa patrona de México es _____ .

EXERCISE B. Relacione ambas columnas. En el espacio provisto, escriba la letra con la definición correspondiente a cada punto geográfico de la columna A.

A	B
_____ *1.* Zócalo	*a.* museo histórico
_____ *2.* Taxco	*b.* petróleo
_____ *3.* Xochimilco	*c.* ruinas
_____ *4.* Popocatépetl	*d.* plaza principal
_____ *5.* Chapultepec	*e.* Santa Patrona
_____ *6.* Tenochtitlán	*f.* ciudad pintoresca
_____ *7.* Acapulco	*g.* jardines flotantes
_____ *8.* Chichén-Itzá	*h.* capital azteca
_____ *9.* Tampico	*i.* playa
_____ *10.* Basílica de Guadalupe	*j.* volcán

LA AMÉRICA CENTRAL Y LAS ANTILLAS

La América Central

1. Guatemala está situada al sur de México y es un país de montañas y de lagos. Su topografía variada le proporciona un clima variado que le ha permitido desarrollar una agricultura también muy variada. Sus productos principales incluyen las bananas, el café, las maderas finas y el chicle que se usa para fabricar la goma de mascar (*chewing gum*). Guatemala es el país de mayor población de la América Central y el que tiene el mayor porcentaje de indígenas puros (40% de la población). Guatemala fue la sede de los mayas, la civilización precolombina más avanzada. Su capital es la **Ciudad de Guatemala.**

2. Honduras es el país más montañoso de Centroamérica. Tiene un clima muy variado. También es un país agrícola. Sus productos principales son las bananas, el café, el tabaco, la caña de azúcar y las maderas finas. La capital es **Tegucigalpa.**

3. El Salvador es la nación más pequeña de Centroamérica y es el único país que no limita con el Océano Atlántico. Tiene más de 350 ríos, muchos lagos y lagunas. Su producto más importante es el café. También produce algodón y caña de azúcar. La capital es **San Salvador.**

4. Nicaragua es la república más grande de Centroamérica. Es también un país agrícola y produce maíz, algodón, café, plátano, caucho y maderas finas. Es el país de mayor producción ganadera de Centroamérica. Su capital es **Managua.**

5. **Costa Rica** es el único país de América que no tiene ejército. Ha sido tradicionalmente un país democrático y ha fomentado la educación pública. Sus principales productos de exportación son el café y los plátanos, aunque produce también cacao, caña de azúcar, papas y una gran variedad de frutas. Su capital es **San José.**

6. **Panamá** es el país más al sur de América Central. El famoso **Canal de Panamá** atraviesa el país y conecta los océanos Atlántico y Pacífico. Su producto principal es el plátano. La capital del país es la **Ciudad de Panamá** y el puerto principal es **Balboa** en la Zona del Canal.

Las Antillas

Las Antillas son un grupo de islas en el Mar Caribe que incluye a Cuba, la República Dominicana y Puerto Rico.

1. **Cuba** es la isla más grande de las Antillas. Es conocida como «la Perla de las Antillas». Produce caña de azúcar y tabaco. Su capital es **La Habana.**

2. **La República Dominicana** comparte la isla de La Española con Haití, una república de habla francesa. Su capital es **Santo Domingo,** la ciudad más antigua de América, fundada en 1496. Es un país agrícola y sus productos principales incluyen la caña de azúcar, el cacao, el café, el plátano y el maíz.

3. **Puerto Rico** es hoy día un Estado Libre Asociado (*Commonwealth*) de los Estados Unidos. La isla, llamada Borinquén por los indígenas, fue descubierta por Cristóbal Colón en 1493 y nombrada **San Juan Bautista.** Su capital, **San Juan,** fue fundada en 1508 por Ponce de León, el primer gobernador de la isla. Es un puerto comercial muy activo. La ciudad de San Juan aun conserva fortificaciones y hermosos edificios de la época colonial española.

EXERCISE C. Relacione ambas columnas. En el espacio provisto, escriba la letra con la capital para cada país de la columna A.

A

_____ *1.* Nicaragua

_____ *2.* Puerto Rico

_____ *3.* Guatemala

_____ *4.* Costa Rica

_____ *5.* El Salvador

_____ *6.* Panamá

_____ *7.* Honduras

_____ *8.* República Dominicana

_____ *9.* Cuba

B

a. San José

b. Ciudad de Panamá

c. Santo Domingo

d. Tegucigalpa

e. La Habana

f. San Salvador

g. San Juan

h. Managua

i. Ciudad de Guatemala

EXERCISE D. Complete las siguientes. oraciones.

1. La república más grande de la América Central es _____ .

2. La república más pequeña de la América Central es _____ .

3. Un producto importante de Guatemala es _____ .

4. «La perla de las Antillas» es un nombre que se le da a _____ .

5. El plátano es un producto importante de _____ .

6. _____ es el país que conecta a la América del Norte con la América del Sur.

7. La Española es una isla compartida por dos naciones: Haití y _____ .

8. Una isla de las Antillas que mantiene un estado libre asociado con los Estados Unidos es

_____ .

9. Para fabricar la goma de mascar se usa el _____ .

10. El azúcar y el tabaco son productos importantes de _____ .

La América del Sur

a. Montañas y picos

Los Andes cruzan el continente de norte a sur, a lo largo de la costa occidental. El **Chimborazo** y el **Cotopaxi** son dos volcanes localizados en los Andes, en el territorio del Ecuador. El **Aconcagua,** el pico más alto de los Andes y de toda la América del Sur, está situado en Argentina.

b. Ríos y lagos

El **Amazonas,** que atraviesa Brasil, es el segundo río del mundo en longitud. En los países de habla española los ríos principales son el **Magdalena** (en Colombia), el **Orinoco** (en Venezuela) y el **Plata** (en Argentina). Entre Argentina y Brasil se encuentra la famosa **catarata** (waterfalls) del **Iguazú.** Entre Bolivia y Perú está el lago **Titicaca,** el lago navegable más alto del mundo.

c. Llanuras (*Plains*)

Las **pampas** son grandes llanuras en Argentina, donde se producen trigo y ganado. Aquí se halla el ombú, árbol típico de la pampa. Aquí también vive el gaucho. En Venezuela las llanuras se llaman llanos. En Colombia y el Brasil se encuentran las selvas, densos bosques de gran extensión.

d. Clima

En la América del Sur las estaciones ocurren en orden opuesto a las nuestras. Cuando nosotros tenemos el verano aquí, allí tienen el invierno, y viceversa.

e. Población

La población de los países hispanos de América del Sur consiste en varias razas, que se originan en Europa, África y las tribus indígenas.

f. Países del Este

1. **Argentina** se extiende desde el **Chaco,** en el norte, hasta el extremo sur del continente. Está separada de Chile por los Andes. En la frontera entre Chile y Argentina hay una gran estatua, llamada «el **Cristo de los Andes**», que conmemora el arreglo pacífico de una disputa entre los dos países. Los productos principales de Argentina son la carne, la lana y el trigo. Su capital, **Buenos Aires,** es la ciudad hispana más grande de Sudamérica. Los habitantes de Buenos Aires son conocidos como «porteños».

2. **Uruguay** es el país hispano más pequeño de Sudamérica. Como Argentina, sus productos principales son la carne, la lana y los cereales. Su capital es **Montevideo.**

3. **Paraguay** no tiene puerto de mar, pero puede comunicarse con la costa por medio del río Paraná. Produce yerba mate, un té muy popular allí, y quebracho, una madera muy dura usada para curtir el cuero. Su capital es **Asunción.**

g. Países de los Andes

1. **Chile** se encuentra entre los Andes y el Océano Pacífico. De norte a sur se extiende unas 3.000 millas. Es el país más largo y más estrecho del continente. Sus productos principales son el cobre y el salitre (*nitrates*). Las ciudades principales son **Santiago**, la capital, y **Valparaíso,** el puerto principal.

2. **Bolivia** es el único país de Sudamérica que no tiene contacto con el mar. Para exportar sus productos depende de los países vecinos. Produce mucho estaño (*tin*). Su capital, **La Paz,** es la capital más alta del mundo (a más de 2 millas sobre el nivel del mar).

3. **Perú** fue el centro del gobierno de los incas, que establecieron su capital en **Cuzco.** Hoy día, la capital y ciudad principal es **Lima.** En Lima se encuentra la universidad más antigua de la América del Sur, la **Universidad de San Marcos,** fundada en 1551. **El Callao,** cerca de Lima, es el puerto principal. Perú tiene mucha riqueza minera. También exporta lana (de alpaca) y guano, un fertilizante, que se usa en la agricultura.

4. **Ecuador** está en el centro de la **Zona Tórrida.** La línea geográfica llamada «el ecuador» cruza el país. Aquí se producen los sombreros de jipijapa, que nosotros llamamos «Panama hats». También se produce mucho cacao, del cual se hace chocolate. Las ciudades principales son **Quito,** la capital, y **Guayaquil,** el puerto principal.

5. **Colombia** está en el noroeste del continente. Tiene puertos en los dos mares: el mar Caribe y el Océano Pacífico. Su capital es **Bogotá.** **Medellín** es el centro de la industria del café. Los productos principales del país son el café, el petróleo, el platino (*platinum*) y las esmeraldas.

6. **Venezuela** está en el norte. Es la patria del Libertador, **Simón Bolívar.** Exporta mucho petróleo. Su capital es **Caracas,** y su puerto principal es **La Guaira.**

EXERCISE E.   Combine cada uno de los países en la columna A con su respectiva capital en la columna B.

A	B
_____ 1. Chile	*a.* La Paz
_____ 2. Venezuela	*b.* Bogotá
_____ 3. Perú	*c.* Quito
_____ 4. Ecuador	*d.* Asunción
_____ 5. Colombia	*e.* Santiago
_____ 6. Bolivia	*f.* Lima
_____ 7. Uruguay	*g.* Buenos Aires
_____ 8. Paraguay	*h.* Montevideo
_____ 9. Argentina	*i.* Caracas

EXERCISE F. Relacione ambas columnas. En el espacio provisto, escriba la letra de los productos correspondientes a cada país de la columna A.

A	B
_____ 1. Venezuela	a. salitre, cobre
_____ 2. Bolivia	b. petróleo
_____ 3. Ecuador	c. esmeraldas, platino, café
_____ 4. Chile	d. sombreros de jipijapa
_____ 5. Paraguay	e. estaño
_____ 6. Colombia	f. carne, trigo, lana
_____ 7. Argentina	g. yerba mate

EXERCISE G. Complete las siguientes oraciones.

1. Los habitantes de Buenos Aires son conocidos como _____ .

2. _____ es un país sudamericano con puertos en dos mares.

3. La ciudad más grande de Sudamérica es _____ .

4. Cuzco fue la capital antigua de los _____ .

5. El país más estrecho de la América del Sur es _____ .

6. _____ es una estatua en los Andes entre Chile y Argentina.

7. El país hispano más pequeño de Sudamérica es _____ .

8. San Marcos es el nombre de una _____ antigua de Perú.

9. Del cacao se hace _____ .

10. El único país sudamericano que no tiene contacto con el mar es _____ .

La historia de Hispanoamérica

CIVILIZACIONES INDÍGENAS

Antes de la llegada de los españoles al «Nuevo Mundo», varias civilizaciones indígenas ya existían allí. La civilización de los **mayas** era la más avanzada. Su civilización floreció del siglo III a mediados del siglo XVI. Ocupaban un territorio bastante extenso que hoy incluye la península de Yucatán, Belice, Guatemala y partes de Honduras y El Salvador. Los mayas lograron un desarrollo increíble en la arquitectura, la astronomía y las matemáticas. Tenían su calendario y podían calcular con mucha precisión la duración de un año solar. Fueron la única cultura indígena que desarrolló una forma avanzada de escritura.

Los **aztecas** desarrollaron su imperio en México durante el siglo XV. Construyeron su capital, Tenochtitlán, en lo que hoy es la Ciudad de México. Sus ciudades eran tan grandes como las ciudades europeas de la época. La religión dominaba todos los aspectos de su vida. Edificaron enormes templos en forma de pirámides donde celebraban ceremonias religiosas que incluían sacrificios humanos. Las esculturas aztecas son muy detalladas. La más famosa es La Piedra del Sol, un calendario circular que representa la superficie del sol.

Los **incas** desarrollaron su imperio en los Andes. Se extendió desde lo que es hoy el Ecuador hasta el centro de Chile, incluyendo partes de Bolivia y la Argentina. El centro de la civilización inca estaba en el Perú. Tenían un fuerte y estructurado sistema político y social. Su ejército estaba muy bien organizado y tenían un sistema de caminos que comunicaba todos los puntos del imperio con la capital, Cuzco. En la capital construyeron grandes palacios, templos y edificios del gobierno. Según una leyenda, el emperador de los incas descendía de los dioses. Todas las tierras pertenecían al gobierno. Aunque no desarrollaron la escritura, tenían un sistema especial para escribir y contar: hacían nudos en cuerdas de varios colores y tamaños. Esto era llamado un quipú. Usaban la llama y la alpaca para el transporte y también les servían de alimento y proveían lana para la ropa. Hablaban el quechua, una lengua que se habla aun hoy en el Perú y algunas zonas de Bolivia, el Ecuador y el norte de Chile.

Otras de las civilizaciones indígenas que existían antes de la llegada de los españoles fueron los **caribes,** en las Antillas, los **chibchas** en la región andina de Colombia, los **guaraníes** en Paraguay, y los **araucanos** que vivían en la costa de Chile pero emigraron a la Argentina cuando llegaron los españoles.

DESCUBRIMIENTO, EXPLORACIÓN Y CONQUISTA

1. **Cristóbal Colón** salió de España con tres barcos, la Niña, la Pinta y la Santa María. El 12 de octubre de 1492 descubrió la isla de San Salvador (que hoy se llama Watlings Island). La fecha de este descubrimiento se celebra en todo el mundo hispano como el Día de la Raza.

2. **Vasco Núñez de Balboa** cruzó el istmo de Panamá y en 1513 descubrió el Océano Pacífico, que él llamó el Mar del Sur.

3. **Hernando de Soto** descubrió el río Misisipí en 1541.

4. **Juan Ponce de León** descubrió la Florida en 1513.

5. **Francisco Vázquez de Coronado** exploró el sudoeste de los Estados Unidos, y descubrió el Gran Cañón en 1540.

6. **Álvar Núñez Cabeza de Vaca** exploró Nuevo México, Texas y parte de Kansas de 1528 a 1536.

7. **Fernando de Magallanes** fue un navegante portugués que trató de dar la vuelta al mundo. En 1520, descubrió y pasó por el Estrecho que lleva su nombre. Murió durante el viaje y Juan Sebastián Elcano, un español, completó el viaje.

8. **Hernán Cortés** conquistó México, venciendo a los aztecas y a su emperador, Cuauhtémoc en 1521.

9. **Francisco Pizarro** conquistó Perú. Venció a los incas y a su rey, Atahualpa. Fundó la ciudad de Lima, que él llamó «Ciudad de los Reyes».

10. **Pedro de Valdivia** conquistó Chile (1541), luchando con los araucanos, una tribu de indígenas muy feroces.

GOBIERNO DE LAS COLONIAS

Las colonias eran gobernadas por el Consejo (Council) de Indias, un grupo de hombres nombrados por el rey. La Casa de Contratación dirigía el comercio colonial. Las colonias estaban divididas en cuatro virreinatos (*viceroyalties*), cada uno gobernado por un virrey (*viceroy*). Los virreinatos eran:

Nueva España (México, Antillas, y la América Central).

Nueva Granada (territorio que ocupan actualmente Colombia, Panamá, Venezuela, y el Ecuador).

Perú (territorio que ocupan actualmente Perú, Bolivia, y Chile).

Río de la Plata (Argentina, Uruguay y Paraguay).

LOS MISIONEROS

1. **Fray Junípero Serra** (1713-1784) estableció varias misiones en California.
2. **Fray Bartolomé de las Casas** (1474-1566), el apóstol de los indios, luchó en favor de los indios.

LA INDEPENDENCIA (REVOLUCIÓN CONTRA ESPAÑA)

1. **Francisco Miranda** (1750-1816), de Venezuela, fue el primero de los revolucionarios.
2. **Simón Bolívar** (1783-1830), llamado «El Libertador», es la figura principal de la revolución hispanoamericana. Ganó la libertad de Venezuela, Colombia y el Ecuador.
3. **José de San Martín** (1778-1850) ganó la libertad de la Argentina, Chile y el Perú.
4. **Bernardo O'Higgins** (1778-1842), un general chileno, ayudó a San Martín en la lucha en Chile.
5. **Antonio José de Sucre** (1795-1830) venció a los españoles en la batalla de Ayacucho, en 1824, la última batalla de la revolución.
6. **El padre Miguel Hidalgo** (1753-1811), cura del pueblo mexicano de Dolores, inició el movimiento por la independencia en México con el «Grito de Dolores».
7. **El padre José Morelos** (1765-1815), también sacerdote, continuó el trabajo comenzado en México por Hidalgo.
8. **José Martí** (1853-1895) fue un patriota y poeta cubano que luchó por la independencia de Cuba.

DICTADORES

En muchos países las guerras por la independencia fueron seguidas de una época de dictaduras. Algunos ejemplos incluyen:

1. **Agustín de Iturbide** se declaró Emperador de México (Agustín I) en 1822. La monarquía fue derrocada (*overthrown*) un año después, en 1823.
2. **Maximiliano de Austria** (1864-1867), fue enviado por Napoleón III a ser emperador de México. Fue ejecutado por las fuerzas republicanas de Benito Juárez, un patriota mexicano. Los mexicanos consideran a Juárez el «Abraham Lincoln de México».
3. **Porfirio Díaz** fue dictador de México en dos ocasiones: de 1877 a 1880 y de 1884 a 1911.

También hubo dictaduras en otros países en distintas épocas. Entre los dictadores se encuentran a:

4. **Juan Manuel de Rosas,** Argentina, de 1829 a 1852;
5. **Juan Perón,** Argentina, de 1943 a 1955;
6. **José Gaspar de Francia**, Paraguay, de 1814 a 1840;
7. **Vicente Gómez,** Venezuela, de 1908 a 1935;
8. **Fulgencio Batista,** Cuba, en dos ocasiones: 1934 a 1944 y 1952 a 1958;
9. **Los Somoza** (**Anastasio** y sus hijos **Luis** y **Anastasio**), Nicaragua, de 1936 a 1979;
10. **Alfredo Stroessner**, Paraguay, de 1954 a 1989;
11. **Manuel Noriega**, Panamá, de 1983 a 1989;
12. **Fidel Castro,** Cuba, en 1959. Su dictadura continúa hoy día, bajo la dirección de su hermano Raúl.

RELACIONES INTERNACIONALES

El Panamericanismo es un movimiento que trata de fomentar (*promote*) la paz, el comercio, y la ayuda mutua entre los Estados Unidos y las repúblicas de la América Latina. Con este propósito se fundó la Unión Panamericana en 1910. En 1948 se cambió el nombre a la Organización de Estados Americanos u O.E.A. (O.A.S., por su siglas en inglés). Se celebra el Día Panamericano cada año el 14 de abril.

La Política (*Policy*) del Buen Vecino es una política de amistad hacia los otros países americanos. Fue iniciada por el presidente Franklin D. Roosevelt.

El Cuerpo de Paz (*Peace Corps*) y la Alianza Para el Progreso (*Alliance for Progress*) fueron iniciados por el presidente John F. Kennedy. El Cuerpo de la Paz manda maestros y técnicos a otros países para ayudar a los habitantes a mejorar su condición. La Alianza Para el Progreso ofrecía dinero y ayuda técnica a los países latinoamericanos que querían hacer más democrático su gobierno. El programa no tuvo el éxito esperado y ha sido reemplazado por otros métodos de ayuda económica.

En 1994 entró en vigor el Tratado de Libre Comercio de la América del Norte (TLC; en inglés, North American Free Trade Agreement–NAFTA). Este acuerdo estableció una sola zona comercial y una fuerza laboral entre el Canadá, los Estados Unidos y México.

EXERCISE A. Escoja la palabra o expresión que complete correctamente cada enunciado.

1. Atahualpa fue el rey de los (incas, mayas, aztecas, araucanos).

_____

2. Colombia formaba parte del virreinato de (Nueva España, Nueva Granada, Perú, Río de la Plata).

_____

3. Ciudad de los Reyes es el nombre que Pizarro dio a la ciudad de (México, Buenos Aires, Caracas, Lima).

_____

4. El Libertador de la Argentina, de Chile y del Perú fue (Miranda, Martí, San Martín, Morelos).

_____

5. El jefe de las fuerzas que vencieron a Maximiliano fue (Benito Juárez, Porfirio Díaz, Miguel Hidalgo, Bernardo O'Higgins).

_____

6. El Día Panamericano se celebra (el dos de mayo, el catorce de abril, el doce de octubre, el cinco de mayo).

_____

7. «La Política del Buen Vecino» fue iniciada por (Perón, Roosevelt, Castro, Batista).

_____

8. El patriota que luchó por la independencia de Cuba fue (Martí, Batista, O'Higgins, Sucre).

_____

9. Una libre zona comercial fue establecida por (la Organización de Estados Americanos, la Política del Buen Vecino, el Cuerpo de Paz, el Tratado de libre comercio de la América del Norte).

_____

10. La Florida fue descubierta por (Hernando de Soto, Juan Ponce de León, Vasco Núñez de Balboa, Francisco Vásquez de Coronado).

_____

EXERCISE B. Relacione ambas columas. En el espacio provisto, escriba la letra con los lugares correspondientes a cada explorador o conquistador de la columna A.

A		B	
_____	1. Chile	*a.*	Vasco Núñez de Balboa
_____	2. San Salvador	*b.*	Hernando de Soto
_____	3. el Perú	*c.*	Juan Ponce de León
_____	4. México	*d.*	FranciscoVásquez de Coronado
_____	5. la Florida	*e.*	Álvar Núñez Cabeza deVaca
_____	6. Estrecho de Magallanes	*f.*	Hernán Cortés
_____	7. Nuevo México, Texas y Kansas	*g.*	Pedro deValdivia
_____	8. Océano Pacífico	*h.*	Fernando de Magallanes
_____	9. río Misisipí	*i.*	Cristóbal Colón
_____	10. el Gran Cañón	*j.*	Francisco Pizarro

EXERCISE C. Relacione ambas columnas. En el espacio provisto, escriba la letra de la expresión con que se asocia cada nombre de la columna B.

A		B	
_____	1. Bartolomé de las Casas	*a.*	«el Libertador»
_____	2. Simón Bolívar	*b.*	Maximiliano de Austria
_____	3. Miguel Hidalgo	*c.*	dictador mexicano
_____	4. Napoleón III	*d.*	«apóstol de los indios»
_____	5. Juan Manuel de Rosas	*e.*	dictador cubano
_____	6. Fray Junípero Serra	*f.*	batalla de Ayacucho
_____	7. Cristóbal Colón	*g.*	fundó misiones en California
_____	8. Fidel Castro	*h.*	la Pinta
_____	9. Porfirio Díaz	*i.*	dictador argentino
_____	10. Antonio José de Sucre	*j.*	Grito de Dolores

EXERCISE D. Lea las siguientes oraciones. Indique si son ciertas o falsas. Si son falsas, corríjalas.

1. Las colonias españolas estaban divididas en cinco virreinatos.

_____

2. El Gran Cañón fue descubierto por Juan Ponce de León.

_____

3. El quechua es una tribu india.

_____

4. Cuzco era la capital de los incas.

_____

5. Chichén-Itzá fue la ciudad principal de los aztecas.

_____

6. La gran época de la colonización española fue el siglo XIV.

_____

7. Fulgencio Batista fue dictador de la Argentina.

_____

8. La civilización indígena más avanzada fue la de los araucanos.

_____

9. Los aztecas celebraban ceremonias religiosas en las pirámides.

_____

10. El emperador azteca derrotado por Cortés se llamaba Atahualpa.

_____

11. Moctezuma fue el último rey de los incas.

_____

12. La Piedra del Sol es el calendario de los mayas.

_____

13. El famoso «Grito de Dolores» fue dado por José Morelos.

_____

14. El misionero que luchó más que ningún otro en favor de los indios se llamaba Fray Junípero Serra.

_____

15. Tenochtitlán fue la capital de los aztecas.

_____

EXERCISE E.   **Indentifique a cada personaje histórico como conquistador, descubridor, dictador o patriota.**

1. José Antonio de Sucre   _____

2. Hernán Cortés   _____

3. Vasco Núñez de Balboa   _____

4. Francisco Pizarro   _____

5. Juan Manuel de Rosas   _____

6. Cristóbal Colón   _____

7. Benito Juárez   _____

8. Bernardo O'Higgins   _____

9. Fidel Castro   _____

10. José Martí   _____

11. Miguel Hidalgo   _____

12. Fernando Magallanes   _____

13. José de San Martín   _____

14. Simón Bolívar   _____

15. Francisco Vásquez de Coronado   _____

La vida y las costumbres de Hispanoamérica

Las costumbres y tradiciones hispanoamericanas representan la mezcla de la influencia española e indígena. En las Antillas y en los países del Caribe se nota también la influencia africana, especialmente en la música y los bailes.

TIPOS PINTORESCOS

Todavía se ven tipos tradicionales en varias regiones de Hispanoamérica. Es más notable en las regiones donde se cría el ganado y el caballo es el medio de transporte principal. Allí se encuentran los vaqueros que tienen nombres distintos en diferentes países. En Venezuela y Colombia se les llama «llaneros», y en Argentina y Uruguay se les llama «gauchos».

El charro es el vaquero de México. Vestido de su traje tradicional es el jinete típico mexicano. La china poblana es su compañera. Su vestido típico representa los colores de la bandera mexicana: una falda ancha y larga de color rojo y verde y una blusa de color blanco.

Los mariachis son grupos de músicos y cantantes ambulantes que tocan la música mariachi del estado de Jalisco.

ROPA TÍPICA

1. El **poncho** es una capa que usan los gauchos para protegerse del frío y de la lluvia.
2. El **sarape** es una especie de manta de colores vivos, hecha de lana o de algodón. Es muy popular en México y los países centroamericanos.
3. El **rebozo** es un chal (*shawl*) muy popular entre las mujeres mexicanas y centroamericanas.
4. Los **huaraches** son sandalias populares en México.
5. El famoso **sombrero** de jipijapa (*Panama hats*) no se fabrica en Panamá, sino en el Ecuador.

COMIDAS Y BEBIDAS

Por lo general, las comidas reflejan una mezcla de las culturas española, indígena y africana. Sus ingredientes principales son el maíz, el frijol, el plátano, la carne y la papa. El tamal es un plato muy popular y casi todos los países tienen su propia versión. Es una masa de maíz fresco molido o de harina de maíz que se cuece al vapor dentro de una hoja de maíz o de plátano. Puede rellenarse con pollo, cerdo, carne de res, legumbres, garbanzos, etc. En México se hace la tortilla de maíz y sirve de base en la preparación de los tacos y las enchiladas.

Los frijoles (llamados «habichuelas» en Puerto Rico) son otro plato popular. Se comen en diversos platos típicos. Los frijoles negros son muy populares en el Caribe y en Venezuela. Cuando se preparan con arroz, en Cuba se les llama «moros y cristianos». Los frijoles pintos o colorados se preparan refritos en México y en potajes con jamón o carne y papas en otros países.

Además del café, que se bebe en todas partes, en Argentina y Paraguay también se bebe mate, que se hace de la yerba mate. Se bebe de una calabaza (*gourd*) por medio de un tubo llamado «bombilla».

DÍAS DE FIESTA

La religión católica ha tenido un papel muy importante en la historia y en la vida diaria de los países hispanoamericanos. Las Navidades se celebran de una forma u otra en todas partes. En México empiezan con las «posadas», que consisten en visitas a los vecinos durante los nueve días anteriores a la Nochebuena. En la fiesta que sigue a las posadas, la gente baila alrededor de una piñata (una figura de barro vivamente decorada, que contiene dulces y regalos). Después rompen la piñata y cogen los dulces. Otras fiestas religiosas católicas como la Semana Santa y el Día de Todos los Santos (el primero de noviembre) se celebran en casi todos los países.

Cada país tiene su fiesta nacional que conmemora la fecha en que comenzó la lucha por la independencia de España. Por ejemplo, en México el 16 de septiembre es la fecha de la fiesta nacional que conmemora el principio de la rebelión contra España y el 5 de mayo conmemora la lucha contra Francia y Maximiliano.

Dos días de fiesta que se celebran en toda la América Hispana son el Día de la Raza que corresponde a Columbus Day (el 12 de octubre) y el Día Panamericano, que se celebra el 14 de abril.

LA EDUCACIÓN

Hay variedad y diferencias en los sistemas de educación de los países de Hispanoamérica. En la mayoría de estos países, es común para los estudiantes usar uniformes.

En México, la educación se divide en tres etapas: primaria (grados 1 a 6), secundaria (grados 7 a 9) y preparatoria (grados 10 a 12). La educación es obligatoria y gratuita en las escuelas públicas.

La educación en Guatemala es gratuita y obligatoria por seis años. A pesar de esto, muchos estudiantes dejan la escuela antes, especialmente en las partes rurales del país, donde habita la población indígena.

En Honduras, la educación es gratuita y obligatoria por seis años. La falta de escuelas en el país y los costos de matrícula, uniformes y transportación dificultan el acceso a la educación de muchos niños.

La educación nacional en El Salvador consiste en uno o dos años de kindergarten, nueve años de educación básica (primer ciclo: grados 1 a 3, segundo ciclo: grados 4 a 6 y tercer ciclo: grados 7 a 9); dos años de educación media y un mínimo de cinco años de universidad, aunque coexisten otros sistemas educativos.

La educación en Nicaragua es gratuita para los ciudadanos; la educación primaria es obligatoria. Desde 1869, la educación en Costa Rica es gratuita y obligatoria para todos los ciudadanos. La inversión de ese país en la educación ha producido resultados positivos: más de cuatro mil escuelas, muchos profesores y un 95 porciento de alfabetismo en la población con edades de quince años o más.

En Panamá, la educación es obligatoria durante los primeros siete años de la educación primaria y los tres años de la escuela media. Más del 90 porciento de los panameños saben leer y escribir.

Cuba cuenta con un sistema educativo gratuito en todos los niveles. El gobierno provee también uniformes, comida y demás gastos. La educación primaria dura seis años y la secundaria se divide en educación secundaria básica y educación secundaria preuniversitaria.

En la República Dominicana la educación primaria es obligatoria y gratuita, pero no es obligatoria en el nivel secundario. Se divide en cuatro niveles: inicial (3 a 6 años de edad), básico (6 a 14 años de edad), medio (14 a 18 años de edad) y superior (mayor de 18 años de edad). El nivel básico es obligatorio.

La instrucción en Puerto Rico es obligatoria entre los 5 y los 18 años de edad, o sea, la escuela primaria y secundaria. Los estudiantes pueden asistir a escuelas públicas o privadas.

Argentina cuenta con dos sistemas educativos de cuatro niveles: el inicial (kindergarten), el primario, el secundario y el superior. La educación es obligatoria para todos los niños en ambos sistemas. Argentina financia su sistema educativo a través de los impuestos.

Uruguay ha alcanzado el mayor nivel de alfabetismo. Su sistema educativo es universal y gratuito. La educación primaria requiere un período de instrucción de nueve años, que comienza a los seis años de edad y termina a los quince. La educación secundaria es también gratuita y obligatoria, y consiste en seis años de instrucción, que se divide en dos ciclos de tres años cada uno: el primer ciclo es básico y el segundo es preparatorio para la universidad.

En Paraguay, la educación es obligatoria para los niños de siete a trece años de edad. Aunque la educación es gratuita, mucho alumnos abandonan los estudios. En Chile la educación primaria y secundaria es gratuita y obligatoria, y consiste en tres niveles: básico, para niños de seis a trece años de edad; medio, para estudiantes de 14 a 17 años de edad y superior o universitario.

En Bolivia, el gobierno estableció un sistema obligatorio que incluye un ciclo primario de cinco años (que comienza a los siete años de edad), seguido de un ciclo intermedio y otro secundario. Es necesario completar estos ciclos para matricularse en la universidad.

La educación en Perú es gratuita y obligatoria para estudiantes de siete a dieciséis años de edad. El sistema educativo de Ecuador requiere que los niños asistan a la escuela hasta lograr un nivel de aprendizaje básico, por lo general, nueve años de instrucción. La educación es gratuita, pero las familias tienen que pagar algunos gastos, como la transportación.

En Colombia, el sistema educativo se divide en cuatro etapas: educación preescolar, educación primaria (de 6 a 12 años de edad), educación media (de 12 a 16 años de edad) y educación superior o universitaria. Las etapas primaria y media son obligatorias. La educación primaria es gratuita para todos los ciudadanos. El gobierno colombiano paga 85 porciento de los gastos en el nivel primario, 60 porciento en el medio y 40 porciento en el nivel superior.

En Venezuela, la educación básica (para estudiantes de 6 a 15 años de edad) es obligatoria y gratuita. La educación secundaria dura dos años y es gratuita, pero no es obligatoria.

> **EXERCISE A.**   Complete las siguientes oraciones.

1. Un alimento mexicano es _____ .

2. Los sombreros de jipijapa se fabrican en _____ .

3. La calabaza y la bombilla se usan para beber _____ .

4. Las mujeres mexicanas llevan en los hombros un _____ .

5. Las _____ y las _____ son dos platos que se hacen de maíz.

6. El plato cubano que se prepara con arroz y frijoles se concoce como _____ .

7. En Venezuela el «cowboy» se llama _____ .

8. Las _____ son sandalias populares en México.

9. Los mexicanos celebran el 5 de mayo para conmemorar su independencia de _____ .

10. Para protegerse de la lluvia, el gaucho lleva un _____ .

> **EXERCISE B.**   Relacione ambas columnas. En el espacio provisto, escriba la letra con la expresión correspondiente a cada punto de la columna A.

	A		B
_____	1. taco	a.	cantante
_____	2. 16 de septiembre	b.	manta
_____	3. mariachi	c.	Columbus Day
_____	4. sarape	d.	alimento mexicano
_____	5. china poblana	e.	bebida
_____	6. 14 de abril	f.	Día Panamericano
_____	7. Día de la Raza	g.	pintos
_____	8. yerba mate	h.	Panama hat
_____	9. sombrero de jipijapa	i.	charro
_____	10. una clase de frijol	j.	día de la independencia mexicana

> **EXERCISE C.**   Lea las siguientes oraciones. Indique si son ciertas of falsas. Si son falsas, corríjalas.

1. Los gauchos son los vaqueros de Venezuela y Colombia.

   _____

2. Se celebran las posadas en todos los países de la América Latina.

   _____

3. La china poblana es la compañera del charro.

_____

4. El sarape es una manta usada por los chilenos.

_____

5. Se usan una calabaza y una bombilla para beber la yerba mate.

_____

6. Una piñata es una figura de barro.

_____

7. Se celebran las posadas en todos los países de Hispanoamérica.

_____

8. El mariachi lleva un rebozo.

_____

9. El 16 de septiembre es el Día de la Independencia de Colombia.

_____

10. El tamal se cuece al vapor.

_____

EXERCISE D.   **Identifique cada palabra como bebida, comida, tipo, traje o fiesta.**

1. taco _____

2. rebozo _____

3. llanero _____

4. tamal _____

5. posada _____

6. huaraches _____

7. mariachi _____

8. mate _____

9. frijol _____

10. china poblana _____

La contribución de Hispanoamérica a la literatura, el arte y la música

LA LITERATURA

Hispanoamérica tiene una literatura rica y abundante cuyos orígenes se encuentran desde los tiempos de la conquista. Los cronistas de Indias fueron historiadores españoles que vinieron al Nuevo Mundo y registraron los sucesos de la conquista. Uno de los grandes soldados y cronistas fue **Bernal Díaz del Castillo** (1492-1581). Acompañó a Hernán Cortés y describió la conquista de México en su famosa **«Historia verdadera de los sucesos de la conquista de la Nueva España»**.

1. **Alonso de Ercilla** (1533-1594) escribió **«La araucana»**, un poema épico acerca de las luchas entre los conquistadores españoles y los indios araucanos de Chile. Fue la primera obra literaria importante escrita en el Nuevo Mundo.

2. **Sor Juana Inés de la Cruz** (1651-1695), de México, escribió la mejor poesía de la época colonial. Los temas de la obra de esta monja son el pesimismo, la angustia y la vanidad de la vida.

3. **Andrés Bello** (1781-1865), de Venezuela, fue poeta, crítico y erudito. Su **«Gramática castellana»** fue escrita hace más de cien años y aun se considera una de las mejores y más completas.

4. **Domingo Faustino Sarmiento** (1811-1888), de la Argentina, fue profesor y también presidente de su país. Escribió **«Facundo»**, biografía de un jefe gaucho.

5. **José Hernández** (1834-1886) escribió **«Martín Fierro»**, un poema épico que describe la vida del gaucho. Es el mejor ejemplo de la literatura gauchesca.

6. **Jorge Isaacs** (1837-1895), de Colombia, escribió la novela romántica **«María»**.

7. **José Martí** (1853-1895) fue un poeta y patriota cubano. Sus **«Versos Sencillos»** son muy famosos.

8. **Rubén Darío** (1867-1916), de Nicaragua, fue uno de los mejores poetas de la América Hispana. Fundó un nuevo movimiento de poesía llamado **«el Modernismo»**. Sus obras principales son **«Prosas profanas»** y **«Cantos de vida y esperanza»**.

9. **Ricardo Palma** (1833-1919), del Perú, fue el autor de **«Tradiciones peruanas»**, cuentos de la época colonial.

10. **José Enrique Rodó** (1872-1917), del Uruguay, fue el ensayista más famoso de Hispanoamérica. Su obra maestra es **«Ariel»**, un libro de ensayos.

11. **Gabriela Mistral** (1889-1957), poetisa de Chile, ganó el Premio Nobel de Literatura en 1945.

12. **Ricardo Güiraldes** (1886-1927), de la Argentina, escribió **«Don Segundo Sombra»**, una novela gauchesca.

13. **Rómulo Gallegos** (1873-1952), de Venezuela, escribió **«Doña Bárbara»**, una novela que se desarrolla en los llanos de Venezuela.

14. **Mariano Azuela** (1873-1952), de México, escribió una novela acerca de la revolución mexicana, **«Los de abajo»**.

15. **Ciro Alegría** (1909-1967), de Perú, escribió sobre los indios de su país en su novela **«El mundo es ancho y ajeno»**.

16. **Jorge Luis Borges** (1899-1986), de la Argentina, fue uno de los escritores más destacados de la literatura del siglo XX.

17. **Pablo Neruda** (1904-1973), de Chile, ganó el Premio Nobel de Literatura en 1971.

18. **Ernesto Sábato** (1911-2011), de Argentina, recibió en 1981 el Premio Cervantes, considerado el premio más prestigioso del mundo hispano. Fue autor de tres novelas: **«El túnel»**, **«De héroes y tumbas»** y **«El ángel de la oscuridad»**.

19. **Octavio Paz** (1914-1998), poeta de México, ganó el Premio Nobel de Literatura en 1990.

20. **Gabriel García Márquez** (1928-2014), de Colombia, escribió la novela **«Cien años de soledad»**, que cuenta la historia de un pueblo colombiano ficticio. García Márquez ganó el Premio Nobel de Literatura en 1982.

21. **Julio Cortázar** (1914-1984), de Argentina, revela una intensa preocupación por la relación entre la realidad y la fantasía y por la condición absurda del hombre moderno. Su obra más famosa es **«Rayuela»**.

22. **Juan Rulfo** (1918-1986), de México, presenta en su obra literaria una voz y una visión muy profundas de su país. Es muy conocido por su novela **«Pedro Páramo»**.

23. **José Donoso** (1924-1996), de Chile, es un autor que ha contribuido a la renovación de la novela hispanoamericana. Sus novelas **«Este domingo»** y **«El lugar sin límites»** son muy conocidas.

24. **Carlos Fuentes** (1928-2012), de México, tuvo mucha fama internacional. Una de sus obras más conocidas es **«Cambio de piel».**

25. El cubano **Guillermo Cabrera Infante** (1929-2005), vivió en el exilio en Inglaterra y fue conocido como un gran innovador de la novela. Su obra **«Tres tristes tigres»** ganó varios premios literarios internacionales.

26. **Manuel Puig** (1932-1990), de Argentina, ganó mucha fama internacional. Entre sus novelas más importantes están **«Boquitas pintadas»** y **«El beso de la mujer araña».**

27. **Mario Vargas Llosa** (1936-   ), de Perú, es un novelista que ha logrado mucha fama internacional. Muestra preocupación social y humana en todas sus obras. Entre sus novelas más famosas están **«La ciudad y los perros»** y **«La casa verde».**

EL ARTE

En el siglo XX surgieron varios pintores hispanoamericanos de gran fama internacional. En su obra se reflejan sus raíces indígenas y la realidad sociopolítica de su país. Los más importantes son los pintores y muralistas mexicanos. Ellos rechazaron el dominio cultural europeo y cultivaron sus rasgos característicos y utilizaron la pintura como instrumento de protesta social.

1. **Diego Rivera** (1886-1957), es el más conocido de los pintores mexicanos. Sus murales, que adornan muchos edificios públicos de toda la república mexicana, tratan temas sociales, políticos e históricos.

2. **José Clemente Orozco** (1883-1949), es otro muralista mexicano que defendió la causa de la revolución mexicana. Durante los años que vivió en los Estados Unidos pintó una serie de frescos importantes en Dartmouth College.

3. **David Alfaro Siqueiros** (1896-1974), de México, fue uno de los defensores más prominentes del arte como expresión de ideología política en la segunda mitad del siglo XX.

4. **Rufino Tamayo** (1899-1992), es uno de los pintores mexicanos contemporáneos más famosos. Por medio del uso de colores vivos y formas semi-abstractas ha captado las alegrías y tragedias de su país.

5. **Miguel Covarrubias** (1904-1957), de México, fue famoso por sus caricaturas de personas famosas.

6. **Cesáreo Bernaldo de Quirós** (1879-1969), de Argentina, captó lo pintoresco de la vida gauchesca en sus obras.

7. **José Sabogal** (1888-1956), de Perú, representó la cultura indígena en sus cuadros.

8. **Wifredo Lam** (1902-1982), de Cuba, fue influido por el surrealismo. Uno de sus cuadros más famosos «La jungla» está en la entrada del Museo de Arte Moderno de la ciudad de Nueva York.

9. **Frida Kahlo** (1907-1954), de México, fue la esposa de Diego Rivera. Su obra artística fue influida por el dolor que sufrió durante su vida. En su juventud tuvo polio y también fue víctima de un accidente de tránsito. Su obra incluye varios autorretratos.

10. **Roberto Matta** (1911-2002), de Chile, fue un pintor contemporáneo de tendencia abstracta y surrealista.

11. **Oswaldo Guayasamín** (1919-1999), de Ecuador, fue un famoso pintor de tendencia cubista.

12. **Alejandro Obregón** (1920-1992) de Colombia, fue un pintor de tendencia abstracta.

13. **Rómulo Macció** (1931-), de Argentina, es un pintor vanguardista.

14. **Fernando Botero** (1932-), de Colombia, es un pintor de tendencia expresionista figurativa.

15. **Gerardo Chávez** (1937-), de Perú, es un pintor de tendencia surrealista.

LA MÚSICA

Mucha de la música hispanoamericana tiene sus raíces en temas folklóricos y sociales. Hay mucha variedad en la música tradicional y popular de los diversos países y de las distintas regiones dentro de un país. La música alegre, con influencia de ritmos africanos se halla en la región del Caribe, que incluye a Puerto Rico, Cuba, la República Dominicana y las costas de Honduras, Panamá, Venezuela y Colombia. Perú también muestra influencias africanas en su música. Por otra parte, las canciones indígenas de los Andes son casi siempre lentas y tristes. En medio de estos dos extremos se halla una gran variedad de ritmos que incluye el **corrido mexicano,** el **candombe** uruguayo, el **joropo venezolano** (música de los llaneros), los **valses** peruanos, ecuatorianos y argentinos, las canciones guaraníes del Paraguay y el **tango** argentino.

INSTRUMENTOS MUSICALES

La **guitarra** española es muy popular en Hispanoamérica. Además hay otros instrumentos musicales de ascendencia indígena o africana. Estos incluyen el **cuatro venezolano** (una especie de guitarra con sólo **cuatro** cuerdas), la **marimba** (semejante al xilofono), el **bongó** (un tambor de origen africano), el **güiro** (hecho de un fruto seco parecido a la calabaza y que se toca con un palito), **la quena** (una flauta de los incas), **las maracas** (calabazas secas con piedritas o granos de maíz adentro) y **las claves** (dos palitos de madera dura que se usan para marcar el ritmo). También se usa una versión del arpa europea del siglo XVI.

EL BAILE

Los bailes tradicionales hispanoamericanos son tan ricos y variados como su música. Muchos de los ritmos como el **corrido,** el **tango** y el **joropo** son también bailes. Otros bailes tradicionales incluyen el **bambuco** colombiano, la **cueca** chilena, la **milonga** argentina y uruguaya, la **plena** puertorriqueña y el **jarabe tapatío** mexicano.

De la música bailable popular, hay ritmos como la **conga,** la **rumba,** el **mambo** y el **chachachá** cubanos, la **guaracha** puertorriqueña y cubana, el **merengue** dominicano y la **cumbia** colombiana. Se conocen estos bailes por todo el mundo.

COMPOSITORES

Dos compositores hispanoamericanos se destacan internacionalmente en la música clásica. **Carlos Chávez** (1899-1978), de México, fundó la **Orquesta Sinfónica de México** y la **Orquesta Sinfónica Nacional**. Entre sus obras más conocidas están el ballet **«El fuego nuevo»** y la **«Sinfonía india»**. **Alberto Ginastera** (1916-1983), de la Argentina, fue compositor moderno de óperas, ballets, sinfonías y conciertos. Compuso la ópera **«Bomarzo».**

En el campo de la música popular se distinguen varios compositores. **Manuel Ponce** (1882-1948), de México, debe su fama a canciones popularísimas como **«Estrellita».** El compositor y director de orquesta **Gonzalo Roig** (1890-1972) compuso muchas zarzuelas y canciones muy populares como **«Quiéreme mucho».** Otro cubano, **Ernesto Lecuona** (1896-1963) compuso canciones muy famosas como **«Siboney»** y **«Malagueña». Agustín Lara** (1897-1970), de México, debe su fama a canciones muy conocidas como **«María Bonita»** y **«Granada».**

ARTISTAS

Muchos cantantes y músicos gozan de mucha fama en el extranjero. Entre ellos están el tenor de ópera chileno **Ramón Vinay,** el barítono puertorriqueño **Justino Díaz** y la gran cantante peruana **Yma Sumac. Claudio Arrau** es un famoso pianista chileno que interpreta música clásica.

El venezolano **José Luis Rodríguez (El Puma),** los mexicanos **José José, Emmanuel, Marco Antonio Muñiz** y **Rocío Banquels,** el argentino **José Luis Perales,** y las puertorriqueñas **Ednita Nazario, Nidia Caro** y **Lucecita Benítez** son conocidos internacionalmente por su interpretación de canciones populares.

Tres actores mexicanos tienen fama mundial por su actuación en películas norteamericanas y dentro de su propio país: **Pedro Armendáriz, Selma Hayek** y el cómico **Cantinflas,** seudónimo de Mario Moreno.

Otros artistas que han logrado fama mundial son: **George López** y **Edward James Olmos,** actores de ascendencia mexicana, y **Rita Moreno, Rosie Pérez** y **Roselyn Sánchez,** actrices de ascendencia puertorriqueña.

EXERCISE A. Escoja la palabra o expresión que complete correctamente las oraciones.

1. (José Enrique Rodó, Ricardo Güiraldes, Alonso de Ercilla) escribió una novela de la vida de los gauchos.

_____

2. Una cantante de Perú que tuvo fama mundial fue (Nidia Cara, Yma Sumac, Iris Chacón).

_____

3. «Los de abajo» fue escrito por (Rómulo Gallegos, David Alfaro Siqueiros, Mariano Azuela).

_____

4. El padre del modernismo en la poesía es (Rubén Darío, Gabriela Mistral, Agustín Lara).

_____

5. Andrés Bello y Domingo Sarmiento eran dos (pintores, educadores, compositores).

_____

6. Una famosa poetisa mexicana de la época colonial fue (Yma Sumac, Gabriela Mistral, Sor Juana Inés de la Cruz).

_____

7. Un célebre pintor de origen cubano fue (José Clemente Orozco, David Alfaro Siqueiros, Wifredo Lam).

_____

8. Un baile típico de México es (el jarabe tapatío, la rumba, la quena).

_____

9. Un pianista famoso de Chile fue (Ernesto Lecuona, Cantinflas, Claudio Arrau).

_____

10. «El mundo es ancho y ajeno» describe la vida y los problemas de los (indios, gauchos, actores).

_____

EXERCISE B.   **Relacione ambas columnas. En el espacio provisto, escriba la letra con la expresión asociada a cada nombre de la columna A.**

	A		B
_____	**1.** José Martí	*a.*	poeta argentino
_____	**2.** Justino Díaz	*b.*	«Doña Bárbara»
_____	**3.** Diego Rivera	*c.*	poeta cubano
_____	**4.** Cantinflas	*d.*	ensayista
_____	**5.** José Enrique Rodó	*e.*	cantante
_____	**6.** Jorge Luis Borges	*f.*	compositor mexicano
_____	**7.** Cesáreo Bernaldo de Quirós	*g.*	«María»
_____	**8.** Carlos Chávez	*h.*	pintor argentino
_____	**9.** Jorge Isaacs	*i.*	pintor mexicano
_____	**10.** Rómulo Gallegos	*j.*	cómico mexicano

EXERCISE C.   **Lea las siguientes oraciones. Indique si son ciertas o falsas. Si son falsas, corríjalas.**

1. Las maracas son dos palitos de madera dura.

_____

2. Agustín Lara fue el compositor que escribió «Siboney».

_____

3. «Tres tristes tigres» es una novela de Mario Vargas Llosa.

_____

4. La novela «Cambio de piel» fue escrita por Carlos Fuentes.

_____

5. Wifredo Lam fue un autor cubano.

_____

6. La novela «El beso de la mujer araña» fue escrita por Manuel Puig.

_____

7. José Donoso recibió el Premio Nobel de Literatura.

_____

8. José José y Emmanuel son cantantes populares de Hispanoamérica.

_____

9. La especialidad de Miguel Covarrubias era el mural.

_____

10. Gabriela Mistral se destacó como poetisa.

_____

(**EXERCISE D.**)   **Complete las siguientes oraciones.**

1. En Chile el baile típico es la _____

2. «Don Segundo Sombra», «Facundo» y «Martín Fierro» tratan de la vida de los _____ .

3. La primera obra literaria de importancia escrita en el Nuevo Mundo fue _____ .

4. _____ es el autor de una famosa gramática española.

5. Uno de los mejores ejemplos de la literatura gauchesca es _____ .

6. Para marcar el ritmo de la música se usan las _____ .

7. _____ fue un poeta chileno.

8. Un pintor argentino fue _____ .

9. El tango tuvo su origen en _____ .

10. El instrumento más popular de los países hispánicos es la _____ .

11. _____ fue un famoso autor peruano que escribió cuentos de la época colonial.

12. Dos bailes típicos de Cuba son _____ y _____ .

13. _____ es el autor de «Cien años de soledad».

14. José Clemente Orozco fue un célebre _____ mexicano.

15. La flauta de los indios del Perú se conoce como _____ .

Comprehensive Testing: Speaking, Listening, Reading, Writing

Rating and Scoring the Speaking Section

Rating and scoring. The rating procedures described below provide for a maximum of five points for the performance of each task. Each utterance is worth a maximum of one point and is rated on the basis of comprehensibility, appropriateness, and the characteristics listed in Column 1 below. An utterance is any spoken statement that helps to accomplish the stated task.

Comprehensibility is determined by considering whether the utterance would be understood by a literate native speaker of Spanish who knows no English but is used to speaking with non-native speakers.

Appropriateness is determined on the basis of the utterance's contribution to the completion of the task to be performed.

2 points	1 point	0 points
Utterance is • comprehensible and • appropriate and is strongly characterized by the following: • initiates and/or sustains and/or advances the conversation • uses common verb-tense forms • uses accurate structures • is articulated comprehensibly • uses a variety of vocabulary which may expand or clarify meaning • is extended discourse (may contain more than one short utterance) • uses culturally correct gestures, social conventions, and/or idiomatic expressions	Utterance is • comprehensible and • appropriate but is • a single, short, discrete utterance consisting of limited vocabulary and structures or • contains little or no evidence of the characteristics listed in Column 1	Utterance is • incomprehensible and/or • inappropriate Disregard if it is a • yes/no response • socializing device • restatement of all or essential parts of what the teacher said • proper noun(s) in isolation

Informal Speaking Rubric

Dimension	4	3	2	1
Initiation	Eagerly initiates speech. Utilizes appropriate attention-getting devices. Asks questions easily. Speaks spontaneously.	Willing to initiate speech. Uses appropriate attention-getting devices. Asks questions. Speaks evenly.	Sometimes initiates speech using attention-getting devices. Sometimes asks questions. Speaks hesitantly.	Relunctant to initiate speech. Struggles to ask questions. Speech is halting.
Response	Almost always responds appropriately to questions or statements.	Frequently responds appropriately to questions or statements.	Sometimes responds appropriately to questions or statements.	Rarely responds appropriately to questions or statements.
Conversational Strategies	Clarifies and continues conversation. Uses all or some of the followings strategies: circumlocution, survival strategies, intonation, self-correction, verbal cues.	Uses all or some strategies but may need occasional prompting.	Uses some strategies. Needs frequent prompting to further the conversation.	Uses few strategies. Relies heavily on conversational partner to sustain conversation. Rarely responds, even with frequent prompting.
Vocabulary	Incorporates a variety of old and new vocabulary. Uses idiomatic expressions appropriate to topic. Speaks clearly and imitates accurate pronunciation.	Utilizes a variety of old and limited new vocabulary. Attempts to use idiomatic expressions appropriate to topic. Speaks clearly and imitates accurate pronunciation.	Relies on basic vocabulary. Speech is comprehensible, in spite of mispronunciations.	Uses limited vocabulary. Mispronunciations impede comprehensibility.
Structure	Makes few errors in the following areas. Verbs in utterances when necessary with appropriate subject or verb agreement; noun and adjective agreement; and correct word order. Errors do not hinder comprehensibility.	Makes several errors in structure which do not affect overall comprehensibility.	Makes several errors in structure which may interfere with comprehensibility.	Makes utterances which are so brief that there is little evidence of structure. Comprehensibility is impeded.
Cultural Appropriateness	Almost always uses/interprets cultural manifestations when appropriate to the task.	Frequently uses/interprets cultural manifestations when appropriate to the task.	Sometimes uses/interprets cultural manifestations when appropriate when appropriate to the task.	Rarely uses/interpretes cultural manifestations when appropriate to the task.

A zero can be given in any of the above dimensions when the student's performance falls below the criteria described for a score of **1**.

If a paper scores a zero on purpose/task, the entire response receives a zero.

Conversion Chart				
19-25 = 5	14-18 = 4	10-13 = 3	5-9 = 2	1-4 = 1

1. SPEAKING: ORAL INTERPERSONAL-COMMUNICATION TASKS [20 points]

Directions: The speaking test consists of communication tasks to be performed by a student with his/her teacher. Each task is a simulated conversation in which the student always plays the role of himself/herself and the teacher assumes the specific role indicated in the task. The tasks may involve one or more of the four communication functions: socializing, providing and obtaining information, expressing personal feelings or opinions, and getting others to adopt a course of action.

You will perform a total of four tasks. Each task consists of a brief statement in English to indicate the purpose and setting of the communication, the role of the teacher, and the person who is to initiate the conversation. Each task should be completed in five interactions between the student and the teacher. These interactions are called utterances.

2. LISTENING COMPREHENSION

a. MULTIPLE CHOICE (ENGLISH) [18 points]

This part consists of nine questions. For each question, you will hear some background information in English. Then you will hear a passage in Spanish twice, followed by a question in English. Listen carefully. After you have heard the question, read the question and the four suggested answers in your book. Choose the best-suggested answer.

1. What do the teachers want to do?
   1. Work with the students after school.
   2. Begin a pen pal exchange for their students.
   3. Arrange a trip to Costa Rica.
   4. Set up a homestay for Costa Rican students.

2. What does your mother say about the dress in the window?
   1. She would like to buy it.
   2. It is her size.
   3. She would like to wear it to a party.
   4. It is too expensive.

3. What does the waiter want you to do?
   1. Leave the restaurant.
   2. Pay the bill.
   3. Move to another table.
   4. Order now.

4. Where does your friend live?
   1. On the Calle Mayor.
   2. Next to a restaurant.
   3. On the left side of the street.
   4. Past the drug store and the restaurant.

5. What does Alicia want you to do?
   1. Help her clean the house.
   2. Come to the party for her mother.
   3. Buy a gift for her mother.
   4. Go shopping with her.

6. When does your friend prefer to eat lunch?
   1. At noon.
   2. Before 12:00.
   3. After 3:00.
   4. At about 2:30.

7. How should you go to your friend's house?
   1. on foot
   2. by train
   3. by car
   4. by bus

8. Why is Gloria Acevedo being congratulated?

   1. Her father just became the head technician at the radio station.

   2. This is her first birthday.

   3. She is going to sing with Luis Miguel and Emmanuel.

   4. She is the daughter of a famous musical artist.

9. What is the topic of this announcement?

   1. An outdoor celebration of Hispanic culture.   3. An exhibit of folkloric art.

   2. A street fair on 44th Street.   4. A meeting of the Hispanic nations.

b.   MULTIPLE CHOICE (SPANISH) [12 points]

This part consists of six questions. For each question, you will hear some background information in English. Then you will hear a passage in Spanish twice, followed by a question in Spanish. Listen carefully. After you have heard the question, read the question and the four suggested answers in your book. Choose the best-suggested answer.

1. ¿Qué anuncian?

   1. Noticias sobre los desastres nacionales.

   2. Información para protegerse en un desastre.

   3. Folletos de promoción turística.

   4. Cursos sobre los primeros auxilios.

2. ¿Qué pasa hoy en el Parque del Retiro?

   1. Habrá una competencia.

   2. Representarán dos obras infantiles con títeres.

   3. Pasarán varios dibujos animados.

   4. El alcalde va a leer unos cuentos infantiles.

3. ¿Qué le asombró a esta persona?

   1. La explicación sencilla que le dieron.

   2. La introducción de un nuevo medio de transporte.

   3. La facilidad de manejo de este vehículo.

   4. La popularidad de esta invención.

4. ¿Quiénes gozarán de esta actividad?

   1. Las personas a quienes les gustan los deportes acuáticos.

   2. Las personas que aprenden a pintar.

   3. Las personas que trabajan cerca de la playa.

   4. Las personas que no saben nadar.

5. ¿De qué se trata este mensaje?

   1. De una invitación a una comida.

   2. De un cambio de horario.

   3. De la cancelación de una cita.

   4. De una inconveniencia para todo el mundo.

6. ¿Quiénes deben prestar atención a este anuncio?

   1. Las personas que pasan mucho tiempo al aire libre.

   2. Las personas que estudian la ciencia.

   3. Las personas que se dedican a la estética.

   4. Las personas que trabajan con computadoras.

3. READING COMPREHENSION

a. READING (MULTIPLE CHOICE, SPANISH) [10 points]

This part consists of a passage followed by five questions or incomplete statements in Spanish. For each, choose the expression that best answers the question or completes the statement according to the meaning of the passage.

¿Conoce Ud. una temporada del año que sea más anhelada que la de las vacaciones? Todo el mundo suele esperar las vacaciones con entusiasmo y con grandes deseos de estar libre de la rutina diaria. Pero, al fijarnos bien en esta temporada y los preparativos que las personas hacen para disfrutarla, nos encontramos con una perspectiva muy diferente.

El período de las vacaciones llega a ser agitado, estresante y cansador porque esta semana significa diferentes cosas para las personas. Mucha gente deja acumularse diversas tareas para llevarlas a cabo durante esta semana disponible. Otras personas salen de la casa y viajan a otro sitio. Pero para estar completamente libre durante siete días, muchas personas trabajan de diez a doce horas con el fin de poner en orden todos los asuntos pendientes del trabajo. En consecuencia, el ritmo en la oficina llega a ser frenético. También, hay que hacer todos los preparativos para esa semana que pasarán fuera de la casa.

El viaje, sea en carro, en autobús, en tren o en avión, requiere mucha preparación: lavar ropa, comprar los boletos, encontrar un mapa o plano de la ciudad a donde se va, hacer la maleta, cerrar la casa, suspender el periódico y el correo, regar las plantas, etc. Y como es la temporada de las vacaciones, las carreteras, las terminales y los aeropuertos están llenos de personas que tienen la misma intención que Ud.: ir a un lugar desconocido o volver a visitar un lugar favorito como alguna playa. El viaje ocupa todo el primer día de esa semana de libertad y llegan cansados por lo general.

El cambio de clima, los sonidos y ruidos distintos y desconocidos del nuevo lugar y la sensación de estar de vacaciones hacen que las personas se despierten antes de la hora a que acostumbran despertarse. Entonces hay que crear una nueva rutina y acostumbrarse a ella... vestirse en seguida para salir a un restaurante a desayunar. Además, hay muchas decisiones que tomar... ¿cómo pasar el día?, ¿dónde comer?, ¿ir a la playa?, etc. Por fin se deciden a ir a la playa y disfrutar del sol. Regresan al cuarto del hotel para ponerse el traje de baño, buscar una toalla y todo lo que se necesita para protegerse del sol. Llegan a la playa y se acuestan en una toalla en la arena. El cansancio que se ha acumulado de los preparativos y del viaje mismo les agobia y se quedan dormidos por largas horas en la playa. Cuando se despiertan, empiezan a sentir que tienen una quemadura de grandes proporciones. Están obligados a permanecer el resto del tiempo en la sombra y sin facilidad de movimiento por la quemadura. Entran los deseos de volver a casa.

A pesar de todo, ya de regreso a la vida normal, las personas vuelven a soñar con las próximas vacaciones.

1. ¿Por qué da la gente tanta importancia a las vacaciones?

  1. Es un período de verdadero ocio.
  2. Es una temporada larga y triste.
  3. Es tiempo oportuno para buscar otro empleo.
  4. Es una manera de liberarse de los jefes.

2. Los días anteriores al comienzo de las vacaciones se caracterizan por

  1. el estrés
  2. la pereza
  3. la alegría
  4. el miedo

3. Por lo general, las personas que salen fuera para pasar las vacaciones llegan

  1. rápidamente por la eficacia del transporte público
  2. a paso de tortuga porque muchas personas viajan en esta época
  3. listos para divertirse el mismo día que llegan
  4. desanimados por los problemas de tránsito

4. ¿Qué tienen que hacer los viajeros al llegar a su destino?

  1. despertarse más tarde
  2. llamar a unos amigos que viven allí
  3. acostumbrarse a una nueva rutina
  4. buscar a un médico

5. A pesar de todos los contratiempos que ha aguantado durante el viaje, ¿en qué piensa el viajero al regresar a casa?

    1. imprimir las fotos que sacó

    2. entregar los regalos que compró para los parientes

    3. permanecer en casa durante las próximas vacaciones

    4. planear un viaje para el otro año

b. SHORT READINGS (MULTIPLE CHOICE, ENGLISH) [10 points]

This part consists of five short readings. For each selection, there is a question or incomplete statement in English. For each, choose the expression that best answers the question or completes the statement. Base your choice on the content of the reading selection.

LUNAUTO

En caso de rotura de un cristal llame al teléfono

900 73 07 07
Llamada gratuita
524 60 18

24 horas

Primer instalador nacional de parabrisas

1. Who should pay attention to this ad?

    1. Homeowners.   3. Car owners.

    2. Mechanics.   4. Waiters.

El Paraíso del Jamón

San Fernando, 10 (Esquina a Gran Vía) • Tel.: 523 81 93

Todos los días   950
Menús a elegir   PTAS.

4 primeros 4 segundos

2 Menús Especiales

Platos combinados desde 550 Ptas.
Especialidad en salchichas ibéricas
(Gran Variedad de Quesos • Patés)

Raciones

Pulpo gallega
Pulpo vinagreta
Callos
Almejas marinera
Ensaladilla rusa
Mejillones con tomate
Pepinillo relleno
Gambas al ajillo

2. What is the specialty of this restaurant?

    1. Meals for tourists.   3. Regional dishes of Spain.

    2. Seafood.   4. Fast service.

Este fin de año compre 2 y estrene 3

No pierda la oportunidad que nuestra venta de fábrica le ofrece: este fin de año lo invitamos a vestir las mejores y exclusivas marcas de ropa para dama y caballero a precios de fábrica. Además, con la compra de 2 prendas, se lleva una más completamente gratis.*

Visítenos en París No. 119, casi esquina con Centenario, de lunes a domingo de 9 a 18 horas

- trajes
- sacos
- blazers
- pantalones
- camisas
- corbatas
- chamarras
- traje sastre
- faldas
- blusas
- vestidos

*Gratis la prenda de menor precio.

Promoción valida hasta el 30 de diciembre o agotar existencia

3. What is the attraction of this sale?

    1. This is the store's policy for the new year.   3. It offers one article of clothing free.

    2. The sale ends only when no stock is left.   4. The stock is replenished daily.

BARAJAS INFORMA

El aeropuerto de Madrid/Barajas está creciendo muy deprisa. Hace ya tiempo que se quedó pequeño. En un aeropuerto en transformación permanente, la información es vital. Vamos a ampliar los medios, para que su tránsito por el aeropuerto sea lo más cómodo posible.

Una sonrisa para ayudarle sale a su encuentro: el equipo de Chaquetas Verdes:

Hemos reforzado el equipo de atención al público, para poder acudir allí donde surjan dada o dificultades. Usted podrá reconocerlos por sus chaquetas verdes.

4. Why has this notice been published?

    1. The Barajas Madrid airport is being moved to a new location.

    2. To alert the public to possible air traffic delays.

    3. To publicize new services to help the traveler.

    4. The uniform of the travelers' aid staff has changed.

MOVIMIENTO EN RUTA

Estamos muy cerca. Para llevarte muy lejos.

Siempre que salga a la carretera aprovéchese de la última tecnología que le ofrece Movimiento para conocer el estado de las carreteras españolas: Servicio **"Movimiento en Ruta "**. Su funcionamiento es muy sencillo. Envíe un mensaje de texto con el código de la carretera o provincia de la que desee la información al número **101**. Por ejemplo, si quiere conocer el estado de las carreteras de la provincia de Salamanca, escriba "SA" en la opción de mensajes de su Movimiento y envíelo al **101**, en pocos segundos recibirá un mensaje de texto con la información requerida en su móvil. Confíe en Movimiento y olvídese de los imprevistos.

5. This service provides information concerning
1. weather patterns
2. road conditions
3. tourist accommodations
4. air traffic

c. **READING (MULTIPLE CHOICE, ENGLISH)** [10 points]

This part consists of a passage in Spanish followed by five questions or incomplete statements in English. For each, choose the expression that best answers the question or completes the statement according to the meaning of the passage.

Los mayores de edad recordarán, sin duda, que el tomate era uno de los sabore del verano: había tomates en verano y no en el resto del año. Hoy, hablar de la temporada del tomate suena rarísimo, porque hay tomates todo el año. Pero es cierto que se trata de un fruto esencialmente veraniego cuando realmente apetece en ensaladas o como ingrediente básico del gazpacho.

El tomate procede de América, de donde se trajo ya en el siglo XVI. Hoy es un ingrediente fundamental en la cocina que llamamos mediterránea, compañero inseparable de las pastas. Normalmente, a un tomate, tal como viene de la verdulería, le sobran tres cosas: la piel, las semillas y el agua de vegetación. Al menos, pelarlos siempre nos ofrece otra dimensión.

Tengan en cuenta que el tomate se combina muy bien con casi todo y deben practicar usarla en nuevas recetas, especialmente durante el verano, cuando los hay en gran abundancia y a menor costo. Y siempre que puedan, háganse usted su propia salsa de tomate porque así sabrán a qué sabe de verdad.

1. Why was the tomato a special treat for older generations?
1. their cost
2. their seasonal availability
3. their special harvesting procedures
4. their unique growing conditions

2. The tomato originated in
1. the Mediterranean region.
2. the Iberian peninsula.
3. Latin America.
4. Africa.

3. The tomato is a basic ingredient in
1. Latin American cooking.
2. all fine cuisines.
3. Mediterranean cuisine.
4. outdoor cooking fests.

4. What makes the tomato most popular in summer?
1. its juices and seeds
2. its inclusion in special recipes
3. its indifference to climate changes
4. its availability and lower price

5. It is suggested that the readers prepare their own sauces

1. to understand the skill it takes.
2. to appreciate the true taste of the tomato.
3. to avoid discarding over-ripened tomatoes.
4. to be able to recognize the point of origin of the tomato.

4. WRITING

Writing Rubric

Dimension	Performance Level			
	4	3	2	1
Purpose/Task	Satisfies the task, connects all ideas to task/purpose, and exhibits a logical and coherent sequence of ideas throughtout.	Satisfies the task; connections are implied with few irrelevancies.	Satisfies the task; connections may be unclear with some irrelevancies.	Makes at least one statement which satisfies the task. Remaining statements are irrelevant to the task.
Vocabulary	Utilizes a **wide variety** of vocabulary that expands the topic in the statement/question to include nouns, verbs and/or adjectives, as appropriate to the task.	Utilizes a **variety** of vocabulary relevant to the topic in statements/questions to include nouns, verbs, and/or adjectives, as appropriate to the task.	Utilizes vocabulary some of which is inaccurate or irrelevant to the task.	Utilizes **limited** vocabulary, most of which is inaccurate or irrelevant to the task.
Structure/ Conventions	Exhibits a **high degree** of control of structures or conventions: • subject/verb agreement • noun/adjective agreement • correct word order • spelling **Errors do not hinder overall comprehensibility of the task.**	Exhibits **some** degree of control of structures or conventions: • subject/verb agreement • noun/adjective agreement • correct word order • spelling **Errors do not hinder overall comprehensibility of the task.**	Exhibits **some** degree of control of structures or conventions: • subject/verb agreement • noun/adjective agreement • correct word order • spelling **Errors do hinder overall comprehensibility of the task.**	Demonstrates **little** control of structure or convention or **errors impede overall comprehensibility of the task.**
Word Count	Uses 60 or more comprehensible words in target language that contribute to the development of the task.	Uses 45-59 comprehensible words in target language that contribute to the development of the task.	Uses 30-44 comprehensible words in target language that contribute to the development of the task.	Uses 15-29 comprehensible words in target language that contribute to the development of the task.

A zero can be given in any of the above dimensions when the student's performance falls below the criteria described for a score of **1**. If a paper scores a zero on purpose/task, the entire response receives a zero.

Conversion Chart					
14–16 = 5	11–13 = 4	8–10 = 3	5–7 = 2	2–4 = 1	0–1 = 0

a. INFORMAL NOTE [10 points]

Choose one of the topics below and write a well-organized note in Spanish as directed. Your note must consist of at least six clauses. A clause must contain a verb, a stated or implied subject, and additional words necessary to convey meaning. The six clauses may be contained in fewer than six sentences if some of the sentences have more than one clause.

EXAMPLES: One clause: Ayer fui de compras.
Two clauses: Ayer fui de compras y di con Emilio en la calle.
Three clauses: Ayer fui de compras y di con Emilio en la calle quien me invitó al cine.

Note that the salutation and closing will not count as part of the six clauses.

1. Your parents left you a note on the kitchen counter telling you the chores they wanted you to complete. Write a note in which you tell them why you didn't do the chores.

Use the following:
Salutation: Padres:
Closing: [your name]

2. You and a friend are not talking because of a misunderstanding or quarrel. Write a note to your friend in which you apologize for your actions.

Use the following:
Salutation: Estimado(a) [your friend's name]:
Closing: [your name]

b. NARRATIVE OR LETTER [10 points]

Write a well-organized composition as directed below. Choose either the narrative or the formal letter. Follow the specific instructions for the topic that you select. Each composition must consist of at least ten clauses. A clause must contain a verb, a stated or implied subject, and additional words necessary to convey meaning. The ten clauses may be contained in fewer than ten sentences if some of the sentences have more than one clause.

A. Narrative

Write a story in Spanish about the situation shown in the picture. It must be a story about the situation in the picture, not a description of the picture.

KEY WORDS: la banda *band*   el espectador *spectator*
la bandera *flag*   el globo *balloon*
la carroza *float*   marchar *to march*
el desfile *parade*

B. Formal Letter

Write a letter in Spanish. Follow the specific instructions. Note that the dateline, salutation, and closing will not count as part of the required ten clauses.

Your school is offering a homestay in a Spanish-speaking country. As part of the application process, you have to write a letter in which you explain why you are interested in this program. Write a letter in which you explain your reasons for applying for this homestay. Suggested subtopics are: your qualifications, reasons for wanting the homestay, what you will learn, what you will do upon returning, effect on your career goals. You may use ideas suggested by any or all of these subtopics, or may use your own ideas. Either way, you must accomplish the purpose of the letter, which is to explain your interest in this homestay experience.

Use the following:

Dateline: el _____ de _____ de _____

Salutation: Estimado (a) Señor(a), [Muy Señores Míos]

Closing: Atentamente.

[your name]

Appendix

◆ 1 ◆ REGULAR VERBS

INFINITIVE		
entr**ar**	corr**er**	viv**ir**

PRESENT		
entr**o**	corr**o**	viv**o**
entr**as**	corr**es**	viv**es**
entr**a**	corr**e**	viv**e**
entr**amos**	corr**emos**	viv**imos**
entr**áis**	corr**éis**	viv**ís**
entr**an**	corr**en**	viv**en**

PRETERIT		
entr**é**	corr**í**	viv**í**
entr**aste**	corr**iste**	viv**iste**
entr**ó**	corr**ió**	viv**ió**
entr**amos**	corr**imos**	viv**imos**
entr**asteis**	corr**isteis**	viv**isteis**
entr**aron**	corr**ieron**	viv**ieron**

IMPERFECT		
entr**aba**	corr**ía**	viv**ía**
entr**abas**	corr**ías**	viv**ías**
entr**aba**	corr**ía**	viv**ía**
entr**ábamos**	corr**íamos**	viv**íamos**
entr**ábais**	corr**íais**	viv**íais**
entr**aban**	corr**ían**	viv**ían**

FUTURE		
entra**ré**	corre**ré**	vivi**ré**
entra**rás**	corre**rás**	vivi**rás**
entra**rá**	corre**rá**	vivi**rá**
entra**remos**	corre**remos**	vivi**remos**
entra**réis**	corre**réis**	vivi**réis**
entra**rán**	corre**rán**	vivi**rán**

CONDITIONAL		
entra**ría**	corre**ría**	vivi**ría**
entra**rías**	corre**rías**	vivi**rías**
entra**ría**	corre**ría**	vivi**ría**
entra**ríamos**	corre**ríamos**	vivi**ríamos**
entra**ríais**	corre**réais**	vivi**ríais**
entra**rían**	corre**rían**	vivi**rían**

COMMANDS (IMPERATIVE)		
entra no entr**es** } (tú)	corre no corr**as** } (tú)	vive no viv**as** } (tú)
entra**d** no entr**éis** } (vosotros)	corre**d** no corr**áis** } (vosotros)	viv**id** no viv**áis** } (vosotros)
entr**e** (Ud.)	corra(Ud.)	viv**a** (Ud.)
entr**emos** (nosotros)	corr**amos** (nosotros)	viv**amos** (nosotros)
entr**en** (Uds.)	corr**an** (Uds.)	viv**an** (Uds.)

PRESENT SUBJUNCTIVE		
entr**e**	corr**a**	viv**a**
entr**es**	corr**as**	viv**as**
entr**e**	corr**a**	viv**a**
entr**emos**	corr**amos**	viv**amos**
entr**éis**	corr**áis**	viv**áis**
entr**en**	corr**an**	viv**áis**

PRESENT PERFECT

he
has
ha   entrado/corrido/vivido
hemos
habéis
han

PLUPERFECT

había
habías
había   entrado/corrido/vivido
habíamos
habíais
habían

◆ 2 ◆ STEM-CHANGING VERBS

a. **-ar** Verbs

INFINITIVE	pensar (**e** to **ie**)	mostrar (**o** to **ue**)	jugar (**u** to **ue**)
PRESENT	p**ie**nso	m**ue**stro	j**ue**go
	p**ie**nsas	m**ue**stras	j**ue**gas
	p**ie**nsa	m**ue**stra	j**ue**ga
	pensamos	mostramos	jugamos
	pensáis	mostráis	jugáis
	p**ie**nsan	m**ue**stran	j**ue**gan
SUBJUNCTIVE	p**ie**nse	m**ue**stre	j**ue**gue
	p**ie**nses	m**ue**stres	j**ue**gues
	p**ie**nse	m**ue**stre	j**ue**gue
	pensemos	mostremos	j**u**guemos
	penséis	mostréis	j**u**guéis
	p**ie**nsen	m**ue**stren	j**ue**guen

b. -er Verbs

INFINITIVE	perder (**e** to **ie**)	volver (**o** to **ue**)
PRESENT	PIERDO	VUELVO
	pierdes	vuelves
	pierde	vuelve
	perdemos	volvemos
	perdéis	volvéis
	pierden	vuelven
SUBJUNCTIVE	pierda	vuelva
	pierdas	vuelvas
	pierda	vuelva
	perdamos	volvamos
	perdáis	volváis
	pierdan	vuelvan

c. -ir Verbs

INFINITIVE	pedir (**e** to **i, i**)	sentir (**e** to **ie, i**)	dormir (**o** to **ue, u**)
PRESENT	pido	siento	duermo
	pides	sientes	duermes
	pide	siente	duerme
	pedimos	sentimos	dormimos
	pedís	sentís	dormís
	piden	sienten	duermen
PRETERIT	PEDÍ	SENTÍ	DORMÍ
	pediste	sentiste	dormiste
	pidió	sintió	durmió
	pedimos	sentimos	dormimos
	pedisteis	sentisteis	dormisteis
	pidieron	sintieron	durmieron
SUBJUNCTIVE	pida	sienta	duerma
	pidas	sientas	duermas
	pida	sienta	duerma
	pidamos	sintamos	durmamos
	pidáis	sintáis	durmáis
	pidan	sientan	duerman

COMMANDS	pide $\Big\}$ (tú) no pidas	siente $\Big\}$ (tú) no sientas	duerme $\Big\}$ (tú) no duermas
	pida (Ud.)	sienta (Ud.)	duerma (Ud.)
	pidamos (nosotros)	sintamos (nosotros)	durmamos (nosotros)
	pedid $\Big\}$ (vosotros) no pidáis	sentid $\Big\}$ (vosotros) no sientan	dormid $\Big\}$ (vosotros) no durmáis
	pidan (Uds.)	sientan (Uds.)	duerman (Uds.)

◆ 3 ◆ VERBS WITH SPELLING CHANGES

a. Verbs in **-cer** or **-cir**

INFINITIVE	ofrecer (c to zc)	conducir (c to zc)	convencer (c to z)
PRESENT	ofrezco	conduzco	convenzo
	ofreces	conduces	convences
	ofrece	conduce	convence
	ofrecemos	conducimos	convencemos
	ofrecéis	conducís	convencemos
	ofrecen	conducen	convencen
SUBJUNCTIVE	ofrezca	conduzca	convenza
	ofrezcas	conduzcas	convenzas
	ofrezca	conduzca	convenza
	ofrezcamos	conduzcamos	convenzamos
	ofrezcáis	conduzcáis	convenzáis
	ofrezcan	conduzcan	convenzan
COMMANDS	ofrece $\Big\}$ (tú) no ofrezcas	conduce $\Big\}$ (tú) no conduzcas	convence $\Big\}$ (tú) no convenzas
	ofrezca (Ud.)	conduzca (Ud.)	convenza (Ud.)
	ofrezcamos (nosotros)	conduzcamos (nosotros)	convenzamos (nosotros)
	ofreced $\Big\}$ (vosotros) no ofrezcáis	conducid $\Big\}$ (vosotros) no conduzcáis	convenced $\Big\}$ (vosotros) no convenzái
	ofrezcan (Uds.)	conduzcan (Uds.)	convenzan (Uds.)

b. Verbs That Change **i** to **y**

INFINITIVE	leer	caer	oír	incluir
PRETERIT	leí	caí	oí	incluí
	leíste	caíste	oíste	incluíste
	le**y**ó	ca**y**ó	o**y**ó	inclu**y**ó
	leímos	caímos	oímos	incluímos
	leísteis	caísteis	oísteis	incluísteis
	le**y**eron	ca**y**eron	o**y**eron	inclu**y**eron
PAST PARTICIPLE	leído	caído	oído	incluído

c. Verbs Ending in **-ger** or **-gir**

INFINITIVE	co**ger**	diri**gir**
PRESENT INDICATIVE	co**j**o	diri**j**o
	coges	diriges
	coge	dirige
	cogemos	dirigimos
	cogéis	dirigís
	cogen	dirigen
PRESENT SUBJUNCTIVE	co**j**a	diri**j**a
	co**j**as	diri**j**as
	co**j**a	diri**j**a
	co**j**amos	diri**j**amos
	co**j**áis	diri**j**áis
	co**j**an	diri**j**an

d. Verbs Ending in **-guir**

INFINITIVE	distin**guir**
PRESENT INDICATIVE	distin**g**o
	distingues
	distingue
	distinguimos
	distinguís
	distinguen

PRESENT SUBJUNCTIVE	distin**g**a
	distin**g**as
	distin**g**a
	distin**g**amos
	distin**g**áis
	distin**g**an

e. Verbs Ending in **–car, –gar,** and **–zar**

INFINITIVE	sa**c**ar (**c** to **gu**)	pa**g**ar (**g** to **gu**)	go**z**ar (**z** to **c**)
PRETERIT	sa**qué**	pa**gué**	go**cé**
	sacaste	pagaste	gozaste
	sacó	pagó	gozó
	sacamos	pagamos	gozamos
	sacasteis	pagasteis	gozasteis
	sacaron	pagaron	gozaron
SUBJUNCTIVE	sa**que**	pa**gue**	go**ce**
	sa**que**s	pa**gue**s	go**ce**s
	sa**que**	pa**gue**	go**ce**
	sa**que**mos	pa**gue**mos	gocemos
	sa**qué**is	pa**gué**is	go**cé**is
	sa**que**n	pa**gue**n	go**ce**n

◆ 4 ◆ VERBS WITH IRREGULAR FORMS

NOTE: Only the tenses containing irregular forms are given.

INFINITIVE	and**ar**
PRETERIT	and**uve**, and**uviste**, and**uvo**, and**uvimos**, and**uvisteis**, and**uvieron**
IMPERFECT SUBJUNCTIVE	and**uviera**, and**uvieras**, and**uviera**, and**uviéramos**, and**uviérais**, and**uvieran** and**uviese**, and**uvieses**, and**uviese**, and**uviésemos**, and**uviéseis**, and**uviesen**

INFINITIVE	cab**er**
PRESENT	**quep**o, cabes, cabe, cabemos, cabéis, caben

PRETERIT	**cupe, cup**iste, **cup**o, **cup**imos, **cup**isteis, **cup**ieron
CONDITIONAL	**cabr**ía, **cabr**ías, **cabr**ía, **cabr**íamos, **cabr**íais, **cabr**ían
PRESENT SUBJUNCTIVE	**quep**a, **quep**as, **quep**a, **quep**amos, **quep**áis, **quep**an

INFINITIVE	c**aer**
PRESENT	**caig**o, caes, cae, caemos, caéis, caen
PRETERIT	caí, caíste, ca**y**ó, caímos, caísteis, cayeron
PRESENT SUBJUNCTIVE	ca**ig**a, ca**ig**as, ca**ig**a, ca**ig**amos, ca**ig**áis, ca**ig**an
PAST PARTICIPLE	caído
GERUND	cayendo

INFINITIVE	d**ar**
PRESENT	d**oy**, das, da, damos, dais, dan
PRETERIT	d**i**, d**iste**, d**io**, dimos, disteis, di**e**ron
PRESENT SUBJUNCTIVE	d**é**, des, d**é**, demos déis, den

INFINITIVE	dec**ir**
PRESENT	di**g**o, dices, dice, decimos, decís, dicen
PRETERIT	**dij**e, **dij**iste, **dij**o, **dij**imos, **dij**isteis, **dij**eron
FUTURE	**dir**é, **dir**ás, **dir**á, **dir**emos, **dir**éis, **dir**án
CONDITIONAL	**dir**ía, **dir**ías, **dir**ía, **dir**íamos, **dir**íais, **dir**ían
PRESENT SUBJUNCTIVE	**dig**a, **dig**as, **dig**a, **dig**amos, **dig**áis, **dig**an
COMMAND	**di** (tú), **dig**a (Ud.), **dig**amos (nosotros)

PAST PARTICIPLE	**dicho**

GERUND	diciendo

INFINITIVE	es**tar**
PRESENT	est**oy**, estás, está, estamos, estáis, están
PRETERIT	est**uve**, estuviste, estuvo, estuvimos, estuvisteis, estuvieron
PRESENT SUBJUNCTIVE	est**é**, est**és**, est**é**, estemos, estéis, est**én**

INFINITIVE	hab**er**
PRESENT	**he, has, ha, h**emos, habéis, **h**an
PRETERIT	**hube, hub**iste, **hubo, hub**imos, **hub**isteis, **hub**ieron
FUTURE	**habr**é, **habr**ás, **habr**á, **habr**emos, **habr**éis, **habr**án
CONDITIONAL	**habr**ía, **habr**ías, **habr**ía, **habr**íamos, **habr**íais, **habr**ían
PRESENT SUBJUNCTIVE	**hay**a, **hay**as, **hay**a, **hay**amos, **hay**áis, **hay**an

INFINITIVE	hac**er**
PRESENT	**hag**o, haces, hace, hacemos, hacéis, hacen
PRETERIT	**hice, hic**iste, **hizo, hic**imos, **hic**isteis, **hic**ieron
FUTURE	**har**é, **har**ás, **har**á, **har**emos, **har**éis, **har**án
CONDITIONAL	**har**ía, **har**ías, **har**ía, **har**íamos, **har**íais, **har**ían
PRESENT SUBJUNCTIVE	**hag**a, **hag**as, **hag**a, **hag**amos, **hag**áis, **hag**an
COMMAND	**haz** (tú), **hag**a (Ud.), **hag**amos (nosotros), **hag**an (Uds.)
GERUND	**hecho**

INFINITIVE	**ir**
PRESENT	**voy, vas, va, vamos, vais, van**
IMPERFECT	**iba, ibas, iba, íbamos, ibais, iban**

PRETERIT	**fui, fuiste, fue, fuimos, fuisteis, fueron**
PRESENT SUBJUNCTIVE	**vay**a, **vay**as, **vay**a, **vay**amos, **vay**áis, **vay**an
COMMAND	ve (tú), **vay**a (Ud.), **vay**amos (nosotros), **vay**an (Uds.)
GERUND	**y**endo

INFINITIVE	o**í**r
PRESENT	**oig**o, **oy**es, **oy**e, oímos, oís, **oy**en
PRETERIT	oí, oíste, o**y**ó, oímos, oísteis, o**y**eron
PRESENT SUBJUNCTIVE	o**ig**a, o**ig**as, o**ig**a, o**ig**amos, o**ig**áis, o**ig**an
COMMAND	o**y**e (tú), o**ig**a (Ud.), o**ig**amos (nosotros), o**ig**an (Uds.)
PAST PARTICIPLE	o**í**do
GERUND	o**y**endo

INFINITIVE	pod**er**
PRESENT	p**ue**do, p**ue**des, p**ue**de, podemos, podéis, p**ue**den
PRETERIT	p**u**de, p**u**diste, p**u**do, p**u**dimos, p**u**disteis, p**u**dieron
FUTURE	**podr**é, **podr**ás, **podr**á, **podr**emos, **podr**éis, **podr**án
CONDITIONAL	**podr**ía, **podr**ías, **podr**ía, **podr**íamos, **podr**íais, **podr**ían
GERUND	p**u**diendo

INFINITIVE	pon**er**
PRESENT	pon**g**o, pones, pone, ponemos, ponéis, ponen
PRETERIT	**pus**e, **pus**iste, **pus**o, **pus**imos, **pus**isteis, **pus**ieron
FUTURE	**pondr**é, **pondr**ás, **pondr**á, **pondr**emos, **pondr**áis, **pondr**án
CONDITIONAL	**pondr**ía, **pondr**ías, **pondr**ía, **pondr**íamos, **pondr**íais, **pondr**ían

PRESENT SUBJUNCTIVE	ponga, pongas, ponga, pongamos, pongáis, pongan
COMMAND	pon (tú), ponga (Ud.), pongamos (nosotros), pongan (Uds.)
PAST PARTICIPLE	puesto

INFINITIVE	querer
PRESENT	quiero, quieres, quiere, queremos, queréis, quieren
PRETERIT	quise, quisiste, quiso, quisimos, quisisteis, quisieron
FUTURE	querré, querrás, querrá, querremos, querréis, querrán
CONDITIONAL	querría, querrías, querría, querríamos, querríais, querrían
PRESENT SUBJUNCTIVE	quiera, quieras, quiera, queramos, queráis, quieran

INFINITIVE	saber
PRESENT	sé, sabes, sabe, sabemos, sabéis, saben
PRETERIT	supe, supiste, supo, supimos, supisteis, supieron
FUTURE	sabré, sabrás, sabrá, sabremos sabréis, sabrán
CONDITIONAL	sabría, sabrías, sabría, sabríamos, sabríais, sabrían
PRESENT SUBJUNCTIVE	sepa, sepas, sepa, sepamos, sepáis, sepan

INFINITIVE	salir
PRESENT	salgo, sales, sale, salimos, salís, salen
FUTURE	saldré, saldrás, saldrá, saldremos, saldréis, saldrán
CONDITIONAL	saldría, saldrías, saldría, saldríamos, saldríais, saldrían
PRESENT SUBJUNCTIVE	salga, salgas, salga, salgamos, salgáis, salgan
COMMAND	sal (tú), salga (Ud.), salgamos (nosotros), salgan (Uds.)

INFINITIVE	ser
PRESENT	soy, eres, es, somos, sois, son
IMPERFECT	era, eras, era, éramos, erais, eran
PRETERIT	fui, fuiste, fue, fuimos, fuisteis, fueron
PRESENT SUBJUNCTIVE	sea, seas, sea, seamos, seáis, sean
COMMAND	sé (tú), sean (Uds.)

INFINITIVE	tener
PRESENT	tengo, tienes, tiene, tenemos, tenéis, tienen
PRETERIT	tuve, tuviste, tuvo, tuvimos, tuvisteis, tuvieron
FUTURE	tendré, tendrás, tendrá, tendremos, tendréis, tendrán
CONDITIONAL	tendría, tendrías, tendría, tendríamos, tendríais, tendrían
PRESENT SUBJUNCTIVE	tenga, tengas, tenga, tengamos, tengáis, tengan
COMMAND	ten (tú), tenga (Ud.), tengamos (nosotros), tengan (Uds.)

INFINITIVE	traer
PRESENT	traigo, traes, trae, traemos, traéis, traen
PRETERIT	traje, trajiste, trajo, trajimos, trajisteis, trajeron
PRESENT SUBJUNCTIVE	traiga, traigas, traiga, traigamos, traigáis, traigan
PAST PARTICIPLE	traído
GERUND	trayendo

INFINITIVE	valer
PRESENT	valgo, vales, vale, valemos, valéis, valen
FUTURE	valdré, valdrás, valdrá, valdremos, valdréis, valdrán

CONDITIONAL	valdr**í**a, **valdrías**, **valdría**, **valdríamos**, **valdríais**, **valdrían**
PRESENT SUBJUNCTIVE	val**g**a, val**g**as, val**g**a, val**g**amos, val**gáis**, val**g**an

INFINITIVE	ven**ir**
PRESENT	ven**g**o, v**i**enes, v**i**ene, venimos, venís, v**i**enen
PRETERIT	v**i**ne, v**i**niste, v**i**no, v**i**nimos, v**i**nisteis, v**i**nieron
FUTURE	**vendr**é, **vendrás**, **vendrá**, **vendr**emos, **vendréis**, **vendrán**
CONDITIONAL	**vendrí**a, **vendrías**, **vendría**, **vendríamos**, **vendríais**, **vendrían**
PRESENT SUBJUNCTIVE	ven**g**a, ven**g**as, ven**g**a, ven**g**amos, ven**gáis**, ven**g**an
COMMAND	**ven** (tú), ven**g**a (Ud.), ven**g**amos (nosotros), ven**g**an (Uds.)
GERUND	v**i**niendo

INFINITIVE	v**er**
PRESENT	v**e**o, ves, ve, vemos, veis, ven
IMPERFECT	v**eí**a, v**eí**as, v**eí**a, v**eí**amos, v**eí**ais, v**eí**an
PRESENT	v**e**a, v**e**as, v**e**a, v**e**amos, v**eá**is, v**e**an
PAST PARTICIPLE	v**isto**

◆ 5 ◆ PUNCTUATION

Although Spanish punctuation is similar to English, it has the following major differences:

(a) In Spanish, questions have an inverted question mark (¿) at the beginning and a normal one at the end.

¿Quién es?   *Who is it?*

(b) In Spanish, exclamatory sentences have an inverted exclamation point (¡) at the beginning and a normal one at the end.

¡Qué día!   *What a day!*

(c) The comma is not used before **y, e, o, u,** or **ni** in a series.

El lunes, el martes y el   There are classes on Monday,
miércoles hay clases.   Tuesday, and Wednesday.

(d) Spanish uses a comma with decimals where English uses a period.

3,5 (tres coma cinco)   *3.5 (three point five)*

(e) Spanish final quotation marks precede the comma or period.

Cervantes escribió   Cervantes wrote
«Don Quijote».   "Don Quijote."

◆ 6 ◆ SYLLABICATION

Spanish words are generally divided at the end of a line according to units of sound.

(a) A syllable normally begins with a consonant. The division is made before the consonant.

te-**n**er   di-**n**e-ro   a-**m**e-ri-**c**a-**n**o   re-**f**e-**r**ir

(b) Letter combinations **ch, ll,** and **rr** are never divided.

pe-**rr**o   ha-**ll**a-do   di-**ch**o

(c) If two or more consonants are combined, the division is made before the last consonant, except in the combinations **bl, br, cl, cr, pl, pr,** and **tr.**

tran**s**-**p**or-**t**e   de**s**-**c**u-bie**r**-to   con-**t**i-nuar   al-ber-ca

BUT

ha-**bl**ar   a-**br**ir   des-**cr**i-bir   a-**pr**en-**d**er   dis-**tr**i-buir

(d) Compound words, including words with prefixes and suffixes, may be divided by components or by syllables.

sur-a-me-ri-ca-no   OR   **su**-**r**a-me-ri-ca-no
mal-es-tar   OR   **ma**-**l**es-tar

◆ 7 ◆ STRESS

In Spanish, stress follows three general rules.

(a) If the words ends in a vowel, **n,** or **s,** the next-to-the-last syllable is stressed.

espa**d**a   des**a**stre   j**o**ven   señ**o**res

(b) If the words ends in a consonant, except **n** or **s,** the final syllable is stressed.

comprend**e**r   alab**a**r   recib**i**r   señ**o**r

(c) All exceptions to the above rules have a written accent mark.

s**á**bado   j**ó**venes   Ad**á**n   C**é**sar   franc**é**s

Spanish-English Vocabulary

The Spanish-English Vocabulary is intended to be complete for the context of this book.

Nouns are listed in the singular. Regular feminine forms of nouns are indicated by **(-a)** or the ending that replaces the masculine ending: **niño(-a)** or **alcalde(-esa).** Irregular noun plurals are given in full: **voz** *f.* voice; (*pl.* **voces**). Regular feminine forms of adjectives are indicated by **-a.**

> ## ABBREVIATIONS
>
> | | | | |
> |---|---|---|---|
> | *adj.* | adjective | *irr.* | irregular |
> | *aux.* | auxiliary verb | *m.* | masculine |
> | *f.* | feminine | *pl.* | plural |
> | *inf.* | infinitive | *sing.* | singular |

a to, at; **a eso de** about (*time*); **a menudo** often

abajo below, downstairs, down

abeja *f.* bee

abierto, -a open

abogado(-a) lawyer

abrigo *m.* overcoat

abril *m.* April

abrir to open

abuela *f.* grandmother

abuelo *m.* grandfather

aburrido,-a boring

acabar to finish, end; **acabar de** to have just

acampar to camp

accidente *m.* accident

aceite *m.* oil; **aceite de oliva** olive oil

aceituna *f.* olive

aceptar to accept

acera *f.* sidewalk

acercarse to approach

acero *m.* steel

acompañar to accompany

aconsejar to advise

acontecimiento *m.* event

acordarse (de) [ue] to remember

acostarse (ue) to go to bed

actividad *f.* activity

activo, -a active

actor *m.* actor

actriz *f.* actress

actuar to act

acuarela *f.* watercolor

adelantar to advance, to move forward

adiós goodbye

admirar to admire

adolescencia *f.* adolescence

adolescente *m. & f.* adolescent

adorno *m.* decoration

aduana *f.* customs

aduanero(-era) customs official

aerolínea *f.* airline

aeropuerto *m.* airport

afecto *m.* affection, love

afeitarse to shave

aficionado(-a) fan

agobiar to overwhelm, to weigh down

agosto *m.* August

agradecer (zc) to thank (for)

agregar (gu) to add

agrícola agricultural

agua *f.* water; **agua mineral** mineral water

aguacate *m.* avocado

aguardar to wait (for)

agudeza *f.* sharpness

aguinaldo *m.* Christmas or New Year's gift

ahora now; **ahora mismo** right now

ahorrar to save

aire *m.* air; **al aire libre** out-of-doors

ajeno of or belonging to another, another's; foreign; different

ala *f.* wing

alabar to praise

alcalde(-esa) mayor

alcanzable attainable, reachable

alcanzar (c) to reach, to attain

aldea *f.* village, town

alegre happy

alegría *f.* joy

alejar to separate; **alejarse (de)** to move away from

alemán (*f.* **alemana)** German

alergia *f.* allergy

alfabeto *m.* alphabet

alfombra *f.* rug, carpet

álgebra *m.* algebra

algo something

algodón *m.* cotton

alguien someone

alguno, -a some, any

allí there

almacén *m.* department store

almohada *f.* pillow

almorzar (ue) (c) to eat lunch

almuerzo *m.* lunch

alojamiento *m.* lodging

alpargata *f.* sandal

alpinismo *m.* mountain climbing

alquilar to rent, to hire

alquiler *m.* leasing, rent

alrededor (de) around

altavoz *m.* loudspeaker

alto, -a tall; high

altura *f.* height

alumno(-a) student, pupil

alzar (c) to raise

amable friendly, nice

amanecer (zc) to dawn

amar to love

amargo, -a bitter

amarillo, -a yellow

ambicioso, -a ambitious

ambiente *m.* atmosphere, environment; **medio ambiente** environment

ambulancia *f.* ambulance

ambulante wandering

amigo(-a) friend

amistad *f.* friendship

amo(-a) master, mistress, owner, boss

amor *m.* affection, love

amoroso, -a lovable

amplio, -a large, ample

amueblar to furnish

anaranjado, -a orange

ancho, -a wide

andar (*irr.*) to walk

anhelado, -a craved, longed for

anillo *m.* ring

año *m.* year

anoche last light

anochecer to grow dark

anteojos *m. pl.* eyeglasses

antes (de) before; **cuanto antes** as soon as possible

antiguo, -a old, ancient

antipático, -a unpleasant, disagreeable

anuario *m.* yearbook

anunciar to announce

anuncio *m.* announcement

apagar (gu) to put out; **apagarse** to shut off

aparato *m.* ride

aparecer (zc) to appear

apartado *m.* box; **apartado postal** post office box

apartamento *m.* apartment

apellido *m.* last name (family name)

apenas hardly, barely

apendicitis *f.* appendicitis

apetito *m.* appetite

aplauso *m.* applause

aplicado, -a studious, smart

apoyador(-ora) supporter

apoyar to support

aprender to learn

aprisa quickly, rapidly

aprovecharse de to take advantage of

aquel that; **aquél** that one

aquí here

árabe *m. & f.* Arab

araña *f.* spider

árbol *m.* tree

arder to burn

ardilla *f.* squirrel

arena *f.* sand

arete *m.* earring

argolla *f.* wedding band

argumento *m.* theme, plot

armario *m.* wardrobe, closet

arquitecto(-a) architect

arreglar to arrange, fix

arreglo *m.* arrangement

arriba above, upstairs

arrojar to throw

arroyo *m.* stream

arroz *m.* rice

arte *f.* art; **artes industriales** shop

artesanía *f.* arts and crafts

artista *m. & f.* artist, performer

asado roasted

asamblea *f.* assembly

asar to roast

ascensor *m.* elevator

asiento *m.* seat

asistir to attend

asma *f.* asthma

aspiradora *f.* vacuum cleaner

aspirina *f.* aspirin

asustarse to be frightened

ateneo *m.* literary club

aterrizaje *m.* landing

atleta *m. & f.* athlete

atlético, -a athletic

atletismo *m.* athletics

atracciones *f. pl.* attractions; **parque de atracciones** amusement park

atravesar (ie) to cross

atreverse to dare

atún *m.* tuna fish

aula *f.* classroom

aún still, yet

aún yet

ausente absent

autobús *m.* bus

automóvil *m.* car

autopista *f.* highway

auxilio *m.* aid, help; **primeros auxilios** first aid

ave *f.* bird

avenida *f.* avenue
aventura *f.* adventure
aventurero(-era) *m.* adventurer
averiguar (gü) to investigate
avión *m.* airplane
aviso *m.* notice
ayer yesterday
ayudante *m. & f.* aide
ayudar to help
ayuntamiento *m.* town hall
azúcar *m.* sugar
azul blue
azulejo *m.* tile

babero *m.* bib
bailar to dance
baile *m.* dance
bajar to go down, descend; to lower; **bajar de peso** to lose weight; **bajar(se) de** to get off (the train, etc.)
bajo, -a short
balcón *m.* balcony
ballena *f.* whale
baloncesto *m.* basketball
bañarse to take a bath
banco *m.* bank; bench
banda *f.* band
bandera *f.* flag
baño *m.* bath; **cuarto de baño** bathroom; **traje de baño** *m.* bathing suit
banquero(-era) banker
barata *f.* sale
barato, -a inexpensive, cheap
barba *f.* beard
barbilla *f.* chin
barco *m.* boat; **barco de vela** sailboat
barrer to sweep
barrio *m.* neighborhood
barro *m.* clay
bastante enough
basura *f.* garbage
bata *f.* robe
batalla *f.* battle, fight, struggle

batear to hit (with a bat)
batido *m.* shake
baúl *m.* trunk
bebé *m. & f.* baby
beber to drink
bebida *f.* drink, beverage
béisbol *m.* baseball
belleza *f.* beauty
beso *m.* kiss
biblioteca *f.* library
bicicleta *f.* bicycle
biftec *m.* steak
bigote *m.* mustache
bilingüe bilingual
billete *m.* bill, ticket
biología *f.* biology
blanco, -a white
blando, -a soft
blusa *f.* blouse
boca *f.* mouth
bocado *m.* snack
bodega *f.* grocery store
boleto *m.* ticket
boliche *m.* bowling
bolígrafo *m.* ballpoint pen
bolos *m. pl.* bowling
bolsa *f.* purse, handbag; **Bolsa** *f.* stock market
bolsillo *m.* pocket
bombero(-era) firefighter
bondadoso, -a kind
bonito, -a pretty, beautiful
borrado, -a erased, blurred
borrar to erase
bosque *m.* woods
bota *f.* boot
botella *f.* bottle
brazo *m.* arm
brillante *m.* diamond
brincar to jump
broche *m.* brooch, pin
brócoli *m.* broccoli
brújula *f.* compass
brutalidad *f.* brutality
bucear to snorkel; to dive
buceo *m.* diving

bueno good
buey *m.* ox
bufanda *f.* scarf
buque *m.* boat, ship
burlarse (de) to make fun of
buró *m.* night stand
burro *m.* donkey
buscar (qu) to look for, seek
butaca *f.* armchair (upholstered)
buzón *m.* mailbox

caballo *m.* horse; **a caballo** on horseback
cabello *m.* hair
caber (*irr.*) to fit
cabeza *f.* head
cabina *f.* cabin, booth: **cabina telefónica** telephone booth
cabra *f.* goat
cada each, every
cadena *f.* chain
caer (*irr.*) to fall; **dejar caer** to drop
café *m.* cafe; coffee; *also adj.* brown
cafetería *f.* cafeteria
caja *f.* box; cashier, cash register, teller's window; **caja fuerte** safe
cajero(-era) cashier, teller
calcetín *m.* sock
calculadora *f.* calculator
caldo *m.* broth, soup
calendario *m.* calendar
calentar (ie) to heat
cálido, -a warm
caliente hot
callarse to be silent, keep still
calle *f.* street
callos *m. pl.* tripe (*Spain*)
calor *m.* heat; **hace calor** it is hot (*weather*); **tener calor** to be warm
calvo, -a bald
cama *f.* bed
cámara *f.* camera; chamber;

cámara de diputados house of representatives

camarero(-era) waiter (waitress)

camarón *m.* shrimp

camarote *m.* cabin

cambiar to change

cambio *m.* change; exchange rate

caminar to walk

camino *m.* road

camión *m.* truck

camionero(-era) truck driver

camioneta *f.* station wagon, van

camisa *f.* shirt; **camiseta** T-shirt

campamento *m.* camp

campeonato *m.* championship

campesino(-a) farmer

campo *m.* country, field

caña *f.* cane; **caña de azúcar** sugar cane

canal *m.* channel (television)

canasta *f.* basket

cancha *f.* court (*sports*)

canción *f.* song

candelero *m.* candleholder

candidato(-a) candidate

canguro *m.* kangaroo

cansado, -a tired

cantante *m. & f.* singer

cantar to sing

canto *m.* song; singing

capacidad *f.* capacity

capítulo *m.* chapter

cara *f.* face

carabela *f.* caravel, boat

carbón *m.* coal

cariño *m.* affection, love

cariñoso, -a loving

carne *f.* meat; **carne de res** beef

carnet *m.* card; **carnet telefónico** calling card

carnicería *f.* butcher shop

carnicero(-era) butcher

caro, -a expensive

carpeta *f.* (file) folder

carpintero(-era) carpenter

carrera *f.* track; race; career, profession

carretera *f.* highway, road

carro *m.* car

carta *f.* letter

cartel *m.* poster

cartera *f.* wallet, billfold

cartero(-era) mail carrier

casa *f.* house

casado, -a married

casamiento *m.* marriage

casarse con to marry

casimir cashmere

castigar to punish

castillo *m.* castle

catedral *f.* cathedral

caucho *m.* rubber

cebolla *f.* onion

cebra *f.* zebra

ceja *f.* eyebrow

célebre famous

celoso, -a jealous

cemento *m.* cement

cena *f.* dinner, supper

cenar to eat supper

centro *m.* center, downtown; **centro comercial** mall; **centro juvenil** youth center

cepillarse to brush (one's teeth, hair, clothes)

cerca (de) near; close to

cerdo *m.* pork

cereal *m.* cereal

cereza *f.* cherry

cerrado, -a closed

cerrar (ie) to close

cesar to stop

césped *m.* lawn, grass

cesta *f.* basket

ceviche *m.* raw fish, sushi

chaleco *m.* vest

chaqueta *f.* jacket

charlar to chat

chícharo *m.* pea

chimenea *f.* fireplace

chino, -a Chinese

chisme *m.* rumor, gossip

chiste *m.* joke

chocar (qu) to crash, to collide

chocolate *m.* chocolate

chofer *m. & f.* driver

choza *f.* hut

chuleta *f.* chop

ciego, -a blind, visually-impaired

cielo *m.* sky

cien (ciento) one hundred; **por ciento** percent

ciencia *f.* science

científico(-a) scientist

cierto, -a sure; true; certain

cincuenta fifty

cine *m.* movies (movie theater)

cinta *f.* tape, ribbon

cinturón *m.* belt

circo *m.* circus

círculo *m.* club; **círculo de matemáticas** math club; **círculo dramático** drama club; **círculo español** Spanish club; **círculo internacional** international club

ciruela *f.* plum

cirugía *f.* surgery

cirujano(-a) surgeon

cisne *m.* swan

cita *f.* appointment, date

ciudad *f.* city

ciudadano(-a) citizen

claro, -a clear, light-colored

clase *f.* class; kind

clásico, -a classical

cliente *m. & f.* client, customer

clima *m.* climate

cobarde cowardly

cobrar to collect

coche *m.* car

cochero(-era) cab driver

cochino *m.* pig

cocido *m.* stew

cocina *f.* kitchen

cocinar to cook

cocinero(-era) chef, cook

cocodrilo *m.* crocodile

código *m.* code; **código postal** zip code

codo *m.* elbow

coger (j) to seize, to catch

cola *f.* line (of people); tail

colchón *m.* mattress

coleccionar to collect

colegio *m.* school, academy

colgar (ue) (gu) to hang

coliflor *m.* coliflower

colina *f.* hill

collar *m.* necklace

colocar (qu) to place, to put

colorear to color

columpio *m.* swing

comedor *m.* dining room

comentario *m.* comment

comenzar (ie, c) to begin

comer to eat

comerciante *m. & f.* merchant, businessperson

cometer to commit; **cometer un error** to make a mistake

cómico, -a funny

comida *f.* meal, food

como as; **¿cómo?** how?

cómoda *f.* dresser

cómodo, -a comfortable

compañero(-era) companion, friend

compañía *f.* company

compartimento *m.* compartment

compartir to share

compás *m.* compass; (music) beat, time

compilar to compile

comprar to buy

compras: ir de compras to go shopping

comprender to understand

computadora *f.* computer

comunidad *f.* community

con with

concierto *m.* concert

concluir (y) to conclude

concurso *m.* contest

conducir (zc) to lead, to drive

conejo *m.* rabbit

conferencia *f.* conference

confesar (ie) to confess

confiar (en) to rely (on), to confide (in)

congelador *m.* freezer

congreso *m.* congress; convention, meeting

conocer (zc) to know (a person)

conocido, -a known

conocimiento *m.* knowledge

conquistador(-ora) conqueror

conseguir (i) (g) to get, to obtain, to succeed in

consejero(-era) counselor

consejo *m.* advice

consentir (ie, i) to spoil

constar (de) to consist (of)

construir (y) to construct, to build

consultorio *m.* office (medical)

contaminación *f.* pollution

contar (ue) to count; to tell; **contar con** to count on

contenido *m.* content

contento, -a happy

contestar *to* answer

contigo with you

continuar (ú) to continue

contra against

contrato *m.* lease

contribuir (y) to contribute

convencer (z) to convince

conversar to converse

convidar to invite

copa *f.* (wine) glass

copiar to copy

corazón *m.* heart

corbata *f.* tie

corcho *m.* cork

cordero *m.* lamb

coreano, -a Korean

coro *m.* chorus

corregir (i) (j) to correct

correo *m.* mail, post office; **correo electrónico** e-mail

correr to run

correspondencia *f.* correspondence; **amigo por correspondencia** pen pal

corrida *f.* run, dash; **corrida de toros** bullfight

cortar to cut

corte *f.* court (house)

cortejar to court

cortés polite

cortesía *f.* courtesy

cortina *f.* curtain

cosa *f.* thing

coser to sew

costa *f.* coast

costar (ue) to cost

costumbre *f.* custom, habit

crecer (zc) to grow

creer to believe

crucero *m.* cruise

crucigrama *m.* crossword puzzle

cruzar (c) to cross

cuaderno *m.* notebook

cuadra *f.* (street) block

cuadro *m.* painting

¿cuál, -es? which?, which one(s)?

cuando when; **¿cuándo?** when?; **de cuando / de vez en cuando** from time to time

cuanto, -a as much; **¿cuánto?** how much?; **¿cuántos, -as?** how many; **¡cuánto, -a... !** how much ... !

cuarenta forty

Cuaresma *f.* Lent

cuartel *m.* barrack; **cuartel de la policía** police precinct

cuarto, -a fourth; quarter; **un cuarto** one quarter; **cuarto** *m.* room; **cuarto de baño** bathroom

cubiertos *m. pl.* cutlery, utensils

cubrir to cover

cuchara *f.* spoon

cucharada *f.* tablespoon

cucharita *f.* teaspoon

cuchichear to whisper

cuchillo *m.* knife

cuello *m.* neck

cuenta *f.* bill, (restaurant) check; account; **cuenta de ahorros** savings account; **cuenta de cheques** checking account

cuento *m.* story; **cuento infantil** childrens' story

cuero *m.* leather

cuerpo *m.* body

cuidado care; **con cuidado** carefully; **tener cuidado** to be careful

cuidar to take care of

culpa *f.* blame; **tener la culpa** to be at fault

cultivar to cultivate

cumpleaños *m.* birthday

cumplir to fulfill, to accomplish; **cumplir con la palabra** to keep one's word

cuñada *f.* sister-in-law

cuñado *m.* brother-in-law

cuota *f.* fare

cura *f.* cure; *also m.* priest

curiosidad *f.* curiosity

curioso, -a curious

curso *m.* course, class

cuyo, -a whose

dama *f.* lady; **primera dama** first lady; **juego de damas** checkers

daño *m.* harm, damage

dar to give; **darse cuenta de** to realize; **dar limosna** to give alms (make a donation)

de of, from; **de repente** suddenly

debajo de beneath, under

deber to have to (should, ought); to owe

debido a due to

débil weak

decano(-a) dean

decidir to decide

décimo, -a tenth

decir (*irr.*) to say, to tell; **decir la verdad** to tell the truth

decisión *f.* decision; **tomar una decisión** to make a decision

dedo *m.* finger; **dedo del pie** toe

defender (ie) to defend

dejar to let, allow, leave (behind)

delante de in front of, ahead of

deletrear to spell

delgado, -a thin

demasiado too much, too many

democracia *f.* democracy

demora *f.* delay

dentista *m. & f.* dentist

dentro de inside of

dependiente *m. & f.* clerk, salesperson

deporte *m.* sport

deportivo, -a sporty

depositar to deposit

depósito *m.* deposit

derecho, -a right; **derecho** straight ahead; **derecho** *m.* right

desacuerdo *m.* disagreement

desaparecer (zc) to disappear

desarrollo *m.* development

desastre *m.* disaster

desayunarse to have breakfast

desayuno *m.* breakfast

descansar to rest

descolgar (ue) (gu) to pick up (the phone)

desconocido, -a unknown

descontento, -a unhappy

descortés impolite

describir to describe

descripción *f.* description

descubridor(-ora) discoverer

descubrimiento *m.* discovery

descuento *m.* discount

desde from; since

desear to want, wish

desembocar to flow out, empty

desempleo *m.* unemployment

desgracia *f.* misfortune; **por desgracia** unfortunately

deshuesado, -a deboned

desierto *m.* desert

desilusionado, -a disillusioned

despacio slowly

despedirse (de) (i) to take leave (of), to say goodbye (to)

despegar (gu) to take off (plane)

despegue *m.* takeoff

despertarse (ie) to wake up, awaken

después later; **después de** after

destacarse to stand out

destruir (y) to destroy

desván *m.* attic

detrás (de) behind

devolver (ue) to return (something); to give back

día *m.* day; **día feriado** legal holiday; **día libre** day off; **de día** by day; **hoy día** nowadays

diamante *m.* diamond

diario, -a daily; **a diario** every day; *also m.* diary

diccionario *m.* dictionary

dicho *m.* saying

diciembre *m.* December

dictado *m.* dictation

dictador(-ora) dictator

dictadura *f.* dictatorship

diente *m.* tooth

dieta *f.* diet

difícil difficult

difunto(-a) deceased

diligente diligent, hard-working

dinero *m.* money

diputado(-a) representative

director(-ora) manager, principal

dirigir (j) to direct; **dirigirse (j)**

a to make one's way toward; to address

discoteca *f.* discotheque

disculpa *f.* excuse, apology

diseñador(-ora) designer

diseñar to design

diseño *m.* drawing

disfraz *m.* disguise

disfrutar to enjoy

disminuir (y) to diminish, to decrease

disponible available

distinguir (g) to distinguish

distinto, -a different

distribuir (y) to distribute

diversión *f.* diversion; **parque de diversiones** amusement park

divertido, -a fun

divertirse (ie) to enjoy oneself

dividir to divide

doblar to fold

docena *f.* dozen

dólar *m.* dollar

doler (ue) to ache

dolor *m.* pain, ache; **dolor de cabeza** headache; **tener dolor de cabeza** to have a headache

doloroso, -a painful

domingo *m.* Sunday

dona *f.* doughnut

donde where; **¿dónde?** where?; **¿de dónde?** (from) where?; **¿a dónde?** (to) where?

dormir (ue) to sleep; **dormirse (ue)** to fall asleep

dormitorio *m.* bedroom

dote *m. & f.* dowry

dramaturgo(-a) playwright

ducha *f.* shower

ducharse to take a shower

duda *f.* doubt; **sin duda** undoubtedly

dudoso doubtful

dueño(-a) owner

dulce sweet; **dulces** *m.* candy, sweets

durante during

duro, -a hard

echar to throw; **echar de menos** to miss; **echar una carta** to mail; **echarse a...** to begin; **echar a perder** to spoil

economía *f.* economy

edificio *m.* building; **edificio de apartamentos** apartment house

educación *f.* education; **educación física** gym

educado, -a educated; polite

efectivo *m.* cash

eficacia *f.* efficiency

egoísta selfish

ejecutivo (-a) executive

ejercer (z) to exert; to exercise; to practice (a profession)

ejercicio *m.* exercise

ejercitar to exercise

ejército *m.* army

elector(-ora) elector, voter

elefante *m.* elephant

elegir (j) to elect, choose

elevar to raise, lift

elote *m.* green bean

embajada *f.* embassy

embajador(-ora) ambassador

embarazoso, -a embarrassing

emisión *f.* broadcast

empate *m.* tie (sports)

empezar (ie) (c) to begin

empresa *f.* business

en in, on; **en seguida** immediately

enamorarse de to fall in love with

encaje *m.* lace

encantador, -a enchanting, charming

encarcelado, -a imprisoned

encargarse (de) to take charge

(of)

encender to light, to burn

encima de on top of

encontrar (ue) to find, to meet

energía *f.* energy

enero *m.* January

enfadarse to get angry

enfermedad *f.* disease, illness

enfermería *f.* infirmary; nursing

enfermero(-era) nurse

enfermo(-a) sick person, patient; *also adj.* sick, ill

enfrente in front of, opposite

enfriar to chill

ensalada *f.* salad

ensayista *m. & f.* essayist

enseñar to teach, show

entender (ie) to understand

enterrar (ie) to bury

entonces then

entrada *f.* entrance; admission

entrar to enter

entre between, among

entregar to deliver

entrenador(-ora) trainer, coach

entrenamiento *m.* training

entrevista *f.* interview

enviar (í) to send

envidia *f.* envy

envolver (ue) to wrap up

enojarse to get angry

época *f.* epoch, era

equipaje *m.* luggage

equipo *m.* team; equipment; **equipo de béisbol** baseball team; **equipo de fútbol** soccer team

equitación *f.* horseback riding

equivocado, -a mistaken, incorrect

equivocarse to be mistaken

error *m.* error

esbelto, -a svelt, slim

escala *f.* stop (air travel)

escalera *f.* stairs

escaparse to elope

escoger (j) to choose, to select

escolar school

esconder to hide (something)

escribir to write

escrito, -a written; **por escrito** in writing

escritor(-ora) writer

escritura *f.* writing

escuchar to listen (to)

escudero *m.* squire

escuela *f.* school; **escuela primaria** elementary school; **escuela secundaria** high school

escurrir to strain

ese that; **ése** that one

esmeralda *f.* emerald

espada *f.* sword

espalda *f.* back

español(-ola) Spanish

espantar to frighten, to scare

espejo *m.* mirror

esperar to wait for, await, hope, expect

espinaca *f.* spinach

esposa *f.* wife

esposo *m.* husband

esquí *m.* skiing; **esquí acuático** waterskiing

establecer (zc) to establish

establecimiento *m.* establishment

estación *f.* train station; season

estadio *m.* stadium

estado *m.* state

estallar to explode, to burst

estampilla *f.* stamp

estar *(irr.)* to be

estatua *f.* statue

este, -a this; **éste, -a** this one

este *m.* east

estéreo *m.* stereo

estética *f.* esthetics

estilo *m.* style

estimar to esteem

estómago *m.* stomach

estornudar to sneeze

estrecho, -a narrow

estrella *f.* star

estrenar to open (a play, a movie)

estreno *m.* opening (movie)

estricto, -a strict

estuche *m.* case

estudiante *m. & f.* student, pupil

estudiar to study

estudio *m.* study; den

estufa *f.* stove

examen *m.* examination, test

excursión *f.* field trip

excursionista *m. & f.* hiker

exigente demanding

exigir to demand

existencia *f.* stock

éxito *m.* success; **tener éxito** to be successful

explicación *f.* explanation

explicar to explain

explorador(-ora) explorer; **el niño explorador** Boy Scout

exposición *f.* exhibit, show

expulsar to expel, to eject

extinguir (g) to extinguish

extrañar to miss

extranjero(-era) foreigner; **al extranjero** abroad

extraño, -a strange, rare

fábrica *f.* factory

fabricar to manufacture

facultad *f.* faculty; **facultad de medicina** medical school

falda *f.* skirt

falta *f.* error, mistake

faltar to lack

fama *f.* fame

familia *f.* family

farmacéutico(-a) pharmacist

farmacia *f.* pharmacy, drugstore

farol *m.* street lamp

fascinar to enjoy, to like

febrero *m.* February

fecha *f.* date

felicidad *f.* happiness

felicitar to congratulate

feliz happy

feo, -a ugly

feria *f.* fair

ferretería *f.* hardware store

ferrocarril *m.* railroad

fiebre *f.* fever

fiel faithful

fieltro *m.* felt

fiesta *f.* holiday, celebration, party

fijarse en to look at

fila *f.* line (of people)

filósofo(-a) philosopher

fin *m.* end; **fin de semana** weekend; **por fin** at last; **al fin** finally

firmar to sign

física *f.* physics

flaco, -a skinny

flan *m.* custard

flor *f.* flower

florería *f.* florist shop

florero *m.* vase

fogata *f.* bonfire

folleto *m.* pamphlet

fomentar to foster, to promote

formación *f.* formation

formulario *m.* form; formula

fotografía *f.* photograph; **sacar fotografías** to take pictures

fotógrafo *m.* photographer

fracaso *m.* failure

fractura *f.* fracture

franco, -a frank

franela *f.* flannel

franqueza *f.* frankness

frase *f.* sentence

frecuencia *f.* frequency

frecuentemente frequently

fregadero *m.* kitchen sink

frenar to brake (stop)

frente *f.* forehead

frente a facing, in front of

fresa *f.* strawberry
fresco, -a fresh; also *m.* cool
frijol *m.* bean
frío *m.* cold; **hacer frío** to be cold (*weather*); **tener frío** to be cold
frito, -a fried
frontera *f.* border
fruta *f.* fruit
frutería *f.* fruit store
fuego *m.* fire
fuente *f.* fountain
fuera outside
fuerte strong
fuerza *f.* strength
función *f.* function, showing
funcionar to function, to work
fundador(-ora) founder
furia *f.* fury
furioso, -a furious
fútbol *m.* soccer; **el fútbol americano** football

gabinete *m.* cabinet
gallego, -a Galician
galleta *f.* cookie, cracker
gallina *f.* hen
gallo *m.* rooster
galón *m.* gallon
gambas *f. pl.* shrimp
gamusa *f.* suede
gana *f.* desire; **tener ganas de** to feel like
ganado *m.* cattle
ganador(-ora) winner
ganancias *f. pl.* earnings
ganar to win
garaje *m.* garage
garganta *f.* throat
gasolinera *f.* gas station
gastar to spend (money)
gasto *m.* expense
gato(-a) cat
gemelo(-a) twin
género *m.* genre

generosidad *f.* generosity
generoso, -a generous
geografía *f.* geography
gerente *m. & f.* manager
gimnasio *m.* gymnasium
giro *m.* money order
gitano(-a) Gypsy
globo *m.* balloon
gobernador(-ora) governor
gobernar (ie) to govern
gobierno *m.* government
gol *m.* goal (*sports*)
golf *m.* golf
goma *f.* eraser
gordo, -a fat
gorra *f.* cap
gozar de to enjoy
grabado, -a etched, recorded
grabado *m.* etching
grabar to record
gracias thank you
gracioso, -a cute, adorable
grado *m.* degree
graduarse de to be graduated from
gramática *f.* grammar
gran great
grande large, big
grandeza *f.* greatness
granja *f.* farm
gratis free (of charge)
griego, -a Greek
gripe *m.* flu
gris gray
gritar to shout
grito *m.* shout
groseramente vulgarly, impolitely
grosería *f.* vulgarity
grupo *m.* group
guante *m.* glove
guapo, -a handsome, pretty
guardar to keep; **guardar cama** to stay in bed
guardarropa *m.* checkroom
guardia *m. & f.* guard

guerra *f.* war
guerrillero(-era) guerrilla fighter
guía *m.* guide; *also f.* guide book; **guía telefónica** telephone book
guiar to guide, to drive (a vehicle)
guisado *m.* stew
gustar to please
gusto *m.* pleasure

haber to have (*aux. verb*)
habichuela *f.* bean
habilidad *f.* skill
habitación *f.* room
hablador, -a talkative
hablar to speak, talk
hacer (*irr.*) to make, to do; **hacer de** to act as; **hacer la(s) maleta(s)** to pack; **hacer una pregunta** to ask a question; **hacer un viaje** to take a trip; **hacerse** to become
hacha *f.* ax
hacia toward
hallar to find
hamaca *f.* hammock
hambre *f.* hunger; **tener hambre** to be hungry
hamburguesa *f.* hamburger
hasta until
hazaña *f.* deed
heladería *f.* ice-cream shop
helado *m.* ice cream; **helado, -a** iced
herencia *f.* heredity; inheritance
herida *f.* wound, injury
hermana *f.* sister
hermano *m.* brother
hermoso, -a handsome, beautiful
héroe *m.* hero
heroína *f.* heroine
hielo *m.* ice

hierba *f.* grass

hierro *m.* iron

hija *f.* daughter

hijo *m.* son; *pl.* sons, children

historia *f.* history

hockey *m.* hockey

hoja *f.* leave; sheet (of paper, etc.)

hombre *m* man

hombro *m.* shoulder

honesto, -a honest

honrado, a honorable, honest

hora *f.* hour

horario *m.* schedule; **horario de clases** class schedule

horno *m.* oven; **horno de microondas** microwave oven

hospital *m.* hospital

hotel *m.* hotel

hoy today

hoyo *m.* hole

huarache *m.* sandal

huelga *f.* strike

huérfano(-a) orphan

hueso *m.* bone

huésped *m. & f.* guest

huevo *m.* egg

huir (y) to flee

humanidad *f.* humanity

idioma *m.* language

iglesia *f.* church

igualmente the same to you, likewise

imaginario, -a imaginary

imaginativo, -a imaginative

imán *m.* magnet

impedir (i) to prevent

impermeable *m.* raincoat

imprenta *f.* press

impuesto *m.* tax

impulsivo, -a impulsive

inalcanzable unattainable, unreachable

incendio *m.* fire

infancia *f.* infancy

infección *f.* infection

inflación *f.* inflation

inflar to inflate

influir (y) to influence

informática *f.* computer science

ingeniero(-era) engineer

ingenuo, -a naive

inglés (*f.* **inglesa**) English

iniciar to start, begin

injusto,-a unjust

inquilino(-a) tenant

insecto *m.* insect

insistir (en) to insist on

insurrección *f.* rebellion

inteligente intelligent

intención *f.* intention

interesante interesting

intermedio *m.* intermission

interrumpir to interrupt

inundación *f.* flood

investigador(-ora) researcher

invierno *m.* winter

invitación *f.* invitation

invitar to invite

inyección *f.* injection

ir *(irr.)* to go; **irse** to leave

isla *f.* island

italiano, -a Italian

itinerario *m.* itinerary

izquierdo, -a left

jabón *m.* soap

jamás never, not . . . ever, ever

jamón *m.* ham

japonés (*f.* **japonesa**) Japanese

jardín *m.* garden

jefe *m.* chief, head; **jefe de estado** head of state

jirafa *f.* giraffe

joven young; *also m. & f.* young person

joya *f.* jewel

joyería *f.* jewelry store

joyero(-era) jeweler

jubilado, -a retired

judías verdes *f. pl.* green beans

juego *m.* game

jueves *m.* Thursday

juez(-a) judge

jugada *f.* play

jugador(-ora) player

jugar (ue) (gu) to play (a sport)

jugo *m.* juice

juguete *m.* toy

julio *m.* July

junio *m.* June

junto together; **junto a** beside

juventud *f.* youth

ketchup *m.* ketchup

labio *m.* lip

lado *m.* side; **al lado de** next to, alongside

ladrido *m.* bark

ladrillo *m.* brick

ladrón *m.* (*f.* **ladrona**) thief

lago *m.* lake

laguna *f.* lagoon

lamentar to be sorry about, to regret

lámpara *f.* lamp

lana *f.* wool

lancha *f.* boat

lápiz *m.* pencil

largo, -a long

lástima *f.* pity, compassion

lastimar to hurt; **lastimarse** to hurt oneself

latín *m.* Latin (language)

lavadora *f.* washing machine

lavandería *f.* laundry

lavaplatos *m.* dishwasher

lavar to wash; **lavarse** to wash oneself

lealtad *f.* loyalty

lección *f.* lesson

leche *f.* milk

lechería milk store

lechero(-era) milk deliverer

lechuga *f.* lettuce
lector de MP3 *m.* MP3 player
lectura *f.* reading
leer (y) to read
legumbre *f.* vegetable
lengua *f.* tongue, language
león *m.* lion
leopardo *m.* leopard
letrero *m.* sign
levantar to raise, lift; **levantarse** to get up
ley *f.* law
leyenda *f.* legend
libertad *f.* liberty
libra *f.* pound
libre free
librería *f.* bookstore
librero *m.* bookcase
libro *m.* book
lidiar to fight
ligereza *f.* lightness
ligero, -a light (weight)
limón *m.* lemon
limonada *f.* lemonade
limosna *f.* alms
limpiar to clean
limpieza *f.* cleanliness
limpio, -a clean
lino *m.* linen
listo, -a ready; **estar listo, -a** to be ready; **ser listo, -a** to be clever
llamada *f.* call
llamar to call; **llamarse** to be named, be called
llanura *f.* plain, prairie
llave *f.* key
llavero *m.* key chain
llegada *f.* arrival
llegar to arrive
llenar to fill
lleno, -a full
llevar to carry, wear; **llevar a cabo** to carry out
llorar to cry, weep
llover (ue) to rain

lluvia *f.* rain
lobo(-a) wolf
locutor(-ora) announcer
lodo *m.* mud
lograr to achieve, to attain; to succeed in
lotería *f.* lottery
lucha *f.* battle, fight, struggle; **lucha libre** wrestling
luchar to fight
luego then
lugar *m.* place; **tener lugar** to take place
luna *f.* moon
lunes *m.* Monday
luz *f.* light

madera *f.* wood
madrastra *f.* stepmother
madrina *f.* godmother
maestro *m.* teacher
maíz *m.* corn
maleta *f.* suitcase
malo, -a evil
mañana *f.* morning; **de la mañana** A.M.; tomorrow
mancha *f.* stain, spot
mandar to send; to order
manejo *m.* handling; operation
manera *f.* way, means; **de manera...** in a . . . way
mano *f.* hand
manta *f.* blanket
mantel *m.* tablecloth
mantequilla *f.* butter
mantilla *f.* shawl
manzana *f.* apple
mapa *m.* map
maquillaje *m.* makeup
maquillarse to put on makeup
máquina *f.* machine; **máquina de contestar** answering machine
mar *m. & f.* sea
maratón *m.* marathon
marca *f.* brand

marcador *m.* marker
marcar (qu) to designate, to show; to dial
marcharse to go away
marido *m.* husband
mariscos *m. pl.* shellfish; seafood
marrón brown
martes *m.* Tuesday
marzo *m.* March
más more, plus
máscara *f.* mask
matemáticas *f. pl.* math
matemático(-a) mathematician
materia *f.* subject
máximo, -a maximum
mayo *m.* May
mayonesa *f.* mayonnaise
mayor older, greater
mayoría *f.* majority
mecánico(-a) mechanic
medalla *f.* medal
mediano, -a medium
medianoche *f.* midnight
medicamento *m.* medicine
medicina *f.* medicine
médico(-a) doctor
medio *m.* means, middle, half; **medio de transporte** means of transportation; *also adj.* half
mediodía *m.* noon
medir (i) to measure
mejilla *f.* cheek
mejillón *m.* mussel
mejor better; best
mejorar to improve
melocotón *m.* peach
memoria *f.* memory; **aprender de memoria** to memorize, to learn by heart
menester *m.* need; **es menester** it is necessary
menor lesser, younger
menos less, minus
mensaje *m.* message
mensajero(-era) messenger
mentir (ie, i) to lie

mentira *f.* lie

menú *m.* menu

mercado *m.* market

merecer (zc) to deserve

mermelada *f.* jam, marmalade

mes *m.* month

mesa *f.* table

mesera *f.* waitress

mesero *m.* waiter

meseta *f.* plateau

meta *f.* goal

meter to put (in); **meterse** to interfere, to meddle

metro *m.* subway

mexicano, -a Mexican

mezcla *f.* mix, mixture, blend

mezclar to mix

miedo *m.* fear; **tener miedo (de)** to fear, to be afraid

mientras while; **mientras tanto** meanwhile

miércoles *m.* Wednesday

mil one thousand

milla *f.* mile

millón *m.* million

mínimo, -a minimum

ministro(-a) minister; **primer(-a) ministro(-a)** Prime Minister

minoría *f.* minority

minusválido, -a handicapped

mirada *f.* look

mirar to look (at)

mismo, -a same; **hoy mismo** this very day

mitad *f.* half

mochila *f.* knapsack, backpack, bookbag

moda *f.* style

modo *m.* way; **de modo...** in a... way

molestar to bother, to annoy

moneda *f.* coin

mono *m.* monkey

monopatín *m.* skateboard

montaña *f.* mountain

montañoso, -a mountainous

montar to ride; **montar a caballo** to go horseback riding; **montar en bicicleta** to ride a bicycle

monumento *m.* monument

morado, -a purple

morder (ue) to bite

moreno, -a brunette

morir (ue) to die

mostaza *f.* mustard

mostrar (ue) to show

motocicleta (moto) *f.* motorcycle

mover (ue) to move

mozo *m.* waiter, server

muchedumbre *f.* crowd

mucho, -a a lot, many

mueble *m.* piece of furniture

muela *f.* molar

muelle *m.* pier

muerte *f.* death

mujer *f.* woman

muleta *f.* red flag used by bullfighters

mundial worldwide

mundo *m.* world; **todo el mundo** everyone

muñeca *f.* doll

murciélago *m.* bat

museo *m.* museum

músico *m.* musician

nacer (zc) to be born

nación *f.* nation

nacionalidad *f.* nationality

nada nothing, (not) anything; **de nada** you're welcome

nadador(-ora) swimmer

nadar to swim

nadie no one, nobody, (not) anyone

naipes *m. pl.* cards

naranja *f.* orange

nariz *f.* nose

natación *f.* swimming

naturaleza *f.* nature

neblina *f.* fog

necesitar to need

necio, -a foolish, stupid

negar (ie) (gu) to deny; **negarse a** to refuse to

negro, -a black

neumonía *f.* pneumonia

nevada *f.* snowfall

nevar (ie) to snow

ni... ni neither . . . nor . . . ; not . . . either . . . or . . . ; **ni siquiera** not even

niebla *f.* fog

nieta *f.* granddaughter

nieto *m.* grandson; *pl.* grandsons, grandchildren

nieve *f.* snow

nilón *m.* nylon

niña *f.* girl

niñez *f.* childhood

ninguno, -a no, none, (not) any

niño *m.* boy

nobleza *f.* nobility

noche *f.* night; **anoche** last night; **esta noche** tonight; **de la noche** P.M.; **de noche** by night

nombrado, -a named

nombre *m.* name; **nombre de pila** first name

norte *m.* north

nota *f.* grade; note

noticias *f. pl.* news

noticiero *m.* news show

novela *f.* novel

noveno, -a ninth

noventa ninety

novia *f.* girlfriend

noviembre *m.* November

novio *m.* boy friend

nube *f.* cloud

nudo *m.* knot

nuera *f.* daughter-in-law

nuevo, -a new

número *m.* number; **número**

equivocado wrong number
numeroso, -a numerous
nunca never, (not) ever

obedecer (zc) to obey
obra *f.* work; **obra de teatro** play
obrero(-era) laborer, worker
océano *m.* ocean
ochenta eighty
ocio *m.* idleness, leisure
octavo, -a eighth
octubre *m.* October
ocupado, -a busy
odio *m.* hate
oeste *m.* west
ofrecer (zc) to offer
oído *m.* (inner) ear; hearing
oír *(irr.)* to hear
ojo *m.* eye
ola *f.* wave
oler (hue) to smell
olla *f.* jug, bowl
olvidadizo, -a forgetful
olvidar to forget
onda *f.* wave
ópera *f.* opera
operación *f.* operation
operador(-ora) operator
opuesto, -a opposite
oración *f.* sentence
ordenador *m.* computer
ordenar to order
oreja *f.* (outer) ear
orgullo *m.* pride
orgulloso, -a proud
orilla *f.* shore
oro *m.* gold
orquesta *f.* orchestra
oscuridad *f.* darkness
oscuro, -a dark
oso *m.* bear
otro, -a other, another
oveja *f.* sheep

paciente *m. & f.* patient
padecer (zc) to suffer
padrastro *m.* stepfather
padre *m.* father
padrino *m.* godfather
paella *f.* paella
pagar (gu) to pay (for)
página *f.* page
país *m.* country
paisaje *m.* landscape
pájaro *m.* bird
palabra *f.* word
palmera *f.* palm tree
palomita (de maíz) *f.* popcorn
pan *m.* bread; **pan tostado** toast; **panecillo** roll
panadería *f.* bakery
panadero(-era) (bread) baker
panecillo *m.* roll
panorámico, -a panoramic
pantalla *f.* screen
pantalón *m.* pants, trousers; **pantalón corto** shorts
pantera *f.* panther
pantimedias *f. pl.* pantyhose
pantorrilla *f.* calf
pañuelo *m.* handkerchief
papa *f.* potato; **papas fritas** french-fried potatoes
Papa *m.* Pope
papel *m.* paper; part
paperas *f. pl.* mumps
paquete *m.* package
par *m.* pair
para for
parabrisas *m.* windshield
parada *f.* stop, bus stop
paraguas *m. sing. & pl.* umbrella
parecer (zc) to seem
parecido, -a similar
pared *f.* wall
pareja *f.* couple
pariente *m. & f.* relative
parlamento *m.* parliament
párpado *m.* eyelid

parque *m.* park; **parque nacional** national park; **parque zoológico** zoo; **parque de bomberos** fire station
parte *f.* part; **en ninguna parte** not anywhere, nowhere; **en otra parte** elsewhere; **en todas partes** everywhere
partidario(-aria) fan
partido *m.* game, match; party (political)
partir to leave, depart
pasado, -a past; **el año pasado** last year
pasadomañana day after tomorrow
pasajero(-era) passenger
pasar to pass, spend (time)
pasatiempo *m.* hobby, pastime
pasearse to take a walk
paseo *m.* walk, path
pasillo *m.* hall
pasión *f.* passion
paso *m.* step
pasta *f.* macaroni
pastel *m.* cake
pastelería *f.* pastry shop
patear to kick
patín *m.* skate
patinar to skate
patio *m.* patio, schoolyard
patria *f.* native country; fatherland, mother country
pavo *m.* turkey
paz *f.* peace
peaje *m.* toll
pecho *m.* chest
pechuga *f.* chicken breast
pedir (i) to ask for, request; to order (food); **pedir prestado** to borrow
peinarse to comb one's hair
peine *m.* comb
pelar to peel
pelear to fight
peligro *m.* danger

peligroso, -a dangerous

pelo *m.* hair

pelota *f.* ball

peluche: **animal de peluche** stuffed animal

peluquería *f.* hair salon, barber shop

peluquero(-era) barber, hair stylist

pendiente pending

pensar (ie) to think; to intend

peor worse

pepino *m.* cucumber

pequeño, -a small

pera *f.* pear

perder (ie) to lose

perdido, -a lost

perdón *m.* apology

pereza *f.* laziness

perezoso, -a lazy

perfumería *f.* perfume shop

periódico *m.* newspaper

periodismo *m.* journalism

periodista *m. & f.* reporter, journalist

perla *f.* pearl

permanecer (zc) to remain

permiso *m.* permission

permitir to let, to allow, to permit

perro *m.* dog

perseguir (i) (g) to pursue

persa Persian

persona *f.* person

pertenecer (zc) to belong

pesado, -a heavy

pesas *f. pl.* weights

pesca *f.* fishing

pescado *m.* fish (out of the water)

pescador(-ora) fisherman

peso *m.* weight

pestaña *f.* eyelash

pez *m.* fish (in the water)

piano *m.* piano

picante spicy

pico *m.* peak

pie *m.* foot

piedad *f.* pity

piedra *f.* stone

piel *f.* skin; leather, fur

pierna *f.* leg

pieza *f.* piece

pijama *f.* pajama

pila *f.* battery

píldora *f.* pill

piloto *m. & f.* pilot

pimienta *f.* pepper

pintor(-ora) painter

pintoresco, -a picturesque

pintura *f.* paint; painting

pirámide *f.* pyramid

piscina *f.* swimming pool

piso *m.* floor, story

pizarra *f.* chalkboard

pizza *f.* pizza

planchar to iron

planeta *m.* planet

plano *m.* map (of a city)

planta *f.* plant; **planta baja** ground floor

plata *f.* silver

plátano *m.* plantain

platino *m.* platinum

plato *m.* plate, dish

playa *f.* beach

plaza *f.* square

plazo *m.* term

pluma *f.* pen; feather

población *f.* population

pobreza *f.* poverty

poco few; **dentro de poco** shortly

poder (ue) to be able, can; *also m.* power; **poder ejecutivo** executive power

poderoso, -a powerful

podrir to rot

poesía *f.* poetry

poeta *m.* poet

poetisa *f.* poet

policía *m.* police officer; *f.* the police

poliéster *m.* polyester

política *f.* politics

político(-a) politician

pollo *m.* chicken

polvo *m.* dust

pomada *f.* salve

poner *(irr.)* to put, to place; **poner la mesa** to set the table; **ponerse** to put on; to become; **ponerse rojo (-a)** to blush

por for, by, through; times *(math)*

porque because; **¿por qué?** why?

portátil portable

porteño, -a from Buenos Aires, Argentina

portero *m.* doorman

portugués, -esa Portuguese

posada *f.* inn

posponer *(irr.)* to postpone

postre *m.* dessert

practicar to practice

precio *m.* price

preciso necessary; precise

predilecto, -a favorite

preferir (ie, i) to prefer

pregunta *f.* question

preguntar to ask

premio *m.* prize; **el premio gordo** first prize, jackpot

prenda *f.* article (of clothing)

prendedor *m.* pin

prensa *f.* press, newspapers

preocupado, -a worried

preparar to prepare

presidente(-a) president

prestado, -a borrowed

prestar to lend; **prestar atención** to pay attention

prima *f.* cousin

primavera *f.* spring

primero, -a first

primo(-a) cousin

princesa *f.* princess

principiar to begin

prisa *f.* haste, promptness; **tener prisa** to be in a hurry

probar (ue) to prove, to try, to test

problema *m.* problem

producir (zc) to produce

profesión *f.* profession

profesor(-ora) teacher

profundamente deeply; soundly

profundo, -a deep

programa *m.* program, platform

programador(-ora) programmer

prohibir to forbid

prometer to promise

promoción *f.* promotion

pronosticador(-ora) forecaster

pronosticar to forecast

pronóstico *m.* forecast

pronto soon; **de pronto** suddenly; **tan pronto como** as soon as

pronunciar to pronounce

propietario(-a) owner

propina *f.* tip

propio, -a own

propósito *m.* purpose

prosperidad *f.* prosperity

protagonista *m. & f.* main character

proteger (j) to protect

provecho *m.* benefit; **buen provecho** hearty appetite

próximo, -a next

pueblo *m.* town

puente *m.* bridge

pureza *f.* purity

puerta *f.* door; gate

puerto *m.* port

puesto *m.* position, post; **puesto que** since

pulgada *f.* inch

pulmonía *f.* pneumonia

pulpo *m.* octopus

pulsera *f.* bracelet

punto *m.* sharp; **en punto** sharp

pupitre *m.* (student's) desk

que that; **¿qué?** what?, which?; **¡qué... !** what . . . !, what a . . . !, how . . . !

quebrar (ie) to break

quedar to remain; **quedarse (en)** to stay, to remain; **quedarle a uno** to have left

quehacer *m.* chore, task, errand

queja *f.* complaint

quejarse to complain

quemadura *f.* burn

quemar to burn

querer (ie) to want; to wish; to love

querido, -a dear

queso *m.* cheese

quien who; **¿quién?** who?; **¿a quién (-es)?** whom?, to whom?; **¿con quién (-es)?** with whom?; **¿de quién (-es)?** whose?, of whom?

química *f.* chemistry

quinceañero *m.* birthday party for girls turning fifteen

quinto, -a fifth

quiosco *m.* kiosk

quitar to take away; **quitarse** to take off (clothing)

ración *f.* ration

radiografía *f.* x-ray

raíz *f.* root

rapidez *f.* rapidity, quickness

rápido, -a rapid, fast; **rápidamente** rapidly, quickly

raqueta *f.* racket

rascacielos *m. sing. & pl.* skyscraper

raso *m.* satin

rato *m.* time; **pasar un buen rato** to have a good time

ratoncito *m.* mouse

razón *f.* reason; **tener razón** to be right

realizar to realize, to fulfill

rebeldía *f.* rebellion, revolt

recado *m.* message

receptor(-ora) receiver

recesión *f.* recession

receta *f.* recipe, prescription

recetar to prescribe

rechazar (c) to reject

recibir to receive

reciclaje *m.* recycling

reciclar to recycle

recoger (j) to pick up, to gather

recompensa *f.* reward

reconocer (zc) to recognize

recordar (ue) to remember

recuerdo *m.* remembrance, souvenir

recurso *m.* resource

red *f.* net

redactar to edit

reducir (zc) to reduce

referir (ie i) to tell; to narrate

refrán *m.* saying, proverb

refresco *m.* refreshment; soft drink, soda

refrigerador *m.* refrigerator

regalo *m.* gift, present

regar to water, to irrigate

régimen *m.* diet; regime

regla *f.* rule; ruler

regresar to return

reina *f.* queen

reinado *m.* reign

reinar to reign

reír(se) (i) to laugh

reja *f.* gate, wrought-iron grill

relámpago *m.* lightening

religioso, -a religious

relleno, -a stuffed

reloj *m.* watch, clock; **reloj despertador** alarm clock

relojería *f.* watch shop

relojero(-era) watchmaker

remar to row

Renacimiento *m.* Renaissance

reñir (i) to quarrel; to scold

reparar to repair
repetir (i) to repeat
reposo *m.* rest
repostería *f.* pastry shop
repostero(-era) (pastry) baker
república *f.* republic
res *f.* beef
reseña *f.* review; description
resfriado *m.* cold (illness)
resfriarse to catch a cold
resolver (ue) to solve
responder to answer
responsable responsible
respuesta *f.* answer
restaurante *m.* restaurant
resultado *m.* result
resultar to result
resumen *m.* summary
retirar to withdraw
retiro *m.* withdrawal
retrato *m.* portrait
reunión *f.* meeting
reunirse to meet
revelar to develop (film)
revisar to revise, to check
revista *f.* magazine
revolución *f.* revolution
revolver (ue) to mix
rey *m.* king
ribera *f.* shore, bank (of a river)
rico, -a rich
río *m.* river
riqueza *f.* wealth
robar to rob
rodilla *f.* knee
rogar (ue, gu) to request, to beg
rojo, -a red
romería *f.* pilgrimage, religious excursion
rompecabezas *m. sing. & pl.* puzzle
romper to break
ropa *f.* clothing
rosado, -a pink
rostro *m.* face

rotura *f.* break, crack; fracture
rubí *m.* ruby
rubio, -a blonde
ruido *m.* noise
ruidoso, -a noisy
rumano, -a Romanian
ruso, -a Russian
ruta *f.* route

sábado *m.* Saturday
saber *(irr.)* to know
sabio, -a wise
sabor *m.* flavor, taste
sabroso, -a flavorful
sacar to take out; to take (photo)
sacerdote *m.* priest
sacerdotisa *f.* priestess
saco *m.* jacket
sal *f.* salt
sala *f.* living room; **sala de clases** classroom
salchicha *f.* sausage
salida *f.* departure; exit; **salida del sol** sunrise
salir *(irr.)* to go out, to leave; **salirse con la suya** to get one's way
salsa *f.* sauce
salubridad *f.* public health
salud *m.* health
saludable healthy
saludar to greet
saludo *m.* greeting
salvaje wild, savage
salvavidas *m. & f., sing. & pl.* lifeguard
sandía *f.* watermelon
sándwich *m.* sandwich
sangre *f.* blood
santo(-a) saint
sarampión *m.* measles
sarape *m.* blanket
secador *m.* dryer; **secador de pelo** *m.* hair dryer
secadora *f.* clothes dryer

secar to dry; **secarse** to dry oneself
seco, -a dry
secretario(-a) secretary
sed *f.* thirst; **tener sed** to be thirsty
seda *f.* silk
sede *f.* seat (of government or organization)
seguir (i) (g) to follow, to continue
segundo, -a second
seguridad *f.* safety
seguro sure, safe; **seguro social** *m.* social security
selva *f.* forest, jungle
semáforo *m.* traffic light
semana *f.* week
semejante similar
senado *m.* senate
senador(-a) senator
señal *f.* signal
sentarse (ie) to sit down
sentir (ie) (i) to regret, be sorry; to feel
septiembre *m.* September
séptimo, -a seventh
ser *(irr.)* to be
serio, -a serious
serpiente *f.* snake
servilleta *f.* napkin
servir (i) to serve
sesenta sixty
setenta seventy
severo, -a severe, stern
sexto, -a sixth
siempre always
siesta *f.* nap
siguiente following
silbar to whistle
silencioso, -a quiet, silent
silla *f.* chair
sillón *m.* armchair
simpático, -a nice, pleasant
simple silly, simpleminded; simple, mere

sin without; **sin embargo** nevertheless

sinagoga *f.* synagogue

situar to place, to locate

sobre on top of; *also m.* envelope

sobresaliente outstanding

sobrina *f.* niece

sobrino *m.* nephew

sociedad *f.* society

sofá *m.* sofa

sofreír to sauté

sol *m.* sun

sólamente (sólo) only

soldado(-a) *m.* soldier

soler (ue) to be accustomed to

solo, -a alone

sombrero *m.* hat

sonar (ue) to sound

soñar (ue) to dream

sonido *m.* sound

sonreír(se) (i) to smile

sonrisa *f.* smile

sopa *f.* soup

soplar to blow

sordo, -a deaf, hearing-impaired

sorprenderse (de) to be surprised

sorteo *m.* drawing (for a raffle)

sortija *f.* ring

sótano *m.* basement

subibaja *m.* seesaw

subir to go up, climb; to raise

suburbio *m.* suburb

suceso *m.* event, occurrence

sucio, -a dirty

sudar to perspire, to sweat

sudor *m.* sweat

suegra *f.* mother-in-law

suegro *m.* father-in-law

suelo *m.* ground

sueño *m.* dream; sleep; **tener sueño** to be sleepy

suerte *f.* luck; **tener suerte** to be lucky

suéter *m.* sweater

sufrir to suffer

sugerencia *f.* suggestion

supermercado *m.* supermarket

supersticioso, -a superstitious

suplicar (qu) to implore, to beg

sur *m.* south

surtido *m.* variety, assortment

sustituir (y) to substitute

suyo, -a his, her, your, their

tacaño, -a stingy

tal such

talentoso, -a talented

talla *f.* size

tamaño *m.* size

también also, too

tampoco neither, not either; **ni yo tampoco** me neither

tanto, -a so much, so many; *also m.* score

tapiz *m.* tapestry

tardar (en) to delay (in)

tarde *f.* afternoon; late; P.M. **de la tarde**

tarea *f.* homework, assignment

tarifa *f.* rate, price

tarjeta *f.* card; **tarjeta postal** postcard

tauromaquia *f.* bull fighting

taxi *m.* taxi

taza *f.* cup

té *m.* tea

teatro *m.* theater

tecnología *f.* technology

techo *m.* ceiling, roof

tela *f.* fabric, cloth

teléfono *m.* telephone; **teléfono celular** *m.* cellular telephone

telegrama *m.* telegram

telenovela *f.* soap opera

televisión *f.* television

televisor *m.* television set

tema *m.* theme, topic

temblar (ie) to tremble

temer to fear

temor *m.* fear

temperatura *f.* temperature

templo *m.* temple

temporada *f.* time, period of time; season

temprano early

tenedor *m.* fork

tener (*irr.*) to have; **tener que** to have to

tenis *m.* tennis; *m. pl.* sneakers

tercero, -a third

tercio m. third; **un tercio** one-third

terciopelo *m.* velvet

terminal *f.* terminal; **terminal de autobuses** bus station

ternera *f.* veal

terraza *f.* terrace

tertulia *f.* social gathering

tía *f.* aunt

tiburón *m.* shark

tiempo *m.* time; weather; **a tiempo** on time

tienda *f.* store; **tienda de ropa** clothing store; **tienda de campaña** tent

tierra *f.* earth, ground

tigre *m.* tiger

tijeras *f. pl.* scissors

timbre *m.* bell

tímido, -a timid, shy

tintorería *f.* drycleaner

tío *m.* uncle

tirantes *m. pl.* suspenders

tirar to throw

tiras cómicas *f. pl.* comicstrips

títere *m.* puppet

titulares *m. pl.* headlines

tiza *f.* chalk

toalla *f.* towel

tobillo *m.* ankle

tocador *m.* dresser

tocar to touch; to play (instrument)

tocino *m.* bacon

todavía still, yet

todo, -a all, every

tomar to take, to drink; **tomar una decisión** to make a decision

tomate *m.* tomato

topacio *m.* topaz

tormenta *f.* storm

torpe clumsy

torre *f.* tower

tortuga *f.* turtle

tos *f.* cough

trabajador, -a hardworking

trabajar to work

trabajo *m.* work

traducir (zc) to translate

traer (*irr.*) to bring

traje *m.* suit; **traje de baño** bathing suit

tranquilamente tranquilly

tránsito *m.* traffic

transporte *m.* transportation

tranvía *m.* streetcar

tratado *m.* treaty

tratamiento *m.* treatment

tratar de to try to

travesura *f.* prank

travieso, -a naughty, mischievious

treinta thirty

tren *m.* train

trigo *m.* wheat

tripulación *f.* crew

triste sad

tristeza *f.* sadness

trofeo *m.* trophy

trompeta *f.* trumpet

trono *m.* throne

turista *m. & f.* tourist

último, -a last

ultramarino, -a overseas

uña *f.* fingernail

unidad *f.* unity

universidad *f.* university

urgencia *f.* emergency

usar to use

útil useful; **útiles** *m. pl.* school supplies

uva *f.* grape

vaca *f.* cow

vacaciones *f. pl.* vacation

vacío, -a empty

vacuna *f.* vaccine

valentía *f.* bravery, valor

valer (*irr.*) to be worth

valiente brave

valor *m.* value

vapor *m.* ship, boat

variar to vary

varicela *f.* chicken pox

variedad *f.* variety

varios, -as several

vaso *m.* drinking glass

vecindario *m.* neighborhood

vecino, -a neighbor

veinte twenty

vela *f.* candle

velocidad *f.* speed

vencedor(-ora) winner

vencer (z) to conquer, defeat; end

vendedor(-ora) salesperson

vender to sell

venir (*irr.*) to come

ventana *f.* window

ventanilla *f.* window (for service); small window

ver to see, to watch

veraniego, -a summer

verano *m.* summer

verdad *f.* truth

verdadero, -a true

verde green

verdulería *f.* vegetable shop

verduras *f. pl.* greens, vegetables

vergüenza *f.* shame

vestido *m.* dress

vestirse (i) to dress oneself; to get dressed

vez *f.* time; **a veces** sometimes; **rara vez** seldom; **tal vez** perhaps

viajar to travel

viaje *m.* trip

viajero(-era) *m.* traveler

vicepresidente, -a vice president

vicio *m.* vice

vida *f.* life

videojuego *m.* video game

vidrio *m.* glass

viejo, -a old

viento *m.* wind; **hacer viento** to be windy

viernes *m.* Friday

violeta purple

virtud *f.* virtue

visitar to visit

vista *f.* view, vision

vivir to live

vivo, -a alive

vocabulario *m.* vocabulary

volar (ue) to fly

volcán *m.* volcano

voleibol *m.* volleyball

volver (ue) to return

voz *f.* voice

vuelo *m.* flight

ya already; **ya no** no longer

zafiro *m.* sapphire

zanahoria *f.* carrot

zapatería *f.* shoe store

zapatero(-era) shoemaker

zapato *m.* shoe

zorra *f.* fox

zumbido *m.* buzz

English-Spanish Vocabulary

The English-Spanish Vocabulary includes only those words that occur in the English-to-Spanish exercise.

a lot mucho

about unos

absent ausente

accompany: to accompany acompañar

act: to act like hacer de

address dirección *f.*; **to address** dirigirse a

afraid: to be afraid tener miedo de

after después de

afternoon tarde *f.*

again otra vez, de nuevo; volver a + *inf.*

ago hace... días (meses, años, *etc.*)

air aire *m.*

almost casi

alone solo, -a

aloud en voz alta

among entre

ancient antiguo

angry: to become angry enojarse, enfadarse

another otro

answer: to answer contestar

applaud: to applaud aplaudir

appreciate: to appreciate agradecer, apreciar

arrive: to arrive llegar

as tan... como; **as many . . . as** tantos, -as... como

ask: to ask preguntar; **to ask for** pedir

assignment tarea *f.*

attend: to attend asistir

attendance asistencia *f.*

author autor(-ora)

autumn otoño *m.*

backpack mochila *f.*

bad malo, -a

banner bandera *f.*

bark: to bark ladrar

basement sótano *m.*

become: to become llegar a ser, ponerse, hacerse

before antes de

begin comenzar (ie) (c), empezar (ie) (c), principiar

beginning principio *m.*

bellboy botones *m. sing.*

best mejor

better mejor

bill cuenta *f.*

bird pájaro *m.*

blanket cobija *f.*

blond rubio, -a

bored aburrido, -a

born: to be born nacer (zc)

break: to break romper, quebrar

breakfast desayuno *m.*

bring: to bring traer, llevar

broom escoba *f.*

brunette moreno, -a

build: to build construir (y)

building edificio *m.*

bus autobús *m.*

but pero

camera cámara *f.*

cancel: to cancel cancelar, anular

candidate candidato(-a)

candle vela *f.*

century siglo *m.*

certain cierto, -a

chambermaid camarera *f.*

change cambio *m.*; **to change** cambiar; **to change one's mind** cambiar de opinión

character personaje *m.*

charge: to charge cobrar

chef cocinero(-a)

chess ajedrez *m.*

choose: to choose escoger (j)

Christmas Navidad *f.*

city ciudad *f.*

civilization civilización *f.*

class clase *f.*

clean limpio; **to clean** limpiar

close: to close cerrar

coach entrenador(-a)

coat abrigo *m.*

colleague colega *m. & f.*

colorful colorido, -a

comb peine *m.*; **to comb one's hair** peinarse

comfortable cómodo, -a

commentary comentario *m.*

commit: to commit cometer

competition competencia *f.*

complete: to complete completar, terminar

construct: to construct construir (y)

contaminate: to contaminate contaminar

convince: to convince convencer (z)

cool fresco; **to be cool** hacer fresco (*weather*)

corner (*street corner*) esquina *f.*; rincón *m.*

cosmopolitan cosmopolita

cost: to cost costar (ue)

country campo *m.*; **(nation)** país *m.*

courteous cortés; de manera cortés

critic crítico *m. & f.*

cut: to cut cortar

daily diario

darkness oscuridad *f.*

day día *m.*

daybreak: at daybreak al amanecer

December diciembre

decoration adorno *m.*

defect falta *f.*

demanding exigente

deserve: to deserve merecer

desk escritorio *m.*

develop: to develop desarrollar

different diferente, distinto, -a

difficult difícil

dinner cena *f.*

discuss: to discuss discutir

dish plato *m.*

divide: to divide dividir

dog perro *m.*

doll muñeca *f.*

door puerta *f.*

doorman portero *m.*

doubt duda *f.*; **to doubt** dudar

doubtful dudoso

dream sueño *m.*; **to dream** soñar (ue) con

dress vestido *m.*; **to dress oneself** vestirse

drink: to drink beber, tomar

during durante

each cada

early temprano

earn: to earn ganar

elect: to elect elegir (j)

electricity electricidad *f.*; luz *f.*

empire imperio *m.*

employ: to employ emplear, usar

employee empleado(-a)

end fin *m.*; **to end** terminar, acabar, concluir (y)

English inglés (*f.* inglesa)

enjoy: to enjoy gozar de; **to have a good time** divertirse (ie, i)

entire entero, todo

European europeo, -a

every cada

everything todo

example ejemplo *m.*

exercise ejercicio *m.*

exhibit exposición *f.*, exhibición *f.*

experience experiencia *f.*

explain: to explain explicar

factory fábrica *f.*

fair justo,-a; recto, -a

fall otoño *m.*; **to fall** caer; **to fall asleep** dormirse (ue) (u)

famous famoso, -a

fan aficionado(-a), fanático(-a)

father padre *m.*

festival fiesta *f.*

few poco

finally por fin

finish: to finish terminar, acabar

first primero, -a

flashlight linterna *f.*

follow: to follow seguir (i)

food comida *f.*

fool tonto, inocente; **April Fools Day** Día de los Inocentes

forecast pronóstico *m.*; **to forecast** pronosticar (qu)

French francés (*f.* francesa)

frequently a menudo

friend amigo(-a)

friendly amigable, amable

fun: to make fun of burlarse de

funny cómico, -a

game juego *m.*, partido *m.*

garbage basura *f.*

garden jardín *m.*

gardener jardinero(-era)

generally generalmente, por lo general

get: to get into subir a; **to get up** levantarse

gift regalo *m.*

go: to go ir; **to go out** salir

goodbye adiós; **to say goodbye** despedirse

government gobierno *m.*

grass césped *m.*

green verde

greet: to greet saludar

guest huésped *m. & f.*

guide guía *m. & f.*

hair pelo *m.*

hall pasillo *m.*

Halloween Día de las Brujas *m.*

hang: to hang colgar (ue) (gu)

happy alegre, contento, feliz

hard duro; mucho

help: to help ayudar

hide: to hide esconder

homeowner dueño de casa *m.*

hope esperanza *f.*; **to hope** esperar

hostel hostería *f.*, albergue *m.*

house casa *f.*

immediately en seguida, inmediatamente

include: to include incluir (y)

independence independencia *f.*

information información *f.*

insist: to insist on insistir en

intend: to intend pensar (ie)

introduce: to introduce presentar

itinerary itinerario *m.*

July julio *m.*

key llave *f.*

kind bondadoso, -a

knock: to knock tocar, llamar

know: to know (something) saber; **to know (someone)** conocer

lamp lámpara *f.*

language idioma *m.*, lengua *f.*

large grande

late tarde

lawyer abogado(-a)

lead: to lead conducir (zc)

learn: to learn aprender

leave irse, marcharse, salir; **to leave something (behind)** dejar

letter carta *f.*; **letter opener** abrecartas *m.*

lightning relámpago *m.*

like: to like gustar

live: to live vivir

lobby vestíbulo *m.*

long largo

look: to look at mirar; **to look for** buscar

lose: to lose perder

loud fuerte

love: to love amar

luggage maleta *f.*; equipaje *m.*

machine máquina *f.*

mail correo *m.*; **to mail** echar al correo

main principal

mall centro comercial *m.*

manager gerente *m. & f.*

many muchos, -as

means modo *m.*

meanwhile mientras tanto

meet: to meet encontrar (ue)

member miembro *m. & f.*, socio *m. & f.*

message recado *m.*, mensaje *m.*

mile milla *f.*

mischievious travieso, -a

mistake error *m.*, falta *f.*; **to be mistaken** equivocarse

money dinero *m.*

month mes *m.*

most más

mother madre *f.*

mountain montaña *f.*

move: to move mover (ue)

museum museo *m.*

name nombre *m.*

nature naturaleza *f.*

near cerca de

need necesidad *f.*; **to need** necesitar

neighborhood barrio *m.*

neither tampoco

never nunca, jamás

nevertheless sin embargo

new nuevo, -a; **New Year's** Año Nuevo

news noticia *f.*

newspaper periódico *m.*

next próximo; **the next day** al día siguiente; **next to** al lado de, junto a

nice simpático, -a

night noche *f.*; **last night** anoche

nightfall: at nightfall al anochecer

no one nadie

noise ruido *m.*

noon mediodía *m.*

nothing nada

novel novela *f.*

now ahora

number número *m.*

obtain: to obtain conseguir

offer: to offer ofrecer (zc)

office oficina *f.*

often a menudo

old viejo, -a

older mayor

open: to open abrir

operator operador(-ora); **telephone operator** telefonista *m. & f.*

opportunity oportunidad *f.*

ourselves nosotros; nosotros mismos

outdoors al aire libre

outside afuera

pack: to pack empacar, hacer la(s) maleta(s)

parent padre *m.*, madre *f.*; **parents** padres *m. pl.*

participate: to participate participar

pay: to pay pagar (gu); **to pay attention** prestar atención

people gente *f.*

perhaps quizá, tal vez

photograph fotografía *f.*

place lugar *m.*, sitio *m.*; **to take place** tener lugar; **to place** colocar (qu), poner

plan proyecto *m.*; **to plan** pensar (ie)

plant: to plant plantar, cultivar

play: to play (music) tocar (qu); **(to play a game or sport)** jugar (ue) (gu)

player jugador(-a)

please por favor

polite cortés
pool piscina *f.*
porch balcón *m.*, terraza *f.*
practice práctica *f.*; **to practice** practicar (qu)
praise: to praise alabar
prefer: to prefer preferir (ie, i)
prepare: to prepare preparar
pretty bonito, -a
prize premio *m.*
promise: to promise prometer
proud orgulloso, -a
public público, -a
punish: to punish castigar

quickly rápidamente

racket raqueta *f.*
rain lluvia *f.*; **to rain** llover (ue)
read: to read leer
realistic realista, verdadero, -a
recognize: to recognize reconocer (zc)
recommend: to recommend recomendar (ie)
record disco *m.*
regret: to regret sentir (ie, i)
remain: to remain permanecer (zc), quedarse
respect: to respect respetar
respond: to respond responder, contestar
result resultado *m.*
review: to review repasar
road carretera *f.*
room cuarto *m.*
rule regla *f.*
run: to run correr

saint santo, -a
same mismo, -a
schedule horario *m.*

school escuela *f.*; **elementary school** escuela primaria *f.*; **high school** escuela secundaria *f.*
scream grito *m.*; **to scream** gritar
seat asiento *m.*
seem: to seem parecer
seize: to seize coger (j)
seldom rara vez
serious serio, -a
serve: to serve servir (i)
set juego *m.*
several varios, unos
share: to share compartir
shop: to shop ir de compras
short bajo, -a
show: to show mostrar (ue), enseñar
shower: to shower ducharse
shut : to shut cerrar (ie); **to shut off** apagar (gu)
silent: to be silent callarse
sit: to sit down sentarse (ie)
sleep: to sleep dormir (ue, u)
slowly despacio, lentamente
small pequeño, -a
sneakers zapatos de tenis *m. pl.*
snow nieve *f.*; **to snow** nevar (ie)
someone alguien
something algo
sometimes a veces
soon pronto
soup sopa *f.*
spacious amplio, -a
Spain España
Spanish español
speak: to speak hablar
special especial
specialize: to specialize especializarse
spend: to spend time pasar; **to spend money** gastar

sport deporte *m.*
spring primavera *f.*
stairs escalera *f.*
start out: to start out ponerse en camino
stay: to stay (in) quedarse (en), permanecer (zc)
sternly severamente
stop: to stop dejar de, cesar de
story cuento *m.*
street calle *f.*
student estudiante, alumno(-a); *also adj.* estudiantil
study: to study estudiar
suddenly de pronto, de repente, repentinamente
suggest: to suggest sugerir (ie, i)
summer verano *m.*
sun sol *m.*; **to be sunny** hacer sol
support apoyo *m.*; **to support** apoyar
surprise sorpresa *f.*; **to surprise** sorprenderse (de)
sweep: to sweep barrer
swim: to swim nadar

take: to take tomar; **to take off** quitarse; **to take pictures** sacar fotografías
talkative hablador(-ora)
tall alto, -a
task tarea *f.*
team equipo *m.*
technique técnica *f.*
telephone teléfono *m.*
there allí, allá
thing cosa *f.*
think: to think creer, pensar (ie)
thunder trueno *m.*
thunderstorm tormenta *f.*
ticket boleto *m.*, billete *m.*
time tiempo *m.*; hora *f.*; vez

f.; **on time** a tiempo; **What time is it?** ¿Qué hora es?; **to have a good time** divertirse (ie, i), pasar un buen rato

timid tímido, –a

tired cansado, –a; **to be tired** estar cansado, –a

title título *m.*

today hoy

together junto

tomorrow mañana

too también

tour excursión *f.*

toy juguete *m.*

traffic tráfico *m.*, tránsito *m.*

train tren *m.*

trait característica *f.*

transportation transporte *m.*

tree árbol *m.*

trip viaje *m.*

try: to try (to) tratar de

type clase *f.*, tipo *m.*

umpire árbitro *m.*

under debajo de

understand: to understand comprender, entender (ie)

unoccupied desocupado, –a

usually generalmente

vacation vacaciones *f. pl.*

videogame videojuego

visit visita *f.*; **to visit** visitar

vote voto *m.*; **to vote** votar

wait: to wait (for) esperar

waiter mesero *m.*

walk andar (*irr.*), caminar, pasearse; **to take a walk** dar un paseo

want: to want desear, querer (ie)

water agua *f.*; **to water** regar (ie) (gu)

wear: to wear llevar, usar

weather tiempo *m.*

Wednesday miércoles *m.*

week semana *f.*

well bien

white blanco, –a

willingly de buena gana

win: to win ganar

winter invierno *m.*

word palabra *f.*; **to keep one's word** cumplir con la palabra

work: to work trabajar

worker trabajador(-ora)

worried preocupado, –a

worse peor

worthwhile: to be worthwhile valer la pena

year año *m.*

younger menor; **younger than** menor que

youngest menor; **the youngest** el / la menor, los / las menores

Index